Wishing the Mariners
every success

Steve Ritchie
Oct. 1992

NO DAY TOO LONG—
AN HYDROGRAPHER'S TALE

Rear Admiral G. S. Ritchie, C.B., D.S.C., F.R.I.C.S.

NO DAY TOO LONG—
AN HYDROGRAPHER'S TALE

by

Rear Admiral G. S. Ritchie C.B., D.S.C., F.R.I.C.S.

The Pentland Press Ltd.
Edinburgh · Cambridge · Durham

By the same author:
Challenger – The Life of a Survey Ship (1957)
*The Admiralty Chart – British Naval Hydrography
in the Nineteenth Century* (1967)

First published in 1992 by
The Pentland Press Ltd.
5 Hutton Close
South Church
Durham

ISBN 1 872795 63 3

Jacket design by Geoff Hobbs

Typeset by Spire Origination, Norwich
Printed and bound by Antony Rowe Ltd., Chippenham

Acknowledgements

In addition to setting down a personal account of nearly fifty years of hydrographic endeavour, I have also attempted to record some of the major advances in data-gathering and cartographic techniques which have taken place during my professional lifetime.

To achieve these two aims I have sought assistance from former naval and civilian colleagues, and other friends I have made along the way. There are many such persons around the world who deserve my thanks, only a few of whom I have space to mention here.

First there was the late Rear Admiral Sir Edmund Irving, K.B.E., C.B.; and then Captain Syd Hennessey, O.B.E., from whom I learnt the art of boat sounding over fifty years ago, and under whom I served in H.M.S. *Scott* during the invasion of North-West Europe. Others who have stirred my memory include Captain Chester Read, C.B.E., my navigator in H.M.S. *Dalrymple* in the Persian Gulf, who has also drawn the map of our activities there; and Captains Geoff Hope and Richard Campbell, O.B.E., who served as my first lieutenant and navigator respectively during a memorable commission in H.M.S. *Vidal.*

Lieutenant Commander F. M. Berncastle, D.S.C., and Commander N. C. Glen, O.B.E., have described to me how they made their vital pre-invasion surveys off Arromanches. Lieutenant R. T. Bailey, R.N.V.R. cast his mind back to our days together in H.M.S. *Endeavour* in the Red Sea in 1942; and Lieutenant Denis Todd, R.N., evoked for me the life of a surveyor in the deserts of Qatar over forty years ago.

Commander T. C. Russell, O.B.E., was able to guide me through the history of the Persian Gulf Lighting Service, he having been in command of the tender *Relume* during the time of my visit to the Gulf in *Dalrymple*.

Derek Newson, B.A., former Director of the Charting and Sciences Division of the U.K. Hydrographic Department, traced for me the long story of our cartographers from 1919, when they were founder members of the Institute of Professional Civil Servants, through their conversion to Civil Hydrographic Officers in 1951, and on until 1988 when they were merged with a new class of Mapping and Charting Officers.

Austin Pielou, O.B.E., B.A., former Superintendent of Chart Maintenance at Taunton, recalled the circumstances which led to our decision to 'modernise' the Admiralty Chart and 'go metric' in 1967, and the effect that these decisions had subsequently on the International Chart.

Bob Crowford, who served as a Royal Marine printer onboard H.M.S. *Challenger* in World War II, and who assisted me in writing my book about that ship, came to my aid again with a description of the complex trade union set-up in the Printing Works at Taunton during my time as Hydrographer.

Godfrey Murt, B.Sc., a former Principal Civil Hydrographic Officer, who pioneered our moves towards automated cartography, was able to remind me of our early frustrations and successes in this field.

For the history of the Decca Navigator System I am indebted to my friend Claud Powell, F.R.I.N., C.Eng., F.I.E.R.E., formerly employed by the Decca Company, and to the late Lieutenant Commander John Roberts of Racal Survey Ltd.

Geoffrey Lumsden of 'Scribes' was able to explain to me the complexities of the legal battles between the various oil companies seeking offshore concessions from Trucial Coast Rulers in the 1950s when the Royal Navy was engaged in surveying those waters.

Michael Richey, M.B.E., former Director of the Royal Institute of Navigation, pointed the way through the long chronicle which began in 1959 with a paper by Commandant Oudet of the French Hydrographic Service, and ended in 1972 with the acceptance by the International Maritime Organisation of a shipping separation routing scheme for Dover Strait.

Captain Neil Guy, Chief of the South African Hydrographic Office in 1989, kindly provided me with details of the early days of the invention and production of the Tellurometer in the mid-1950s.

Commander John Pryor, who was a prisoner of war in Germany with Captain E. H. B. Baker, D.S.O., told me of the latter's forthright attitude towards their German captors when acting as Senior British Officer in Marlag-Milag Nord.

In search of elusive facts and figures I have often called to my aid the Hydrographic Information Officer in Lacon House, London. The different officers in that post over the last three or four years never failed to find the answers for me.

In 1989 Rear Admiral Sir David Haslam, K.B.E., C.B., then President of the Directing Committee of the I.H.B. (International Hydrographic Bureau), thoughtfully invited me to stay with him for a couple of weeks in Monaco so that I could work in the Bureau to complete my final chapter. The Directing Committee and their international staff were eager to provide me with all the correspondence and reports generated during my ten years at the Bureau, which refreshed my memory concerning many international projects.

Finally I have to thank my son-in-law, Lieutenant Commander David Griffiths, B.Sc. (Eur. Ing.), C.Eng., M.I.Mar.E., for processing my manuscript on his Amstrad.

Once again my wife has piloted me through a labyrinth of grammar, spelling and proof-reading dangers into the final haven.

G. S. Ritchie
Collieston, Aberdeenshire
July 1992

Contents

List of Illustrations

Frontispiece:
Rear Admiral G. S. Ritchie, C.B., D.S.C., F.R.I.C.S.
(© British Crown copyright 1991/M.O.D. reproduced with the permission of the Controller of Her Britannic Majesty's Stationery Office)

Palais de Monaco

FOREWORD
By His Serene Highness Prince Rainier III of Monaco

At the first International Hydrographic Conference in London in 1919, it was decided that a permanent International Bureau be established to be administered by a committee of three Directors elected by the Member States of an International Hydrographic Organisation.

My great grandfather, Prince Albert I, an oceanographer of world renown who built the Musée Océanographique on the face of the Rocher in 1910, invited the newly elected Directing Committee to establish their Bureau within the Principality.

On 20th April 1929, my grandfather, Prince Louis II, laid the foundation stone of a building to be erected on the Quai de Plaisance to house the International Hydrographic Bureau (IBH); this edifice has been maintained by the Monégasque Government ever since. Today, the IBH provides the nucleus around which the fifty-five Member States of the Organisation promote the exchange of hydrographic data and the standardisation of their seacharts.

o

o   o

During forty years in the Royal Navy (UK), Steve Ritchie rose to become Hydrographer of the Navy, representing his country at the International Hydrographic Conference in Monaco in 1967.

On joining the Surveying Service of the Navy as a sub-Lieutenant in 1936, he was informed by the then Hydrographer of the significance of the IBH, and advised to keep up-to-date by reading its technical journal - "The Hydrographic Review".

I welcome Admiral Ritchie's "No Day Too Long" - which chronicles the professional life of a sea surveyor. While he records the many technical advances in hydrography and chart-making that have taken place over the past fifty years, the author never loses sight of the influence of the International Hydrographic Organisation in stimulating and spreading the news of such innovations to the increasing benefit and safety of mariners world-wide.

xiii

Steve Ritchie finally came to Monaco in 1972 to serve for ten years as President of the Directing Committee of the Bureau. Clearly, he enjoyed life in the Principality and looks back with satisfaction, I am sure, on the advances which were made in international hydrographic collaboration during his term of office, as well as all the significant technical progress made in that time.

We enjoyed Admiral Ritchie's charisma and great knowledge in the many areas of our local life and activities ... and, last but not least, we are proud to count him as one of our distinguished "boule" player champions!

RAINIER, Prince de Monaco

Chapter I

'Who Are the Hydrographers?'

'Hydrographia' was used by seventeenth-century Spanish and Portuguese writers to embrace the widest concepts of navigation. The Jesuit priest Georges Fournier used *Hydrographie* as the title for his massive work published in Paris in 1643 which covered every aspect of the study of the sea, ships and navigation; only a single chapter among the twenty was devoted to 'La Carte Marine'.

With the growing number of exploring voyages during the eighteenth century the word hydrography began to be used by Europeans to refer specifically to the surveying of the sea coasts, and sounding the adjacent depths with lead and line, with the aim of making marine charts for the safe navigation of vessels.

In 1720 France established a 'Dépôt des Cartes et Plans' as a repository for hydrographic surveys to which establishment was appointed Nicolas Bellin, at the age of eighteen, as the first 'Ingénieur hydrographe de la marine'. He began at once to prepare for the engraving and printing of charts for the navigator.

By the time the British Hydrographic Office was established seventy-five years later the terms 'hydrographers' and 'hydrographic surveys' were universally understood in maritime circles.

Had he lived to return home from his third Pacific voyage Captain Cook might well have become the first British 'Hydrographer of the Navy'. As it was, a talented civilian, Alexander Dalrymple, already serving as Hydrographer to the East India Company, was appointed to the newly established post in 1795. His task was to gather hydrographic information from all possible sources and pass it on in usable form to the ships of the Royal Navy. With the appointment of its first Hydrographer the Admiralty had in the words of Sir Oswyn Murray, one of its greatest Secretaries, 'put its hand to the continuous charting of the seas'.

A naval officer, Captain Hurd, took over from Dalrymple in 1808, the first of a long line of twenty-three naval Hydrographers of the Navy down to the present day. In 1814 Hurd made a Report to Their Lordships detailing the many areas of the world's oceans which should be surveyed to meet the Fleet's requirements for charts. The Report concludes that,

> . . . *'The return of Peace to this Country makes me consider it as an official duty to represent to the Lords Commissioners of the Admiralty the great deficiency of our National knowledge in almost every part of the World, but more particularly on the coastline of our own Dominions, and also with the hopes that the present favourable moment for remedying these evils will be made use of, by calling into employment those of our Naval Officers, whose scientific merits point them out as qualified for undertakings of this nature – of which description of Officers there are, I am happy to say, many who stand eminently conspicuous.'*

Hurd, like Cook, appears to have learnt the basics of surveying from Samuel Holland, a Dutch army engineer who served in the British Royal American Regiment during the Seven Years' War. Hurd became Surveyor General of Cape Breton sometime after 1780, but by 1788 had commenced a detailed hydrographic survey of Bermuda and remained there to establish a base for the Royal Navy. During the first eight years of the new century Hurd was often on the enemy's doorstep, surveying the Bay of Brest in support of the British blockading forces.

Whether Hurd ever met Cook seems doubtful. Certainly his association with Samuel Holland; his studying of the published volumes of Captain Vancouver's surveying voyages on the east side of the North Pacific and those of Broughton on the west; and his close association with Captain Flinders from 1810 onwards whilst the latter was preparing his manuscript and charts for his 'Voyage to Terra Australis' would together have made Hurd acutely aware of the broad pattern for chartmaking set by the great explorer only thirty years earlier, for all these men employed Cook's methods.

A corps of officers, selected for their mathematical and navigational abilities to carry out the Hydrographer's instructions worldwide, was gradually built up by Hurd. The founding date of what has become known as 'The Royal Naval Surveying Service' may be taken as 7th January 1817, when a Board Minute established special rates of pay for officers specialising in hydrography.

'The Companions of their Researches', as Hurd called these officers, were inculcated with the ideals of Captain Cook – his attention to the health of the ship's company without which no hydrographic venture can be successful; his desire to have onboard the latest and best of nautical instruments; his feeling for ocean science far beyond the confines of navigational interest; and his absolute dedication to chartmaking which still motivates the R.N. Surveying Service today.

Captain Basil Hall was never himself a surveying officer but he openly admired their achievements, and in 1832 in his *Fragments of Voyages and Travels* in a chapter entitled 'Taking a Line in the Service' he describes how 'philosophers' well versed in nautical and scientific studies were coming forward to eclipse the 'tarpaulin men'.

Ten years after Hurd's death, by which time Admiralty charts were on sale to the public, Captain Hall testified to the continuance of Captain Hurd's dedicated corps:

'The Admiralty, without seeking beyond the profession, lay their hands at once upon a competent hydrographer, and, through the skill and diligence of such an authority as Beaufort, ensure not only the fidelity of their numerous charts and other nautical works (now placed at the free disposal of the public), but also give the country an assurance that those officers who are employed afloat in extending and in perfecting our knowledge of almost every part of the navigable world, are judiciously distributed.'

Admiral Sir Francis Beaufort reigned as Hydrographer of the Navy from 1829 until 1855, during which time he had naval surveyors working in every quarter of the globe and was constantly urging zeal, counselling care and commending their achievements. Beaufort set a new pattern during this high noon for British hydrography which the Surveying Service has followed for a further 130 years, maintaining our position in the very forefront of the world's chartmakers.

Writing towards the end of the nineteenth century Captain Wharton, later to become Hydrographer of the Navy, in his Preliminary to his manual on 'Hydrographical Surveying' shows naval surveyors continuing in their now traditional style.

'Happily, it is a profession of volunteers, and the author's experience is, that in no branch of the public service can the juniors be

3

more anxious to do their duty, not only to the letter, but to the utmost of the spirit, and to such as these no day seems long enough. To them the interest is constantly kept up. Every day has its incidents. The accuracy of the work of each assistant, when proved, is an infinite gratification to him, and he has also the continual satisfaction of feeling that of all he does a permanent record will remain, in the chart which is to guide hundreds of fellow-seamen on their way'.

Surveying officers received practical training at sea from their seniors and on the recommendation of their commanding officers gradually advanced from Fourth to First Class 'Surveying Assistants'. Beyond that they required a further recommendation before the Hydrographer of the Navy would advance them to 'Charge Surveyors', qualifying them to take charge of a major survey in command of one of H.M. surveying ships.

To fix a sounding boat at regular intervals it was necessary to observe two sextant angles simultaneously: thus in 1904 the Hydrographer of the day introduced a non-substantive rate 'for intelligent Seamen and Petty Officers'; 'Surveying Recorders' performed the duties of the second officer in the boat. They too advanced on recommendation from sea from Third to First Class Surveying Recorders and have remained an integral part of the Surveying Service. Whereas there are usually sixty to eighty Officers in the Service, double that number of Recorders are normally employed.

In World War I the naval surveyors were widely scattered throughout the Fleet using their precise positioning skills for minesweeping, minelaying, placing of monitors for bombardment and maintaining surveys where they were required for safe passage of the Fleet and allied merchant ships. Many were decorated or mentioned for their skill and courage. Admiral Sir Andrew Cunningham, the great naval leader of World War II, wrote in *A Sailor's Odyssey* of how, in World War I in HMS *Termagant*, he escorted monitors to their assigned bombarding anchorages off the Belgian Coast in a thick fog, and wondered how on earth they could fix their precise location for indirect fire – however, 'I discovered that they had Captain H.P. Douglas of the Hydrographic Department onboard and that he was responsible for the navigation.'

So, in peace or in war, the Royal Naval Surveying Service continued to uphold the standards set for them by Captain Hurd 100 years earlier.

H.M. Ships employed on surveying duties are unarmed in peacetime and may be recognised by their white-painted hulls and superstructures and their buff-coloured funnels. Until recent times such ships were usually converted men-of-

4

war, but to-day the Hydrographer of the Navy commands a squadron of fine custom-built vessels which fly the White Ensign in Home Waters and in many remote parts of the world's oceans.

It was my good fortune to serve for thirty years in the Surveying Service, after which I became the nineteenth Hydrographer of the Navy, an honourable post which I held for five years. Subsequently I was elected for two five-year terms as President of the International Hydrographic Bureau in Monaco where, among the Hydrographers representing the fifty or so Member States of the Organisation, I found a similar dedication to hydrography and the closeness of a brotherhood such as I had known in the Royal Navy.

'In hydrographical surveying,' wrote Admiral Wharton, 'every day has its incidents.' What follows is an account of some of those incidents which have come my way during a long and happy life of hydrographic endeavour.

Chapter II

'Where Were the Hydrographers?'

At the Royal Naval College, Dartmouth, in the Duncan Term of the late 1920s and early 1930s our Term Officers would talk to us about the different specialisations we could opt for after completing three years at sea as midshipmen, and the sub-lieutenants' courses at Greenwich and Portsmouth. Our Term Officer was a 'destroyer man' who revelled in recalling the high speed manoeuvres at sea and the seamanship entailed in berthing three flotillas of destroyers in Sliema creek, the harbour reserved at Malta for destroyers. He urged us not to specialise but to become 'salt horses' – the true seamen.

This course I would surely have followed had I not, during one holiday from Dartmouth, met a venerable Admiral who set the course of my life. He was Sir Frederick Learmonth, a former Hydrographer of the Navy, who in retirement was currently serving on the Board of the Port of London Authority of which my father was then Secretary.

One evening the Admiral came to dinner. He had spent a lifetime in the Surveying Service, commanding surveying ships in many distant waters, and when I was introduced to him as a Dartmouth cadet his eyes sparkled above his well-trimmed white beard – he would no doubt have an attentive listener when the Madeira had been passed and the ladies left us men to ourselves, as was the custom in those days.

His tongue loosened, he warmed to his theme as he carried me with him to the remote north-west coast of British Columbia where, with an Indian pilot beside us on the bridge of *Egeria*, we navigated in treacherous currents through narrow channels flanked by dangerous rocks, the presence of which below the surface was indicated by but a few trailing fronds of seaweed; we spent days together in pulling boats with sextants and lead and line charting the deep inlets confined by towering fir and snow clad mountains; we landed and camped for the night on the fringes of the impenetrable forest, warm in our caribou sleeping bags. Then the Admiral shifted the scene to Borneo where he described similar adventures in a tropical and jungle setting. By now he was convinced he had recruited a young surveyor – 'Steve, my boy, always learn the local language so that you can get on with the natives who will clear the forest survey sites and guide you through the jungle. Sometimes knowing the language can be vital.' He then went on to relate how once in Borneo he had gone with the ship's doctor to shoot wild pig. The doctor had stationed himself on an overgrown track to await what the beaters might flush from the dense undergrowth. There had been a sudden rustling, a brown animal briefly glimpsed, and the doctor had fired, only to find that he had gravely wounded the local chief's son. 'Things could have been very difficult had I been unable to speak Malay – but as it was, matters were soon explained and settled – Yes, always learn the local language.'

Back at Dartmouth I asked those officers I could approach for details of the Surveying Service and how one could become a surveyor. Many had clearly never heard of this specialisation, whilst others did not treat my enquiries as serious. At last I found that our Term C.P.O. had once, many years before, served a commission in the *Mutine*, surveying the channels through the Great Barrier Reef. He had a peculiar way of sucking air in through the side of his mouth before speaking, and having thus taken in an abnormally large supply he pronounced – 'Surveying – that's hard graft all right – away all day sounding in open boats under the tropic sun – seven days a week. Mark you, I never tasted the tot so good as it did night times after the boats were hoisted. Ritchie, your seachest's like a scranbag – you Duncans is all the same, you'll never do no good at sea leavin' all your gear loafing, chokes the pumps in an emergency it does.'

In all my three years at sea as a midshipman I only saw a survey ship on one occasion – when a strange looking white ship with buff coloured funnel steamed into Grand Harbour, Malta. She was moored to buoys astern of my ship in French Creek and she looked more like a steam yacht than a naval vessel; she sported an impressive bowsprit and a crow's nest but carried no visible armament. She was the *Endeavour*, built as long ago as 1910, returning now to U.K. from her surveys in the Red Sea.

One of *Endeavour*'s officers came to dine with an old shipmate of his in our wardroom and I was Midshipman of the Watch when *Endeavour*'s boat came alongside. The boat's crew were suntanned and bearded, as was the officer; the

7

boat was workmanlike, if not immaculate, with chains still rigged for sounding. The coxswain handled the Kitchen rudder, as yet only a novelty in the Fleet, with a skill born of familiarity; 'the Kitchen rudder gives the coxswain the unique ability to box the compass without head-reaching,' said the surveyors. I had glimpsed at last the hydrographers, and my resolve to join them was strengthened, but this was not to be easy to achieve.

Half way through the sub-lieutenants' courses and before volunteering for specialisation we were sent off in great haste to join the Fleet as part of the mobilisation to meet the Abyssinian Crisis of 1935, and I found myself appointed Sub-Lieutenant of the Gunroom in the battleship *Valiant* on guard duty at Port Said. We had little to do but monitor the Italian troopships southward bound for Ethiopia through the Suez Canal, so our captain, being a gunnery specialist, decided to occupy us twice weekly with battalion drill on the beach at Port Said, for which I was made Second in Command to the gunnery officer; most unusually for these specialists he had a weak voice. I had not been called 'Stentor' for nothing at Dartmouth, and being fresh from Whale Island I was well acquainted with battalion drill – so I did the shouting. One morning, whilst I was enjoying my sense of power, marching the battalion to the very edge of the tide before shouting the complex orders to change direction, I was unaware that the captain had stepped from a staff car behind me and was admiring my efforts.

At last I saw an Admiralty Fleet Order calling for volunteers for Surveying, and putting my name forward found myself before the captain. 'Nonsense,' said he, 'I have watched you conducting battalion drill – you are cut out for gunnery specialisation.' I remonstrated but was told sharply to put in again in three months' time if I still persisted with this foolish idea. Twice more, at three monthly intervals, I put my name forward to the captain only to be deferred. Even my efforts as gunnery control officer during a night shoot, when I got the deflection 180° wrong when glimpsing the target vessel briefly in the glare of the searchlights, failed to convince my captain that I was not gunnery material, although it did earn me a resounding blast.

I despaired of becoming a surveyor, but, unknown to me, a golden opportunity lay close at hand. Six armed trawlers, rapidly commissioned with Reserve officers and men from the Fishing Fleet, were patrolling the coast of Palestine in a bid to prevent arms smuggling into that country. When passing through Malta on their voyage from England the double bottoms of these ships had been stocked plentifully with duty free liquor by a well-known firm of wine merchants. 'Pay as you drink,' the wine representative had said – it sounded a remarkably good deal to these fisherman, but eventually it led to a breakdown of efficiency in these vessels, to such an extent that it was decided to replace the officers and men with complements drawn from the larger ships in the Mediterranean Fleet. I found myself in my first command, H.M.S. *Lilac*, a trawler, operating from Haifa.

My mail, including Notices to Mariners from the Hydrographer, was impressively addressed to 'The Commanding Officer' and it took me only a short while to realise that I could now forward my own name direct to the Hydrographer as a volunteer for surveying. Three months later the need for patrolling lapsed and I brought *Lilac* home to Devonport at the end of 1935. Early in the New Year I was embarked in H.M.S. *Suffolk* bound for the China Station to join the surveying ship *Herald*. At last I was on my way to join the hydrographers.

Chapter III

The Pre-war Years

Before sailing for Hong Kong I was called to an interview with Admiral Edgell, the Hydrographer of the Navy, in his office in Whitehall. He presented me with a copy of *Hydrographical Surveying*, a manual which consisted of Admiral Wharton's original work of 1882, updated by Admiral Mostyn-Field, the Hydrographer, in 1908. Admiral Edgell further informed me that on arrival in *Herald* I would find copies of *The Hydrographic Review* which carried articles on modern techniques. It was published, he told me, by the International Hydrographic Bureau in Monaco where a retired British admiral, considerably senior to himself, was currently President. As a very junior 'Acting Fourth Class Surveying Assistant', as I had just become, such age and seniority seemed tantamount to senility. I see it differently now!

Vice Admiral Boyle Somerville, a distinguished hydrographic surveyor of the late nineteenth century, and inventor of an ingenious steam sounding machine, in his book *The Chart Makers* refers to the ships used for surveying.

> *'The Naval Surveying Service has ever had foisted upon it for its work any old castaway ship that has become useless for other branches of the Navy. No one knows except those who have suffered from them how much more difficult that work – and no more essential work for the safety of the Navy can be conceived – is made for us by the aged hoodlums that are handed out for our use. But of all the old clumbungies with which the Surveying Service has been saddled, the* Penguin *would be hard to beat for clumbunginess.'*

Things had changed little in this respect by 1936 and *Herald* could easily be substituted for *Penguin* as a clumbungie. Built twenty years earlier as the

Racehorse Class coal-burning sloop *Merry Hampton* for World War I convoy duties, the adoption of her classic survey ship name, the removal of her armament and the construction of a box-like chartroom aft were the only visible signs, together with her white hull and buff funnel, that *Herald* had become a surveying vessel. She certainly had old world charm. The captain's cabin opened onto the quarterdeck, where a Chinese carpenter had constructed a beautifully carved entrance porch in which potted plants thrived, whilst centrally on the forecastle stood an ancient twelve pounder saluting gun.

By the time I reached Hong Kong *Herald* was secured to a buoy in the harbour at the conclusion of the lie-up, her crew busily engaged in taking onboard coal, spars, bamboos, beacon drums, the wardroom wine stocks and ship's company beer, and generally making ready for surveys in the South China Sea.

I was shown to my cabin in the bowels of the ship and before unpacking I opened the scuttle to clear the fustiness of the compartment. No one had warned me that the old ship carried so much ballast to compensate for top hamper that this was unwise. The first passing ferryboat swamped the cabin.

My first surveying captain was Commander Hardy, a genial and popular man, later to be lost in the North Atlantic when in command of an armed merchant cruiser. The first lieutenant was 'Kechil' Collins, so named by the Malays in view of his small size, a nickname which stuck to him even when he subsequently became Hydrographer of the Navy. He was my instructor in surveying, an excellent man with a bubbling sense of humour. He gave me sound advice far beyond the strict limits of hydrography and introduced me to *The Bogus Surveyor* which he was currently engaged in having reprinted.

The Bogus Surveyor, or a Short History of a Peculiar People by Whitewash was written and published by a disillusioned naval surveyor named Gleig in 1887. There is a great deal of truth in this small work and an extract from Chapter III, 'A Marine Survey in General', although written fifty years earlier, may be used to describe the style of life onboard *Herald* in 1936.

'Before going further, it may be as well to furnish our readers with some few hints on the mode of life on board a surveying ship. There is a great deal more than surveying to be learnt by one desirous of advancement. The social life on board these vessels is of a peculiar nature. One should no more venture to step over the gangway of a surveying ship without some enquiry on this subject, than to invade the territories of a savage monarch single-handed and unarmed.

11

NO DAY TOO LONG – AN HYDROGRAPHER'S TALE

'It is a new life, entirely different from man-of-war routine, and some preparation is absolutely necessary. The ship after taking in sufficient stores of food and coal to last for two or three months, steams away to the barren coast, or unknown bay which it has been decided to examine. The resources of ordinary civilisation are now closed to the surveyor, he is cut off from all communications with his fellow men, and the ship and her surroundings form his entire world.

'The nature of the conversation soon brings home this fact to the novice, not only in working hours, but at all other times; surveying forms the basis of conversation for it is seldom indeed that any other subject is introduced. Never show any symptoms of fatigue during these dialogues, if unable to join in the discussion it is at least possible for the veriest novice to affect a keen interest. Too much stress cannot be laid on this advice; if an officer feels that he cannot keep up this assumption of interest in surveying, there can be little hope of his success, no matter what talents he may display whilst at work, what ingenuity in overcoming difficulties, all will be to no purpose if he cannot convince others that his heart and soul are in the Great Work alone. Even as 'Attitude is the art of Gunnery' so it may be said that 'Bunkum is the secret of Surveying.

'Young assistants are disposed to imagine, after having been away eleven or twelve hours on duty, from 'early morn to dewy eve' that further labour is unnecessary. Such is by no means the case, and it is most dangerous to try and break through established custom of this nature. In common with the rest of your messmates, always make a little show of doing at least one hour's work after dinner. This is one of the secrets of success.

'Thus, whilst taking care to surround himself with a shield of scientific works, rough angle books, etc. the assistant may after a little experience, keep up a running fire of remarks about his day's work. Something in this style: 'I say, Jones, was that your whitewash mark on Saucepan Rock? It showed splendidly.' 'Smith, what was your angle at Cliff Station between Hyde Peak and Sandhill?' or between anything no matter what. 'That theodolite of mine worked splendidly to-day, I wouldn't change it for any other' and so forth. What you say is of no consequence, so long as the proper interest in the work is apparent, for, entre nous, it is quite possible to hear a lot of scientific bosh even in the Chartroom.

'The Captain will nearly always be present on these occasions, for he is as much a part of the proceedings as an usher at evening studies; indeed his duties seem rather similar. À propos *of the Captain, always remember that the only road to advancement is through his favour. Luckily for the surveying service its Captains are specially selected for their impartiality, otherwise it would be difficult to award each assistant according to his merits.*

'The Idlers – the most miserable people on board a surveying vessel – are the Paymaster, the Doctor, and the Chief Engineer. They have no interest in surveying, and consequently dislike the isolated life which they are compelled to lead for about nine months in the year. Their growls, both loud and deep, resound through the after part of the ship; 'like Rachel weeping for her children' they cannot possibly be comforted.

'If only a fourth Idler were carried the case would be less hopeless, as they might while away the weary hours by playing whist, but such is seldom the case; and then again seeing so much of each other, deadly quarrels are no uncommon thing. We see no reason, however, why whist should not be reverted to even under these painful circumstances, if only there were a fourth party, but there's the rub. On no account should the young surveyor allow himself to be made use of to supply the missing link, such a course would be absolutely fatal to his future prospects; he might as well take to playing the fiddle or even pitch and toss . . . .

'The Doctor if he be of a scientific turn, may occasionally find something to interest him in the places visited; but the common or garden Irish surgeons had better be warned to keep away from a surveying ship.'

Hydrographic Surveying had changed little during the first thirty-five years of the twentieth century and it must be remembered that in 1936 *Hydrographical Surveying* by Wharton and Field published in 1908 was our current manual. In order therefore to give the reader some idea of how a marine survey was conducted in *Herald* in those days an extract from Chapter II of this manual – 'A Marine Survey in General' – follows:-

'Under ordinary circumstances, it is often a good plan to begin the survey of a coast from the shelter of some harbour, of which it will

13

*eventually be necessary to make a plan on a larger scale, and to
extend the triangulation outwards from thence.*

*'The base, which is measured primarily for the purpose of the plan,
being connected directly with the main triangulation of the coast
survey, is afterwards utilised for calculating the long side upon which
we shall begin plotting the coast survey. In case of the weather becoming unfavourable for the main triangulation outside, a harbour plan to
fall back on also prevents the loss of time that might otherwise ensue
under those circumstances; this is specially so when a large staff of
assistants has to be considered.*

*'In the survey of a particularly wild, stormy, and exposed coast,
such as the southern coast of Terra del Fuego, the general plan
adopted by Captain Fitzroy, of H.M.S. Beagle, was to measure a base,
and to survey, from the shelter of a harbour fixed astronomically, as
far afield as practicable, fixing·points to the utmost limit in every
direction. The harbour surveys were afterwards connected by sketch
surveys, the ship being fixed on the points already plotted, and all
theodolite shots to intermediate points utilised as far as practicable.
The use of steam now enables this sort of work to be carried out
somewhat differently and more expeditiously.*

*'If circumstances permit the use of floating beacons, the accuracy of
such work is much increased.*

'In the first place, Marine Surveys may be divided into three heads:

1st. Preliminary or Sketch Surveys.

2nd. Surveys for the ordinary purposes of navigation.

3rd. Detailed Surveys.

*'The boundaries between these are by no means strongly marked,
although each differs considerably from the other, and a finished sheet
as sent home is not unfrequently a combination of all three, comprising pieces of work done after very different fashions, according to
needs and circumstances.*

*'A preliminary survey does not pretend to accuracy. The time ex-
pended on it, and the means used, cannot ensure it, and it only repres-
ents what our second name for it indicates, a sketch. A sketch survey
will be founded on a base of some kind, but this will generally be
rough, and in some instances, as in many running surveys, will depend
solely upon the speed of the ship as far as it can be ascertained by*

patent log; so that the whole affair from beginning to end is only a rough approximation.

'The second head comprises the majority of charts now published, and many of those in course of construction in the present day, i.e., they are constructed on such a scale, and with such limitations of time, etc., as to make it impossible either to show small details of land or sea, or to be perfectly certain that small inequalities of the bottom, or detached rocks, may not exist, unmarked. Everything, however, shown in such a survey should be correct, and it is only in its omissions that it should be imperfect.

'A detailed survey is accurately constructed from the commencement, on a scale large enough to admit of close sounding, and time is given up to working out all the minutiae.

'Detailed surveys are normally confined to the more civilised shores of the world, where there is· much trade, and to such ports, harbours, and channels as are largely used in navigation.

'The necessity for these surveys increases to an enormous extent every year, with the prodigious strides trade, more especially trade by means of steam vessels, is taking.

'All surveys are, however, alike in this respect. They are, as it were, built up on a framework of triangles of some kind, the corners of which are the main 'points' of the chart, and to obtain this framework is always the first thing to do, and how to set about it the first thing to consider.

'The construction of this 'triangulation', as it is termed, is of various kinds; ranging, from the rough triangles obtained in a running survey, where the side is obtained by the distance it is supposed the ship has moved, and the angles are sextant angles, taken on board from a by no means stationary position, to the almost exactly formed triangles of a detailed survey, when carefully levelled theodolites observe the foundation of a regular trigonometrical network, which covers the whole portion to be mapped.

'The general plan of a survey may be said to be this:-

1st. A base is obtained, either temporary, as in the case of an extended survey; or absolute, as in a plan. This is the known side of the first triangle.

2nd. The main triangulation, that is, the establishment by means of angles of a series of positions, at a considerable distance apart, from *which, and to which, angles are afterwards taken, to fix other stations. These are the corners of our framework, and are known as the 'main stations', the two ends of the base being the first two, on which everything is built.*

3rd. The fixing by means of angles from these main stations of a sufficient number of secondary stations, and marks, to enable the detail of the chart to be filled in between them. In most cases angles will be required to be taken from the marks themselves as well.

4th. All these points, or those embracing a sufficient area to work on, being plotted on the chart, they are transferred to the field boards, either by pricking through the plotting sheet with a fine needle, or, what is a better way when carefully done, by making a tracing of them on tracing-cloth, and pricking through that on to the boards.

5th. Each assistant then has a portion told off to him to do. It must depend on circumstances, but as a rule it is more satisfactory to have the coast-line put in first, and the soundings taken when this has been done. The topography, or detail of the land, can be done at any time.

6th. Each piece of work is inked in by the assistant on his board, with all the detail, and when complete, is carefully traced on the above tracing of the 'points'. All bits are thus collected together, and the total is retransferred to the plotting sheet by means of transfer paper, and inked in as the finished chart.'

Within the triangulation the sextant and stationpointers provided an accurate method of fixing one's position. The theory of such a fix is shown in the sketch; the system has formed the very keystone of sea surveying for well over 150 years and has only recently been overtaken by electronic forms of positioning.

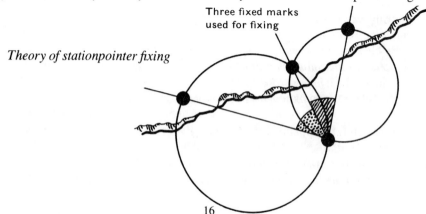

Three fixed marks
used for fixing

Theory of stationpointer fixing

16

Once the triangulation has been plotted the ship and her boats commence covering the sea area to be surveyed. Backwards and forwards they go, first running towards the shore then to seaward along pre-planned lines for sounding; the boats work along the coast in the shallower water; the ship continues the work to seaward from the boats' outer limits. Sextant and station pointer fixes are taken at regular and frequent intervals, the vessel being constantly conned to keep her on the pre-drawn lines. The surveying officer is assisted by his recorder who takes the second angle and records in the sounding book the angles observed and the soundings regularly called by the leadsman.

In the mid-1930s there were eight British surveying ships, four working in Home Waters and four overseas. *Herald* had for some years been progressing surveys off the East Coast of Malaya and the coasts of Sarawak and British North Borneo, the latter being undertaken when the north-east monsoon set in on the coast of Malaya.

These surveys in the South China Sea were of the two types classified by Admiral Wharton as those 'for the ordinary purposes of navigation' along the coast, which were carried out by the ship, and the 'detailed surveys' of the riverine ports and their close approaches which were achieved by detaching a boat and survey party.

My first experience of such a 'camp party' was at Kemaman on the East Coast of Malaya when I accompanied the navigator, Syd Hennessey, as a 'makee learner'.

Syd, then a lieutenant commander, had begun life on the lower deck, and as a seaman torpedoman in 1922 had trained in H.M.S. *Warrior* when Britain's first ironclad formed an integral part of H.M.S. *Vernon*, the torpedo school. He was a perceptive officer with a strong sense of discipline which he could bend to meet the particular circumstances to be found in a camp party. He had learnt his trade under a number of notable surveying captains over the previous ten years and I was fortunate to have Syd as my first tutor in the art of boat-sounding.

By clearing secondary jungle growth around Survey of Malaya triangulation stations on three hilltops we were able, with a minimum of delay, to fix the necesary whitewashed rocks and the flags which we had placed along the shoreline for the sounding and coastlining operations.

The District Officer had previously arranged for us the construction of a bamboo and atap (palm thatch) 'bungalow' on green sward overlooking a golden beach. Our boat was moored safely at a bend in the Kemaman River half a mile inland from our dwelling.

In a detached bathhouse a Malay boy kept a forty-gallon kerosene drum topped up with fresh water from which, by means of a half-coconut baler, we gave ourselves a chilling awakening douche before setting out each morning with our gear for the boat. As we passed through the gloomy palm groves Malays were quietly beginning their day, smoke from their kindled fires slowly rising in the damp morning air. By the time the boat reached the river mouth the sun was warm enough for us to remove our shirts and slip into our sarongs.

As the north-east monsoon began to set in the boat sounding became more boisterous, and on one such day, when the boat was bucking like a bronco, black-bearded 'Fras' Davis, the coxswain, pointed out in vigorous terms that it was in fact August Bank Holiday and, 'By rights I should be on Barnstaple beach with me old woman instead of trying to boat sound in these bloody conditions in the South China Sea.'

Syd and I alternated between boat sounding and coastlining. The latter was always a delight. Accompanied by a survey recorder we walked the shoreline fixing with horizontal sextant angles between our various survey marks at each change of direction of the coast, and sketching in the field book the changing terrain.

The turning of each small point of land opened up new vistas – a dazzling casuarina-backed beach, a rocky cove with sparkling blue water heaving toward the rocks, a hutted village beneath palm trees where a Malay deftly struck the top from a coconut with his parang to provide a cool reviving drink. At night, by the light of a paraffin lamp encircled by flying ants, one plotted the fixes taken during the day, joining them up with the aid of the field book to reveal the trend and intricacies of the coastline.

During my time in *Herald* her main survey ground off Borneo lay in the shallow waters stretching far to seaward from the delta of the Rajang, Sarawak's greatest river. Established triangulation was not available here and resort had to be made to fixing a datum geographical position on one of the low-lying islands in the delta. Here I spent instructive nights with Kechil Collins where we used the 45° fixed astrolabe and mercury horizon to observe the exact times of the passage of thirty-two stars, as each, predicted in our programme, sailed into view in the telescope during the long night watch. By an elegant use of prisms each star was made to pass eight times through a pair of its own reflections, such passage being recorded by the observer pressing a key which pricked a paper tape on which time was being regularly marked by a chronometer. Twice nightly, operations ceased, whilst earphones were put on and knobs twiddled on the radio to receive the series of pips comprising a rhythmic time signal transmitted from Rugby, half the world away.

From this accurately computed geographical position an extensive triangulation network of moored surveying beacons was laid out, these being giant spar buoys which, by means of a huge bamboo lashed to the main barling, enabled calico flags to be displayed to a height of thirty feet, visible for ten miles from the bridge of the ship.

Various sides of the beacon triangulation were measured as controlling baselines with the taut wire measuring gear, an ingenious apparatus fitted on the quarterdeck which allows over 100 nautical miles of piano wire to be pulled from its drum via a flyer arm and round a dynamometer wheel. A modest weight is attached to the end of the wire before lowering it to the seabed, effectively anchoring it as the ship gathers way. The number of revolutions of the dynamometer wheel, which is 6.08 feet in circumference, is recorded on a cyclometer so that the distance between one beacon and another may be read off in decimals of nautical miles as the ship passes close by them.

To plot the position of all the floating beacons within the triangulation it was necessary to observe the angles of all the triangles concerned by bringing the ship to a stop close to each beacon, whilst a team of officers and recorders on the bridge observed the various horizontal angles to other visible beacons with their sextants at the call 'Fix'. Simultaneously a range and bearing of the beacon close to which the ship lay was taken, so that correction to the angles could be made for the true station.

A scientist at the British Admiralty Research Laboratory named A.B. Brown turned his attention, when peace came after World War I, from the detection of submarines by underwater sound, on which he had been engaged, to devising a depth echo-sounding machine. Successful trials were carried out by the Hydrographer from a survey boat in the mid-twenties which resulted in the commercial manufacture by Henry Hughes and Sons Ltd. of 'The British Admiralty Select Super-Sonic Echo Sounder' in 1930.

Six years later such an apparatus was not to be found in *Herald*. In the survey boats we still relied on the traditional lead and line. There were three leadsmen, each capable of heaving the lead six fathoms ahead of the moving boat; in turn they spent an hour in the starboard chains, the port chains and then the forepeak, where they struggled to brew up tea for the crew on a Primus stove.

In deeper reef-infested waters Lucas wire sounding machines were fitted in the boats and it was common practice for a pair of boats to run alternate lines for mutual support. Every cable or so along the line the boat had to be turned into wind and held stopped whilst a sounding was taken. There is a tendency for small Lucas machines to overrun as the lead strikes the seabed, leaving a tangle of wire necessitating tedious unravelling with a pair of pliers. I can still see John Gruning, a fellow surveyor, as his boat surges past on the next line while I am hopelessly tangled with my Lucas wire; his whole great body shakes with laughter as he gestures towards me in a manner more recently adopted by Harvey Smith.

There was an early sonic type of echo-sounder in the ship employing a formidable hammer which, when released at regular intervals by two electromagnetic coils, struck a sharp blow upon a steel plate in the double bottoms, thus emitting a powerful sonic signal towards the seabed. The operator on the bridge manually rotated an inscribed drum back and forth until he received the loudest returning signal in his earphones: he then called out the depth indicated on the drum at that instant.

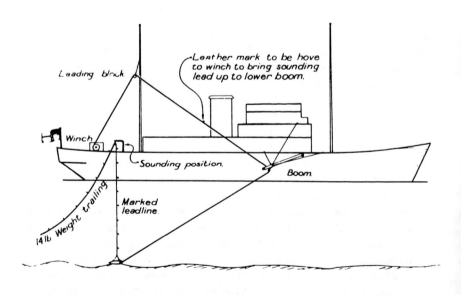

Somerville sounding gear

As soon as depths became less than eleven fathoms confidence in the echo-sounder was lost and the Somerville sounding gear swung noisily into action. By means of a steam winch on the quarterdeck the lead was hauled forward to the end of the lower boom abreast the bridge for each cast; the leadsman was situated in the chains near the winch from where he gently 'felt' the bottom with the leadline as it passed vertically beneath him. A trailing counterweight kept the leadline nicely taut throughout the operation. The winch, emitting steam and noise, was situated directly above the pusser's cabin making it immediately uninhabitable, which sent the Chief Idler, red-faced with fury, to the quarterdeck with the regularity of a cuckoo emerging from its clock.

An occasional weekend in Sarawak was spent at anchor off Pending a few miles down river from the capital Kuching. Sarawak was nearing its centenary of dynastic rule under the third White Rajah, Vyner Brooke, who occasionally invited the officers to the Astana where he held court; the Ranee and her three daughters were far distant, enjoying London's nightlife and the music of Harry Roy (whom Princess Pearl married). We spent the weekends as guests of European government officers, many of whom had Chinese or Malay wives or mistresses whose female relations moved in to entertain us visitors. Curry was always on the menu. Our men seemed happy in the Chinese-owned bars in the town and I cannot remember any troubles ashore ruffling those halcyon weekends.

Once I led a party far inland to observe from the peak of a distant mountain to which we travelled along jungle tracks with the aid of local guides. Pausing for refreshment at a remote Catholic mission in the foothills we were approached by a charming Chinese girl who handed us a chit on which was crudely written 'good for a dollar – Charlie Stirk H.M.S. *Herald*'. Our admiration for our enterprising stoker was considerable – we honoured this as an I.O.U., rather than a recommendation.

The 'survey season', as it was called, lasted eight months, and as winter came *Herald* headed northwards to Hong Kong for the so called 'lie-up', when the ship was docked and repaired and the surveying officers settled down to draw the fair charts resulting from the season's work. Draughtsmanship was still one of the surveyor's major skills, as it had been for 150 years, and we were proud to think that these meticulously drafted and hand coloured sheets might, after being used in the Hydrographic Office to compile new Admiralty charts, lie on the shelves of the archives alongside those penned by Captain Cook, Admiral Beaufort and many other great surveyors of the past.

My first fair chart was that of Kemaman, the drawing of which recalled for me those happy days on detachment there. As the work neared completion I experienced that feeling of personal achievement in adding, however modestly, to the seafarers' fund of knowledge which sustains hydrographers the world over.

The office in which we drew the charts lay close to the Hong Kong Club where we draughtsmen daily took our gin and a leisurely luncheon.

Deprived for eight months of social life, officers and men took full advantage of the nightlife Hong Kong had to offer. Bar and restaurant and many other payments were signed for on the chit system, the debts being collected by the various 'umbrella men' who visited the ship from time to time and especially when there was news of sailing. Even Ethel Morrison accepted chits for services rendered by her young ladies and if her 'umbrella man' failed to collect she put the chit in the Sunday offertory plate and an ecclesiastical umbrella man of great persistence subsequently arrived alongside.

On a sub-lieutenant's pay I could afford to keep a Chinese pony in the army stables in the New Territories. On Saturday afternoons, having imbibed generously at the 'Hunters Arms', I mounted my steed, and in a semi-intoxicated state careered across the rugged countryside in the wake of the Fanling Hunt's racing pack of draghounds.

The 1938 season was spent almost entirely off the north-east coast of Borneo charting the extensive reefs that stretched far to seaward; brief visits to Jesselton and Sandakan were augmented by a monthly visit to Singapore for coal, stores and recreation.

During weekends spent at Singapore, encouraged by the beautiful green golf courses, I took up that game. By then we had a new and somewhat severe captain, Commander Jenks, the only other golfer onboard. Increasingly I found myself his partner, the sombre rounds taking place on sunny afternoons when my fellow officers were 'poodle-faking' on golden beaches. Thus I was delighted when I heard the newly joined first lieutenant say that he was thinking of taking up golf. He could hardly believe his luck when I offered him my matched set of clubs at half the price I had paid for them new but three months earlier. A bargain was quickly struck.

A couple of weeks later I was bidden to the cuddy on a beautiful Saturday morning.

'Golf, Sub?' said the captain. 'We'll go to Tanglin right after lunch.'

'I've given up golf, Sir,' said I. 'I've sold my clubs.'

The captain was dumb with amazement, but quickly recovered.

'Sold your clubs! Who to?'

'The first lieutenant, Sir.'

The captain rang the quartermaster – 'Send No. 1 to me.'

Commander Jenks turned from the 'phone to dismiss me unceremoniously.

As I set out for the beach after lunch I watched with pleasure the first lieutenant humping his bulky bag of clubs over the gangway astern of the captain. I have never again set foot on a golf course.

By 1939 when I returned to England the Admiralty had at last recognised that custom-built ships were best suited for surveying and four Halcyon class minesweepers had been completed as surveying vessels with modern echo-sounders both onboard and in the boats. I served for a few months in the early part of the year in one of these ships – *Jason* under the command of Alun Jones, a slightly pompous but rather shy Welshman.

I recall an incident in *Jason* that occurred early one morning when the captain and I were alone on the bridge as we sailed down the Bristol Channel after week-ending in Avonmouth. Commander Jones, rather short in stature, was on the 'monkey's island' whilst I, as navigator, was at a lower level at the chart table. The captain had recently acquired one of the new-fangled electric razors and was describing to me their efficacy. 'Feel the smoothness of my chin,' said he as he bent down towards me. I was perforce obliged to comply, and as my fingers touched his face I saw beyond him the leading signalman, who had joined the ship that very weekend, mounting the ladder onto the open bridge. His jaw dropped and, wide-eyed, he turned about on the ladder and descended out of sight. Presumably he was off to the messdeck to enquire as to what sort of a ship he had joined where the officers stroked each other, before breakfast!

By midsummer I had been transferred, as a volunteer, to another new vessel, *Franklin*, bound for Labrador (at that time, with Newfoundland, a British Colony) to undertake a survey of St. Lewis Inlet to facilitate timber extraction. Commander Charles Sabine, a polite and courteous man, was our captain, whilst the first lieutenant was a small thick-set Australian named Carl Oom who had a twinkle in his eye and saw the funny side of every situation. Another Australian, Tex Cody, a handsome bibliophile, had accompanied me from *Jason* bringing with him his precious collection of books including the 'Note-books of Leonardo da Vinci'.

The area to be surveyed was large, with many bays and islands, and the first task was to build up the triangulation. The 'balancing' of such a network in those pre-computer days entailed much mathematical work in the chartroom employing Bruhn's logarithmic tables and Shortrede's trigonometrical tables, both running to seven figures. One forenoon when the junior officers were thus engaged, the captain made a visit to the chartroom – 'Oh dear, Cody's faded away again. Ritchie, go and get him.' I descended to the wardroom situated immediately below the chartroom and there found Tex comfortably seated in an armchair, a glass of brandy to hand as he studied Leonardo's plans for a flying machine. 'Tex, the captain wants you up top. Don't you find it worrying sitting here knowing the captain may demand your presence at any moment?' Luxuriously drawing upon his cigarette he replied – 'That element of danger adds piquancy to the pleasure I am experiencing.'

Once a week Stan Brazil, the bulky storekeeper in the distant village, arrived alongside in his noisy trapboat with mail and newspapers which brought news of the increasing imminence of war.

We were in an area of poor radio reception but the receipt of a coded message was sufficient for our captain to decide to sail for our war station at Dover, where *Franklin* was required to provide the control for the laying of the Channel Mine Barrage.

There was a flurry of activity as the boats, including Stan's trapboat, were sent with parties to mark permanently the many triangulation stations and recover detached parties already established. Then to Halifax, where we found a lively scene of activity as British and Canadian naval vessels hurriedly embarked fuel, ammunition and stores to the maximum capacity. We had only to embark fuel before setting off unarmed across the Atlantic, feeling very lonely as we received an Admiralty General Message – 'Fuse all shell arm all warheads. Prepare for war.'

In the Western Approaches we encountered a number of British merchant ships hastening south-westwards to avoid being included in the first convoys. Then came the message 'Winston is back', informing the Fleet that we now had a First Lord of the Admiralty in whom we could have faith.

Vice Admiral H.P. Douglas, previously mentioned for his work in World War I and Hydrographer of the Navy from 1924-1932, had been recalled for war service as Admiral Superintendent Dover. As we steamed into harbour on the Sunday morning on which Chamberlain declared war he sent us a brief message – 'Welcome Home. Paint grey.' We set to work on this task that very afternoon.

Chapter IV

The Early War Years

Franklin's immediate wartime task was to provide the control for the laying of the Channel Mine Barrage from the railway ferry ships *Hampton* and *Shepperton* which, in peacetime, plied daily between Dover and Calais. By modifying the rail tracks already onboard these ships, mines that had been stored in tunnels in the cliffs below Dover Castle could be embarked at the Eastern Breakwater.

Franklin proceeded to sea every other day to lay a line of beflagged beacons across the Channel from the Goodwin Sands to the sandbanks off Calais, fixing them by sextant observations and taut wire measurement.

On return to harbour I took my fieldboard, on which conspicuous shore marks, the beacons and the intended mining lines were plotted, and together with my survey recorder, joined *Hampton*. Tex Cody, similarly equipped, joined *Shepperton*.

At dawn Captain Page, *Hampton*'s peacetime captain and a superb shiphandler, aided by his bow rudders, would be out of harbour within minutes. Keeping as close as we dared to the outer edge of the Goodwin Sands we turned onto the intended line and began, with sextants and station pointers, to plot the ship's position and correct her course as for ship sounding. In low visibility, so often encountered, the beacons were difficult to see and we were acutely aware, as the mines plopped over the stern at regular intervals, that our failure to fix our position correctly might allow us to be set by the strong tidal streams onto the previously laid mines of the barrage. Halfway across the Channel, our mines laid, we pulled out of line and *Shepperton* turned in astern to continue the lay. It was quite a tricky business.

The objects of the mine barrage were two-fold – first by general proclamation of its existence it was designed to divert neutral merchant ships through the Downs where they could be examined for contraband on its way to the enemy and arrangements made for its removal; secondly by laying some mines deeper than others it was hoped to catch U-Boats outward bound for the Atlantic.

Both objects were rapidly achieved. Whilst the Downs became crowded with anchored merchantmen unwillingly awaiting inspection, we saw one morning at daybreak a U-Boat wrecked on the South Goodwins. I was put onboard from a boat in choppy seas but could not descend below the conning tower for she was flooded from a massive hole in her hull. By the time divers arrived from Dover she was already breaking up in a south-east gale and in a few days the Goodwins had claimed every vestige of her. Despite a search of all the neutral shipping in the Downs no survivors from this U-Boat were found.

The next development of consequence was the laying of magnetic mines by parachute from enemy aircaft in the shallow waters around south-east England. To devise an antidote to these new weapons it was essential to recover one of these mines intact for examination.

One of the most desperate plans to achieve such a capture was the gathering in the area of about 100 ancient fishing trawlers together with their skippers and crews from Aberdeen and Grimsby. Twenty-five of these vessels were assigned to each of four harbours, Dover, Sheerness, Harwich and Yarmouth; they were known as 'Look Out Trawlers'. The idea was to anchor at dusk a number of these vessels in carefully fixed locations and with a good watch perhaps three or four trawler skippers might be able to take compass bearings of the point of impact of a parachuted mine so that the position of the fallen mine could be fixed. A surveyor was allocated to each flotilla of trawlers as general co-ordinator, navigator and administrator. I was appointed to the staff of Captain Minesweeping Dover for this task. Once the position of a fallen mine was reasonably well pin-pointed, it was my job to direct selected trawlers to this position where they used their normal fishing trawls to try to catch up the mine. The next step, had we been successful, was to buoy the trawl, cut the warp and await the arrival of a wooden barge and its crew of divers to recover the mine.

Two of my trawlers, one of which had been built in 1903, were lost without trace on their way south from Aberdeen, whilst the remaining twenty-three which reached Dover were daily beset by all manner of breakdowns. There had been no time to outfit the crews with uniform, but when ashore they wore an armband bearing the letters 'R.N.' to preserve their pride in a port where uniform was the order of the day. Captain Simpson, my boss, sat at his defaulters' table to deal with the many and varied cases I brought before him, the great majority of which were alcohol related. On one occasion a skipper was charged for his failure to get his ship to the scene of a minefall soon after dawn.

'I was paralysed,' he said.

'What! At that time of day?' asked Captain Simpson. We had not yet learned the trawlerman's expression for fouling his trawl in a seabed obstruction.

Perhaps we were fortunate that we did not 'catch' a mine before Lieutenant Commander Ouvry was able, with great courage, to dismantle a magnetic mine which was uncovered at low water on Maplin Sands. This led directly to the degaussing of ships as an antidote to these shallow water weapons. This took the strain off the Look Out Trawlers and in the ten days or so that remained before their disbandment we turned our trawling attention to Hythe Bay, a rich ground closed to fishermen under wartime regulations. We fed well, particularly on skate which trawlermen believe has aphrodisiac qualities. Cloth-capped men with R.N. armbands became sought after figures in Dover dockside pubs with their soggy paper parcels of prime fish for barter. It was not long before local fish traders registered a complaint with Flag Officer Dover and it was high time to bid farewell to my trawlers as they headed homewards. I was appointed back to *Franklin*, and I too sailed away northwards, to the Faroe Islands.

Compared with the occupation of Iceland by British forces, the take over of the Faroes in 1940 was a low key affair. Whilst a destroyer took an official delegation to the capital, Thorshavn, *Franklin* entered Scaale Fjord and commenced her survey for use as a fuelling base for allied warships. Two asdic trawlers patrolled the narrow entrance in the interests of safety, whilst our sounding boats criss-crossed the mirror-like waters of the fjord in glorious weather. Faroese fishermen in passing boats raised their caps politely if unenthusiastically; onshore the crofters showed little interest in our diggings in search of Danish triangulation stations.

These would have been halcyon days had it not been for the depressing news filtering in daily on the radio concerning the evacuation of the British Army from the beaches of Dunkirk. Many of our Dover friends were involved – Captain Archie Day (later Hydrographer of the Navy) was Chief of Staff for the operations, and my old chief, Captain Simpson, whose sympathetic handling of the trawlermen I had much admired, had been appointed in command of the destroyer leader *Keith*. He was killed on the bridge when attacked by enemy aircraft in Dunkirk Harbour whilst embarking troops. Lieutenant Commander

Robin Bill, the surveyor who had relieved me on the staff of Captain Minesweeping Dover, was awarded the D.S.O. for his leadership and courage in his small vessel *Conidaw* whilst clearing damaged shipping from that same harbour.

The sinking of *Royal Oak* by Commander Prien in Scapa Flow in October 1939 had exposed the insecurity of this major fleet anchorage. In his U-Boat Prien had entered the Flow through one of the Eastern Sounds despite the numerous blockships and strong currents. Winston Churchill was determined to close this loophole by building causeways across the three sounds; but first it seemed prudent to ensure that such closures would not increase the tidal streams in Hoxa Sound, the main entrance to the anchorage, to such an extent that protective anti-submarine and torpedo booms could not be maintained there.

A model of Scapa Flow was rapidly devised at Liverpool University to resolve this important query and *Franklin* sailed from the Faroes to Scapa to provide the missing data – the strength of the tidal streams flowing through the Eastern Sounds. This survey was to be made by releasing buoyed drogues into the current at the entrances to each Sound. The floats were then plotted through the Sounds by synchronised theodolite observations from shore. The recovery of the floats and their carriage back to the start line at half-hourly intervals, against currents expected to exceed twelve knots, required the use of a speed-boat which was shipped to Scapa Flow for the purpose. It was a thrilling experience to ride the speedboat through the Sounds. One actually travelled downhill as the boat raced through the narrow gaps in the jumble of blockships in pursuit of the drogues; then followed the long slow climb back to the start line. One could not stifle one's admiration for Commander Prien's superb skills as a seaman.

One night whilst at Scapa a signal came in from the Hydrographer ordering our first lieutenant, Carl Oom, to fly to London the following day. A farewell dinner in the wardroom was quickly arranged during which an air raid on the Fleet developed. In hilarious mood we gathered on the bridge with the captain and, whilst our six pounder blazed away from the forecastle, we joined in with stripped Lewis guns. The countless tracer bullets and exploding shells made a magnificent display above the Fleet. It was a great farewell for Carl.

On arrival in the Hydrographer's Office in Whitehall, Oom was ordered to report to a location in Cricklewood in north-west London, not far from Staples Corner which in later years we all came to know so well. He arrived in uniform at the entrance to an impressive new building nearing completion where an official, speaking in hushed tones, ordered Carl to go away and return the following day in plain clothes as this was a highly secret area. An air raid over London developed during the night and on returning to the site next day, suitably clothed in sports jacket and flannels, Carl found the building a smoking ruin and the secretive official nowhere to be seen. Back at the Hydrographic Office Admiral Edgell seemed only mildly surprised – 'Oh well, we'll have to find you another appointment.'

About this time our engineer officer was relieved by Lieutenant Commander Jimmy Maguire R.N.R., who had in peacetime been for some years the staff engineer onboard the luxurious *Queen of Bermuda* which ferried tourists from New York to those happy isles. This had been a social appointment, hosting the chief engineer's table and, in spotless white overalls, conducting passengers around the engineroom, leaving the Chief to perform his engineering duties unhindered.

During his eighteen months in *Franklin* Jimmy was never known to enter the engineroom, his self-appointed action station being on the roof of the chartroom at the after end of the vessel where he manned the Holman projector. This curious weapon consisted of a pipe set at an angle of 65° to the horizontal which could be rotated through a fixed arc astern by means of bicycle handlebars affixed to the pipe. The object was to deflect an aircraft coming in from astern by exploding hand grenades in the air ahead of it. The grenades, stacked in a rack alongside, were pre-set to seven seconds delay, and whilst Jimmy directed the weapon his writer pulled the pins from the grenades as he dropped each one down the pipe. The weight of the grenade on reaching the bottom of the pipe opened a steam valve, the pressure from which projected the grenade skywards. Practising with water-filled beer cans Jimmy and his writer had reached a high standard of Holman efficiency and were probably responsible for saving our lives on our way south for a refit in West India Dock.

Off Lowestoft in the searched channel one evening we were at action stations when an enemy aircraft came in purposefully astern. Jimmy opened his Holman barrage exploding right in the path of the Heinkel which, veering to port, dropped its bombs harmlessly. These shook the ship, and set the adrenalin running, but no damage was done.

The West India Dock was a dreary place in the winter of 1940–1941. The ship was cold and cheerless; the docksides were pitch dark, illuminated only by firebombs which fell nightly. A small party huddled onboard to deal with these, while the rest of the dutywatch did firewatch on the roof of the Port of London Authority Building, headquarters of the Flag Officer London.

Divisions onboard in wartime were an infrequent occurrence and the news that the Hydrographer would be inspecting the ship's company during our sojourn in West India Dock sent everyone jumbling through their kit lockers in search of their No 1s. On the great day Jimmy Maguire arrived onboard, after a night in the West End, only minutes before Admiral Edgell, who later appeared not a little startled when the engineer officer, after saluting, moved to place his arm around the Hydrographer's waist as he addressed him: 'Meet the Stokers, Sir, they're lovely people.'

The passing of the years has blurred the chronology of *Franklin*'s many activities in 1941. I recall nights at anchor off Happisburgh Lighthouse awaiting the dawn call to proceed, together with a Trinity House tender, to survey and buoy a diversion from the shallow swept channel where it had been blocked by merchant vessels sunk by E-Boats during the night. I remember squatting in a darkened trawler, my survey boat moored astern, whilst waiting on site to resume the search in daylight with echo sounder and chain sweeps for a suitable unencumbered area of seabed on which to establish the sea defence towers off the Thames Estuary. These platforms, built ashore, were towed out and sunk in position much as an oil rig is placed today.

Detached parties were a pleasant relief from life at sea on the East Coast; we were sent not to survey areas but to establish trigonometrical networks and transit beacons for the precise laying of shore controlled anti-invasion mines in such diverse locations as the Essex rivers and Peterhead Harbour of Refuge. Our billets varied from a yacht clubhouse to a Scottish farm, whilst everywhere we were regarded with suspicion by the Army, the Police and the public at large as we peered through our theodolites. In those days when invasion seemed imminent such activities as ours never passed unnoticed.

On one occasion *Franklin* was sent to the West Coast of Scotland to survey the irregular and rocky seabed of Kilbrannan Sound which was to be used as a sheltered submarine exercise area. Fitted as the ship was with asdic and depth charges, as well as our six pounder gun, we acted as a convoy escort when moving from one area of operations to another. This was before the days of radar and stationkeeping in a darkened convoy was a nerve-racking business. On passage northwards on our way to the West Coast we were stationed ahead of a convoy which had formed into four columns north of Flamborough Head. Here the searched channel was marked only by single mid-channel buoys every five miles or more, convoys keeping to the starboard side of the channel.

Northwards from Bell Rock we found ourselves in thick fog whilst expecting to pass a southbound convoy during the night. Shortly before midnight I was on my way along the boatdeck, together with two seamen, to relieve the watch on the bridge. The ship had slowed down, whilst sirens wailed all about us in the fog. Suddenly the ship shuddered and heeled over to port and a terrible noise of grinding ensued as the tanker *Donax* crashed along our starboard side. It was the Commodore's ship coming from astern, and as we dashed hither and thither to avoid our heavy boats' davits, which were falling like forest trees in a hurricane, we heard the Commodore, far above, shouting from his flying bridge as he passed – 'Keep calm, men! Keep calm.' Nor was respite to be found on the other side of the boatdeck as a ship of the southbound convoy ground her way aft along our port side. The two convoys had met head on in a gridiron situation but little *Franklin* was the only vessel to sustain severe damage. As dawn broke the fog lifted and the first rays of the sun lit the windows of the white cottages of my home village five miles to the west! We were in Aberdeen for a month for repairs to the hull and davits during which time I often visited Collieston. Our house was empty and chill. My parents were far away: my father at his post as General Manager of the beleaguered Port of London, my mother, as Commandant of the Women's Legion, organising mobile canteens for the hard-pressed stevedores in the London Docks. I was taken in at the Manse where many a shipwrecked mariner had been given succour in the past. The good wives of Collieston put together a bedspread of knitted squares as a parting gift which I used through all my years at sea.

Soon my days in *Franklin* were over and 18th January 1942 found me on an overcrowded train bound from Euston to Liverpool. It was a bitterly cold night in the darkened and unheated carriage; snow lay on the platforms of unnamed stations where interminable delays occurred, whilst the inevitable cups of wartime tea were handed onboard by voluntary women workers from their mobile canteens. This was the beginning of an eighty-day voyage which took me from London to Suez and changed my whole life.

Chapter V

The Middle East

S.S. *Ceramic* was a passenger/cargo liner in which a novel system of automatic coal stoking had been installed. During the war she made an occasional round voyage to Australia and New Zealand via the Cape of Good Hope carrying civilians who had long awaited passage home. Naval personnel bound for the Middle East also sailed in *Ceramic* as far as the Cape, and on this occasion there were about twenty naval officers and 150 Royal Marines. Lieutenant Commander 'Egg' Irving, a fellow surveyor, and I were bound for Suez to join the surveying ship *Endeavour* which was about to sail from Singapore. Carl Oom and his vivacious wife Eve were returning to Australia.

As the convoy gathered in the North Channel on a wet and blustery morning I stood on the sodden deck and gazed across the grey waters. My spirits were at a low ebb, when they were suddenly lifted by the sight of a young woman with flowing corn-blonde hair walking the empty decks. Some few days out from Liverpool I persuaded Eve Oom to invite this young woman to join us for drinks in the Oom's cabin. Disa and I thus met for the first time, and for me this long wartime voyage became one of pure joy.

One night in the North Atlantic the thump of depth charges and the sky alight with starshell signalled a U-boat attack on the convoy; later in the night the convoy was ordered to scatter northwards. In normal times our captain would have retired long since to the 'Anchorage' to relive his memories, but the necessity of war had kept him at sea with all its anxieties. His immediate problem, when the weather had cleared sufficiently for a sight of the sun, was that the ship's northerly position made it impossible to reach Lagos, where stocks of specially graded coal awaited us. He set course for Halifax. The city lay deep in snow and at night was a glorious blaze of reflected light. Unrationed goods were freely available, but no coal of a suitable type for *Ceramic*'s automatic stoking system. Such coal had to be shipped from Prince Edward Island; meanwhile, for four days and nights we revelled in the parties laid on by the Canadian Navy and the butter and cream and other delights so scarce in Britain.

Ceramic was sailing south past the Windward Isles when a message was received ordering the ship to Rio de Janeiro to embark 100 tons of very special but unidentified cargo. As soon as we came to anchor beneath the towering Sugarloaf an officer was despatched to the British Embassy in search of the special cargo; and fortunately the chief steward simultaneously landed the great bulk of the ship's linen for laundering as fresh water was in short supply onboard. No sign of the cargo was found, but the laundry took three days to return our linen. What a bonus befell Disa and me, two nights ashore on the Copacabana in the midst of a war!

On board was a half hogshead of naval rum for the marines' daily ration and I had been put in charge of it. The first officer had begged me to make sure it was empty before the troops left the ship in Cape Town; at the end of a previous voyage some rum had remained in the barrel which had caused tedious accounting difficulties with the Director of Naval Victualling. Fifty-six days after leaving Liverpool we berthed alongside in Cape Town, on every day of which I had quaffed my tot at noon like a good matelot.

Leaving *Ceramic* I remained only four days in Cape Town, but long enough to marry Disa and to enjoy a brief honeymoon in the Mount Nelson Hotel before joining a Norwegian troopship *en route* for Suez. Onboard there were four officers to a single cabin – no wife, no grog, no fun – the honeymoon was truly over.

Tragically *Ceramic* was sunk by a U-boat off West Africa on her voyage home with only four survivors. The aged captain, the first officer and even the empty rum barrel never reached their home port.

In 1941 it had been decided to refit the elderly survey ship *Endeavour*, which had been laid up in Singapore since the outbreak of war. She was then to be sailed to Suez where Irving, myself and others were to join her for work in the Middle East. However, even while we were on our way out in *Ceramic* Singapore had fallen to the Japanese and a crew made up of *Prince of Wales* survivors had made their escape in *Endeavour*. Harassed at times by Japanese aircraft the ship was sailed southwards to Sumatra where, moored alongside a rickety wooden wharf, and camouflaged with giant palm fronds, the bunkers were replenished from a deserted coal mine. Captain Baker, appointed as her surveying commander, was able to join her in Aden to sail on to Suez.

There *Endeavour* lay when Egg and I disembarked from our troopship. She appeared little more than a mobile hulk with a crew of disillusioned survivors who had hoped to be on their way home. There was much to be done. The ship was docked, echo-sounding machines were found and a complement of officers was gathered in; only the engineer officer remained of those who had sailed the ship from Singapore.

By early April we were ready. The first job was to survey the Great Bitter Lake where anchorages were required for merchant ships to be off loaded by barge as the Canal Ports were now fully extended; a chart of the lake and its shores was also required for a combined operations training centre being established there.

Soon I found myself training on the Lake with the Army's Special Boat Section to which I had been seconded. With Lieutenant Allot of the Middlesex Regiment I learnt to use the canvas folding canoes known as 'folboats' for clandestine beach surveys behind enemy lines. It was now the Army's plan to launch tank landings behind the enemy's front line on suitable beaches in Cyrenaica, tank landing craft having become available in the Mediterranean.

Our training was brief but during it the two of us developed a method of measuring the profile of a beach in darkness and determining whether runnels existed. Whilst Allot, who was smaller and lighter than I, paddled in the bows I was free to place a peg in the sand at the water's edge to which was attached a marked distance line. As the canoe moved seaward I took a leadline sounding and recorded it on a scribing board as each tangible mark on the measuring line passed through my left hand. Later in the war this system was perfected and employed by trained navigators and surveyors, but I believe we were the pioneers.

By early May we were in Tobruk, having been flown there with our khaki-brown folboat neatly packed in its two bags. We embarked in a motor torpedo boat and, escorted by another, we were transported across the Gulf of Bomba through the night. I slept soundly and about three hours before dawn we were awakened to launch our folboat about two miles off the enemy's shore; our object being to survey a beach which had been selected from air photographs as a possible landing for tanks.

It was a calm night and as we paddled shorewards the noise of the departing motor launches was horrific and we imagined every enemy soldier along the shoreline would be alerted, but as we grounded gently on the sand all was quiet, and we carried our folboat up the beach and lay down beside it in a cluster of thick bushes about 100 yards above the shore.

The idea was to lie up all day and carry out the survey the following night. The morning passed peacefully, but early in the afternoon we were awakened from our dozing by the sound of motor bikes, first one, then others, to be followed by a dozen trucks from which leapt scores of Italian soldiers shouting as they splashed into the sparkling sea in their swimming trunks. It was recreational bathing, to be followed by a mass game of hide and seek. The majority ran to hide in the bushes, to be sought out by a team of six or so who tried to catch the hiders before they could reach base on the beach. Two of the soldiers actually lay down in our bush. Thankful that I was wearing khaki I squatted tight as a hare in its form as the seekers cast about like beagles in search of the scent. It was an agonizing afternoon and when whistles were sounded we thought we had been discovered; happily it was the sergeant calling the men to return to their trucks; a fortunate escape indeed.

As soon as darkness fell we were afloat engaged on our survey. It was an ideal beach for landing craft and having completed the work we made our way north to find a quieter hiding place for our second day. We found it on a long strand, liberally scattered with bushes, and separated from the mainland by a shallow lagoon.

After a peaceful day, but one of increasingly strong wind from the north east, we set off eastwards across the great Bay of Bomba. The plan was that we were to find our own way back to British lines some twenty miles across the Bay.

The seaworthiness of the folboat was well proved during the gale that night; at times Allot continued to paddle while I perforce had to bail. Soon after dawn we saw to our dismay that a considerable battle was in progress on land to the south of us. We could hear the crump of gunfire and shells exploding, whilst through binoculars we could see tanks slowly probing eastwards. To avoid the battle and reach our own lines we must keep at sea as long as we could, although the north-easterly gale was slowly driving us towards the shore.

We paddled on all day but by late afternoon we were utterly exhausted. Happily things seemed quieter ashore so we allowed ourselves to be driven in to the shallower, calmer water. Suddenly we were spotted and gesticulating soldiers ran to the shore and fired a few shots over our heads. We gave up, so stiff that we could not rise from the canoe. We were lifted out by excited soldiers whose unusual uniform and helmets together with their gutteral tongue identified our captors as Germans. We were in the bag!

We were rushed to a dugout and confronted by an officer for interrogation. 'Names and Units, please.' His accent was unmistakably South African – his men had been speaking Afrikaans.

The battle we had witnessed from seaward had been the opening of a new German offensive which took them within striking distance of the Nile Delta by the end of June. In Cairo the General Staff began to consider contingency plans for the loss of the Canal Zone. The campaign might have to be fought from southern Egypt and the Sudan where Port Sudan, capable of handling only 8,000 tons a day, was the only viable supply base.

Endeavour was sent south in search of harbours from which military supplies could be augmented. The ship was aged, and was sometimes capable of only five knots as the young stokers struggled with shovel and slice to keep up steam; the poor quality coal embarked at Port Sudan frequently coagulated on the fire bars. The officers and survey recorders formed a uniquely skilled and harmonious team the like of which I have never seen bettered. We were led by Captain 'Buck' Baker, idolised in the Surveying Service; he was first and foremost a seaman who could give you a well-deserved and fearsome blast in the morning yet stand you a friendly gin at noon; he had been known to outswear the hardest fishing skipper when the latter had trawled across Buck's bows when sounding.

We surveyed the ancient port of Suakin with its deserted township and tumbled graves of British soldiers who had died in the campaign against the Mahdi; the extensive anchorage of Mersa Halaib lying between an island and the village which surrounded the well where long-haired Nubians watered their white camels, which we learned to ride as the only transport available for setting out the triangulation; then to the legendary Port Berenice of the Ancient Egyptians where we saw but a single old man on the beach crying 'Hakim, Hakim!' until our doctor came ashore to minister to his many afflictions. Port Berenice is formed by a basin bounded by coral reefs with a narrow entrance from the south.

I landed at dawn one morning with my surveying recorder to climb a 600-foot peak in order that, with other observers similarly placed on triangulated stations, I could intersect the masthead of the ship by theodolite angle at given signals as the observers on the bridge 'shot up' the positions of sounding marks erected along the shoreline. By the time I reached the summit, the shadows were still lengthy in the morning sun as I watched through the telescope of the theodolite the ship slowly moving out of harbour. Suddenly the mast stopped moving and remained rigidly in line with the vertical crosswire. The ship was surely aground and within a few minutes the large black recall flag was at the masthead.

In his haste to get on with the work the captain had sailed before the sun was high enough to define the limits of the shallow coral reefs bordering the channel. By the time the observing parties were back onboard kedge anchors were being laid out from the ship's whalers astern, the cables were being veered to the seabed at the bows and the ship's company were mustering aft for the jumping in unison which is sometimes efficacious. But more had to be done – the ship must be rid of a quantity of heavy stores, and here 'Hadji' Bailey came to the fore; a slim, bearded Reserve Officer he had been surveying in the Gulf of Suez long before *Endeavour* arrived and had learnt to speak Arabic tolerably well. Fortunately two large unladen dhows were at anchor nearby awaiting a change of wind to continue their voyage. Hadji was sent over to the dhows and managed to cajole their masters by promises of rewards in kind to berth alongside, and the tedious task of transferrring 150 tons of stores into each of the two vessels began, every officer and man lending a hand. By noon the following day the job was complete and at the height of the feeble tide renewed efforts were made to dislodge the ship from the reef. With the engine going astern, the winches hauling on the kedge anchor cables and the ship's company jumping in unison to No. 1's orders, a slight trembling movement was felt. The magic moment had come as the ship slowly began to move astern. A cheer went up from the men.

Once the bower and kedge anchors had been recovered the ship was again anchored in the harbour and the stores had then to be re-embarked, all except those claimed by the dhow masters. Rope, canvas, timber and tinned victuals in profusion were demanded, each item being haggled over by the first lieutenant, Hadji, the two Arabs and the protesting paymaster, a peacetime bank manager who had never seen such dealings in the High Street. Finally the ship lay ready for sea again, her exhausted crew flaked out around the awning covered decks, for the captain had announced a very hard-earned 'make and mend'.

Meanwhile the tide of war had turned in the Western Desert; the Battle of Alamein had been won by 3rd November and the Eighth Army was once more moving forward. Landing Ships (Tanks) were expected soon to arrive in Suez and the invasion of Southern Europe was already being planned. Training beaches were to be found for ambitious landing exercises and *Endeavour* was sent to Akaba at the head of that Gulf where the two-mile-long beach was found to be eminently suitable, as was the complex of small beaches at Sherm Shaikh at the very tip of the Sinai Peninsula.

Paul Clark was our navigator, his languid manner belying the skill and courage he was later to show in a midget submarine guiding in the invasion fleet to the beaches of Normandy. He was among our number one day when a party of us were given leave to accept an invitation from the Arab Legion to visit the ancient city of Petra.

We were taken in jeeps up the old Akaba-Damascus road many miles until we reached an outpost high above Petra. The plan was to ride down the winding track on horseback, a motley collection of ponies being provided. There was, however, one magnificent white Arab stallion, belonging to the commanding officer, and a competent rider being called for Paul volunteered. He had hardly got into the saddle when the animal was away at full speed down the track, the Arab cloak, which Paul was wearing, streaming out behind him. Parts of the track disappeared behind the contours of the hills and our little party nervously awaited each reappearance of the Gilpin-like figure quite out of control. Far down the track we sighted two old crones driving before them a couple of donkeys, heavily laden with firewood, unaware of impending disaster. Round the bend came the stallion and, unable to pause, leapt the donkeys as the old women jumped aside. The horse's belly scraped the donkeys' loads and they, together with Paul and his mount, crashed to earth in a cloud of dust.

We hurried down the track on our less active steeds to find Paul nursing a bruised knee, the two donkeys still on their backs waving their legs like upturned beetles and the crones clamouring for baksheesh. The stallion was quietly grazing half a mile further on. I was then invited to mount the stallion, but by now its exuberance was spent and we all rode together sedately through the canyon into the city. Despite the beauty of the Treasure House and other towering buildings carved from the multicoloured cliffs surrounding the natural forum, it seemed an anticlimax to the excitement of the ride.

As the Eighth Army advanced into Libya we all began to clamour for more active service. I was the first to join the Army in the 'Blue' (as they called the Western Desert) when in January 1943 I arrived in Tripoli to relieve Commander Kennedy. He was an almost legendary figure who, together with his petty officer surveying recorder 'Zotto' Lloyd, so named after an Egyptian gin of which he was fond, and his leadsman Able Seaman Proctor, had been surveying all over the Middle East – harbour clearances, beach recces, and intelligence surveys. I found the little party in the entrance to Tripoli harbour, sounding from a floating pontoon in the narrow gap recently cleared between the East Mole and the remains of a blockship. Kennedy grinned through his straggling sandy beard in disbelief that I had come to relieve him.

We were known as the Mobile Survey Unit and it was our duty to keep in touch with Main Army H.Q. which ordered us to move forward when an enemy held port seemed likely to fall into our hands. We entered the port as soon as it fell and began at once a survey to locate obstructions left by the enemy either in the port or its approaches, so that we were able to guide in to suitable berths the motley fleet of coasters and caiques which carried military supplies forward from Alexandria.

Lloyd and Proctor remained with me, whilst my team was augmented by two ordinary seamen, survivors from a sunken cruiser, one a Lancastrian from Burnley, the other a Yorkshireman from Barnsley.

Clad in battledress we travelled in our three-ton truck, together with our boat, following the westward-flowing military convoys along the single desert road, learning the ways of the soldier. It was a point of honour to have the tea brewed up over the sandbox three minutes after the convoy halted; at night, before darkness fell, we pulled off the road, pitched our tents and cooked our cornbeef hash.

Proctor, who had been driving most of the day, was then free to indulge in his hobby. Having found a supply of the notoriously unstable red Italian hand grenades, which lay abandoned almost everywhere in the desert, he lobbed them at targets increasingly less distant from himself until the wire shrapnel peppered his bare chest. One had little control over him as he had long ago abandoned naval discipline for a curious blend of loyalty and impudence. However, loyalty was uppermost and, quite fearless, he had been awarded the B.E.M. for his work with Kennedy.

The nights were cold as we got into our sleeping bags and, having scooped a hollow in the sand to accommodate the hip, we chatted for a while under the stars. On such nights the Lancashire lad would often sigh, 'Eee, I wish I was back in Burnley.' Journeying thus we arrived in the port of Sfax where, under the direction of the bluff Naval Officer in Charge, Commander Alexander, who went in ahead of us, we began at once a survey of the harbour and the long approach channel partially blocked by the departing Germans. Then on to Sousse which was even less damaged, for the enemy was now rapidly pulling out of North Africa.

By now Hadji Bailey had joined our party and we retired to a quiet farm in the hills of the Cape Bon Peninsula, where an Italian farmer and his family cooked for us and supplied rough red wine, a quantity of which Zotto stored in a jerrycan.

One dreamy afternoon the peace of the farm was broken by the roar of a despatch rider's motor cycle as he made his way up the dusty lane. He had orders for our Unit to proceed to Bizerta to assist with the clearance of that port; our current instructions to await orders at Sousse were cancelled. As we travelled northwestwards along the straight tar-sealed roads of Tunisia we sat silent and depressed. We had been excited at the prospect of taking part in the expected invasion of Southern Europe where our task had been to survey 'Port A' which, it was planned, should be in our hands by D+2.

At Bizerta we were soon busily engaged in sounding out the vital passage through the wreckage in the channel which led to the Lake from the open sea and which was being steadily widened and deepened by U.S. Navy salvagemen.

Chapter VI

Italy

Suddenly on 7th July 1943 the American soldiers began embarking in the fleet of landing craft and ships assembled at Bizerta. We feared that we had been forgotten until a message from our distant chief, now in Algiers, ordered us to sail from Bizerta with the Americans and join up with the Eighth Army as soon as we could after the landings.

The U.S. Navy staff saw nothing unusual in my request for a hitch-hike to an invasion. There would be no room for our beloved truck, but if we abandoned her we could embark in any landing ship we wished. We lost no time in packing all our gear in one huge crate and in stowing it inside the bow doors of a sturdy looking landing ship, and then settled down to life at sea with the U.S. Army. We were two days at sea, which I remember as a pleasant round of coffee, 'chow' and radio. On the third morning the brown hills of southern Sicily lay before us with here and there a building on fire, and I well remember the sight of a whole railway train derailed and blazing merrily. The scene along the shore was one of vigorous activity as the unloading of the beached landing craft went steadily ahead.

The Americans had invaded Sicily the night before over beaches to the westward of Cape Scalambri, while the British had gone ashore to the north-eastward of this cape. The small port of Licata was already in the hands of the U.S. Army, and our ship, turning to starboard on entering the harbour, berthed easily with her bows on the Molo di Levante. We staggered down the ramp with our massive packing case and the transport began rolling off.

The Americans had been willing enough to take us as passengers at sea, but quite reasonably they now had little time to listen to our pleas to be carried by road to the British sector. An inspection of the maps, no longer secret, showed that the British and United States Armies were separated by a formidable mountain barrier which it was planned to by-pass as the troops headed northwards into the hinterland.

How could we proceed? We clustered around our crate, our only communal possession, as impotent as the Italian townsfolk who stood beside us in the swirling dust, gazing in amazement at the endless stream of vehicles coming ashore. 'Hiya Captain! How's things in good old New York City? I plenty wish we go back there right now. Got a Lucky Strike? Thanks. I been long time in the States - long time Pennsylvania Railroad. Mussolini no good! Tedeschi no damn good!' I was being addressed by an Italian of elderly yet active appearance who was now going through the motions of cutting his throat to indicate his hatred of both Mussolini and the departing Germans.

Tony, for what else could his name be, now wished to reap what benefit he might from some years spent in the United States before the war. He babbled on with all manner of suggestions of how he might be of service to us 'real American guys'. I was taking little notice until Hadji drew my attention to what he was saying. 'Up in Ragusa plenty box-cars, flat cars. Helluva lot. Tedeschi take all locomotives to the mountains. Tony take you.' Hadji was pointing out that Ragusa lay high in the mountains between us and the Eighth Army.

Giving Tony his packet of Lucky Strike, and a carton of K rations to keep him at our sides, we made our way to the railway station where we found a major of the U.S. Army, battling with the aid of his interpreter to find out where the rolling stock of the Italian State Railways had gone. 'The only goddamned freight cars they leave behind the Fleet uses for shootin' targets. How the hell do they reckon I can run a railroad?' he stormed at the uncomprehending little party of Italian railway officials assembled before him. We produced Tony, now chewing gum from his K rations, who told the major of the wealth of rolling stock high in the mountains. The major's men were busy repairing the tracks to the north-west of the town whither the advance was racing ahead towards Palermo. He readily agreed that we Limeys could take a shunting engine and Italian crew, and with Tony as our guide, go eastwards into the mountains in search of the locomotives and rolling stock he needed so badly. As long as Tony brought these back the Limeys could then go where the hell they pleased.

Our little party, seated on a flat-car around our precious crate, set out behind a shunting engine for the mountains far to the eastward. By nightfall we had reached Gela Station, and there we set up our camp beds on the platform. The U.S. Army was busy in every direction, but next day, as we travelled eastwards and entered the foothills, we reached a peaceful countryside, unmolested by the activities of war. Slowly the little train chugged into the mountains; the sun beat down on our small party on the flat-car; Zotto swigged 'plonk' from his jerry can, which he topped up with wine, red or white impartially, whenever the engine paused to take on 'aqua fresca' at the picturesque little stations. The enthusiastic villagers welcomed us with gifts of fruit and Tony was voluble, showing us off to everyone as his personal property.

In the early evening the long climb ended, and we drew into Ragusa, where our delighted gaze fell upon a mass of rolling stock and at least six shining locomotives. The station master was there to greet us, in his high peaked cap with Fascist badge and a uniform brilliant with silver buttons and emblems. He was effusive and willing to please and agreed to let us have an engine, carriage and closed truck for our onward journey on the morrow; but he believed that the railway line was damaged between Ragusa and Pozzallo, our goal near the British beaches fifty miles to the south-eastward. It would be prudent to send an inspection car ahead so that if damaged track was located warning might be given to the oncoming train. By offering generous allowances of our rations, which we had hoarded in our crate for just such an occasion, and by promising that we should send them back to Ragusa and their wives and families just as soon as we arrived at Pozzallo, we persuaded a reluctant driver and fireman to accompany us; and we then selected, from a promising range of locomotives, our own engine for the last stage of our journey.

Ragusa is a delightful town, built perilously on two sides of a deep gorge joined by a spectacular viaduct. There were no troops of any kind here, no damage, no signs of war. Still carrying the sands of the African desert in our beards we went first to the public bath-house and lay in deep hot baths like those we had last enjoyed in Cairo eight months before; we had our hair cut and beards trimmed by a jolly barber; we enjoyed superb pasta and ice creams such as only Italians can make; and we slept, without a thought for our safety, in deep soft mattresses in the town's leading hotel.

Eight o'clock next morning found us in the railway yards where all was bustle as Tony mustered his three or four trains which were to set out for the American beachhead. Our chosen fireman was already lighting a fire in the engine we had selected. The plan was that I should go with two Italian railwaymen on the inspection car. This was a four-wheeled contraption with a pair of double seats back-to-back powered by an erratic two stroke engine; I was pleased that for the most part our journey lay downhill. Three hours later Hadji was to follow with the party, wallowing in the comfort of a first class compartment.

The engine of the inspection car was already spluttering away and I was about to take my seat beside the driver when the station master became very excited and Tony had to be called to interpret. It appeared that it would be unusual to take a train without a receipt; by doing so the files of the State Railways would no longer be in order. War was one thing, but the unauthorised removal of Government property was another. I got out my survey field book and made an entry: 'Received one locomotive No. 4724, one carriage and one box-car. Signed G.S. Ritchie, Lieutenant, Royal Navy.' I tore out the sheet and handed it to the station master; honour was satisfied; he gave a flourishing Fascist salute, our driver let in the clutch and we were swaying and accelerating down the long winding railroad to Pozzallo.

The track coiled like a snake along the precipitous mountain sides, through black tunnels which sometimes completed a circle and emerged some hundred or so feet below their entrance. Had the track been damaged I doubt whether we should have seen it in time to avert disaster as we careered on. After three hours we reached the plain beyond Scicli, and as it had been a warm morning we were now thirsty. We stopped by a melon field and the driver and his companion climbed the fence to select a pair of ripe refreshing watermelons. Not far off was the farmer's cottage and almost at once he was at his door shouting at the thieves, who ran like small boys disturbed in an apple orchard, each with a shining green melon beneath his arm. The driver started the engine at once and we put some miles between ourselves and the irate peasant before we dared stop to quench our thirsts. Obviously this area had yet to experience the attention of 'liberators'.

At about 3.00 p.m. we rounded a bend, and there, anchored close inshore, lay a grey armada busily engaged unloading, and a mile ahead of us lay the trim little railway station of Pozzallo. We drew to a halt to the consternation of the sergeant in charge, running it in the precise service-like manner demanded by a railway operating group of the British Army. He asked where I had come from and seemed both outraged and hurt that we had dared to travel on his railway without permission. He spoke of the disaster which would have taken place had he despatched a reconnaisance train that day and it had met us in the tunnels, for it was a single track for much of the way to Ragusa. The sergeant was simmering down when, from far to the westward, came the unmistakable whistle of a train. He stared like a man who is seeing a ghost and I confessed that my private train was following me. I must admit that I felt a surge of pride as my own little train came into view from behind a range of low hills and puffed its way confidently towards us across the plain. It was only as it neared the station that the full horror of the situation struck me, for out of the windows of the carriage peered the faces of a number of Italian peasants and their families. One of the many unpleasant restrictions that occupying troops find indispensable is that of the movement of civilians, and thus it was many a long day since these Sicilian peasants had enjoyed free movement by rail. They had boarded the train at its frequent stops unbeknown to Hadji and the survey party dozing in their compartment.

By now the sergeant had sized up this unusual situation and he went into action. A guard was summoned to herd the Italian passengers into some sort of custody, and I was called to the telephone to explain my actions to the brigadier in charge of the railways, now installed in an office at Syracuse Station. As the sergeant passed me the handset I had to hold it at some distance from my ear, so violent was the brigadier's reaction. I gathered that for the Navy to have taken over the railway was in no way a part of the invasion plans and that my entire party, together with the engine driver and fireman, were under arrest; we were to travel in our train attached ignominiously to the rear of the very next supply train to leave Pozzallo for Syracuse.

We were a gloomy little party in our carriage in the late evening as we rattled northwards; our only consolation was that Syracuse was Port 'A', and now, for the first time, it seemed certain we should reach it. In fact the train was now travelling very fast indeed and was beginning to sway violently. In the gathering dusk we became aware of a gesticulating figure at the carriage window which, after some difficulty, we lowered to permit entry to a flow of excited Italian. It seemed, even with our elementary knowledge of the language, that there was something very wrong towards the front of the train, so three of our party were soon making their way over the top of our own engine and the swaying ammunition trucks, following the excited and beckoning Italian. On reaching the engine which was drawing both trains it was at once clear to our people that the British railway corporal, who was in general charge of the train, had himself taken over the controls from the Italian driver and was driving with an élan attributable only to a surfeit of 'plonk'; the terrified Italian engine driver pleaded with him in vain. We visualised our train dashing right through Syracuse, for our present driver was obviously in no mood to respect the finer points of signalling, and thus, presumably, we should soon find ourselves in the German lines not far north of the town. Action was required. The soldier was overpowered with the aid of the coal shovel and the Italians were not long in slowing the engine to a speed more suited to a goods train.

At Syracuse Station an officer was waiting to escort me to the brigadier: now I too had a card to play; the arrested had become the arresters and whereas I walked unaided into the lion's den my prisoner, the corporal, now in a deep sleep, was carried in by two of his comrades. This circumstance considerably softened the blow, and inter-service co-operation healed the wound. We set up our camp beds in the dark of the station waiting room, but, tired as we were, sleep was made impossible by German bombers over the town. Beside me lay our engine driver, wrapped in an army blanket on the cold hard floor. He could speak no English, but, between his moans as the bombs fell around the harbour, he made it crystal clear to me that he considered I had shamefully broken my promise to send him home by nightfall to his wife and family and the peace of Ragusa far away in the mountains.

Next morning, as our somewhat bedraggled party made their way towards the harbour, we saw a familiar and commanding figure in naval khaki striding along the quays. He was Commander Alexander whom we had served under at Sfax and now Naval Officer in Charge Syracuse. 'Where the hell have you been, Ritchie? Your boat is that infantry landing craft over there. Get cracking.' Soon we were at our familiar tasks in the harbour while Able Seaman Proctor searched the town with a knowing eye for cosy billets.

As we moved northwards behind the Eighth Army there was little survey work to be done in the Italian Navy's anchorage in the bay of Augusta, whilst Catania is remembered by our little party for the billet we occupied. We set up our camp beds in the passageway between the great wooden casks in a wine vault where the vintner warmly welcomed us; even before our early morning departure for the docks he provided us with refreshing beakers of Vino Etnea drawn through the bunghole of a bulky barrel with a ladle cunningly constructed from a hollow bamboo.

Whilst at Catania Frank Hunt, who had joined *Endeavour* as his first survey ship at Suez, arrived to relieve Hadji Bailey as my assistant surveyor. Hadji embarked for England in a man-of-war taking with him a modest cask of Vino Etnea packed in a crate labelled 'Hydrographic Instruments - Handle With Care', to be bottled on arrival home.

By this time the enemy had been driven from Sicily, and from the countless vehicles they left behind we were able to select a beautiful new Fiat truck the engine of which purred like a contented pussycat. We were mobile again.

ITALY

Egg Irving had arrived in Sicily from Malta, where he had been engaged in harbour clearance surveys, to assist with the Eighth Army's invasion of the 'toe' of Italy which General Montgomery was now planning. Egg and I headed north in his jeep to join the Army's artillery, the whole of which was dispersed in the mountains south of Messina. The Royal Artillery surveyors had co-ordinated both their own gun positions and every notable topographical feature on the enemy-held mainland five miles across the Straits of Messina. We were impressed with the efficacy of the survey when, sitting in an artillery control post in the westering evening sunlight, we saw a single German motorcyclist, crossing a dry watercourse, bring down upon himself the fire from fifty or more British guns. He disappeared in a towering cloud of dust.

We were able, from the control post, to co-ordinate the three beaches selected for the landings on the mainland. The Thirteenth Corps of the Eighth Army were to embark by night at Augusta and Catania. On sailing, the three flotillas of landing craft would hug the Sicilian coast northwards until opposite their respective beaches, when they would turn eastwards. Back transit marks would ensure that the landing craft would arrive precisely where intended.

Egg and I extended the artillerymen's triangulation to include three stations along the beach, often under bombardment from the enemy on the mainland, and three more stations in deep valleys in the mountains behind us. A Royal Marine detachment brought in mobile searchlights and installed them on our stations so that when these were illuminated, pointing vertically upwards, a few minutes before the invasion craft were due to turn eastwards the six pillars of light would form three superb sets of back transit beacons leading the invaders exactly onto their beaches. All went according to plan on the night of 2nd/3rd September 1943.

After a night sleeping in sodden slit trenches on the Messina football ground we found at daylight that tank landing ships were already running a roll-on roll-off shuttle service from Messina to Reggio, Calabria. Our Fiat truck was soon embarked and we were on our way. There was a single narrow coastal road right round the 'instep' of Italy's 'boot' along which we had to travel to reach Taranto. Most of the bridges over the deep river beds had been destroyed by the enemy in retreat, necessitating difficult diversions bulldozed by our sappers high up on the mountainsides. After two days we reached our objective, but there was little survey work required in Taranto and we were soon speeding along the wide and level roads of Apulia.

Somewhere here we picked up a naval war artist, John Worsley, and took him along with us to Bari where he left us for a secret mission in a caique to

Yugoslavia. I didn't see him again until 1985 at a War Artists' Exhibition at the National Maritime Museum at Greenwich. John had been captured during his mission, together with his portfolio of sketches, including one of Proctor and me in our Fiat; strangely these drawings had been returned to Britain after the war, each bearing cryptic notes presumably made by a German Intelligence Officer. Perhaps Proctor and I had been marked men!

There were no signs of destruction when we arrived at Bari, and on stepping down from the truck I was confronted by an impressive statue of Stephano Ricci, my namesake and famed poet son of Bari – I felt at home. Later our party dined in a well conducted restaurant, white napery on the tables, hurrying waiters, carafes of wine; a beautiful raven-haired young woman skilfully twirled and consumed her spaghetti pausing only for snatches of vivacious conversation with a grey-haired gentleman who savoured his wine thoughtfully. What a contrast with our 'corned dog ush' swilled down with 'plonk' from Zotto's jerrycan as we sat by the dusty roadsides.

As autumn came so did the rains in great abundance changing the dust into mud which, churned up by lorries and tanks, turned the roads to quagmires. The Eighth Army's progress became slow but by 11th October they were established in the little seaport of Termoli and were gradually advancing towards the Sangro River where the Germans had decided to make a stand. They had established a 'winter line' of defences along a commanding ridge on the north side of the swollen river. In one of the toughest battles of the war, fought under appalling weather conditions, Montgomery's seasoned army finally broke through the Winter Line on Christmas Eve. Floundering through the mud our Unit finally reached Termoli and as this small harbour was close to the static front line it was necessary to survey on a large scale so that every possible berth for landing craft and ships could be utilised. About this time the Unit had been furnished with two of the American built amphibious vehicles (DUKWS) with R.A.S.C. drivers. These enabled us to send our survey parties on ahead along the beaches or in the sea avoiding holdups on the congested and boggy roads. To augment the limited berths at Termoli the 'Dukws', fitted with echo-sounders, were used to find suitable beach sites for disembarkation of stores north of Termoli itself.

On this occasion, instead of finding our own billets we were allocated a first floor apartment by the town major. There we found Carla, a middle-aged and garrulous woman who readily agreed to cook for us in return for her share of our rations; home-made spaghetti hung like streamers from every projection around our kitchen-cum-living room. There was a large irregular hole in the kitchen ceiling leading to the derelict flat above, and through this on our second evening dropped two Geordie soldiers in search of women. We remonstrated with them and with some difficulty evicted two disgruntled and disbelieving troopers. The following day as I was seated taking my supper at the kitchen table, from which the oversized tablecloth hung to the floor, two military policemen walked in and accused me bluntly of running a brothel. I denied this and informed them that this was our official billet assigned to us by the town major; furthermore, I said that except for Carla, there were no women on the premises. They grudgingly accepted my assurance and departed; then, to my surprise, a smiling teenage girl emerged from under the table, whilst Carla claimed her as her niece with no home to go to. An excited exchange took place between Carla and me, both having but a few words of the other's language, but the message that girls were to be banished eventually sunk in. Intelligence concerning the location of brothels flows freely across battlelines.

It was now my turn to leave for home, so turning the Unit over to Frank Hunt I set out hitch-hiking with the Army to Bari. Apulia is turkey country and as Christmas was near I found myself the sole passenger in a United States DC3 bound from Bari to Algiers surrounded by numerous crates of live turkeys. It was a glorious crisp winter's day as the pilot took the aircraft over Etna's smoking crater, whilst each time the aircraft rocked or dipped in the turbulence a restless ripple of gobbling broke out among my companions. We all spent Christmas in the American Base in Algiers.

Chapter VII

The Second Front

By February 1944 I was first lieutenant of H.M.S. *Scott* which, with *Franklin*, was one of only two surveying vessels in commission in Home Waters. It was generally understood both ships would be involved in the landings in Europe which were to open the Second Front, by now clearly in preparation.

Scott took part in two very cold invasion exercises in the Firth of Forth: a battalion of infantry was landed on the beaches at Gullane, and the port of Methil was 'taken' from the sea. The landing techniques were still somewhat tentative and I was far from clear as a result of these exercises what our rôle in the invasion was to be. In early March the ship moved to Larne ostensibly to survey the port, but it became apparent that Northern Ireland was our 'holding area' for greater things to come.

After two years in South Africa my wife was able to get passage to U.K. in the merchant ship *Glenartney*. At the initial boat drill the first officer informed the dozen passengers that, loaded with ore as she was, the vessel would sink in minutes if torpedoed. Happily the voyage was uneventful and so on a cold and blustery morning I was on the jetty awaiting the arrival of the Stranraer to Larne ferry. I wondered if I would recognise Disa so long after our parting in Cape Town; but there she was coming down the gangway, her golden hair streaming in the breeze.

In mid-April we were ordered to Lough Foyle where shoaling in the long approach channel to the berths at Lisahally was causing difficulties for the many frigates now based there. In mid-May we were ordered south, and Disa went to London where she was taken on as a civilian plotting officer in the depths of the Admiralty Citadel.

By 22nd May *Scott* lay anchored, with many other vessels, in the Solent and, as all leave was now cancelled, our captain, Commander Syd Hennessey, my old tutor of *Herald* days, was able to tell the ship's company something of our task in 'Operation Neptune' which was hourly awaited. The main object of the operation was to land British and American armies across the beaches of the Bay of Seine; to facilitate this two military ports were to be established off the open coast. To form the breakwaters for such a port it was planned to sink blockships and concrete caissons, the latter, known as 'Phoenix', being towed across the Channel to be sunk in their assigned positions on arrival.

To plan the 'Mulberrys', as such ports were to be called, it had been necessary to make, well in advance, sketch hydrographic surveys of the proposed areas. So during the autumn of 1943 two naval surveyors, Lieutenant Commander Berncastle and Lieutenant Glen, using three thirty-two foot personnel landing craft with silenced engines and underwater exhausts, ventured on eight dark nights across the Channel to 'top secret' survey grounds. The craft were fitted with echo-sounding machines, miniature nine-mile range taut-wire measuring apparatus and chart tables under a hooded canopy.

One particular survey was made off Arromanches for Mulberry B, the point of origin being the underwater reef Rocher du Calvados. On arrival off Arromanches the Rocher was identified by soundings so that one of the craft could anchor, whilst the crews of the other two streamed the weighted end of the taut wire and, passing the anchored craft, ran slowly and silently away on a compass course, the distance run by taut wire measurement being regularly recorded whilst the echo-sounding trace was simultaneously marked and fix numbered. At the end of each run the wire was cut and the sounding craft returned past the anchored one and commenced a further measured sounding run on a different compass course until a 'star' of sounded lines had been built up by the two sounding boats around the stationary boat. At the ends of the lines that ran towards the beach it was possible, even on a dark night, to take compass bearings of individual houses silhouetted along the crests of the low cliffs. Each building was subsequently identified and its position plotted from low oblique aerial photographs so that the recorded bearings provided fixes which could be applied to the star of soundings. This clandestine work enabled an excellent sketch chart to be compiled upon which the whole of the port of Arromanches was planned.

Shortly before dawn on 6th June 1944 *Scott* weighed anchor, and at her best speed of fifteen knots joined a veritable armada streaming out to sea. Southwards we sailed, flanked as far as the eye could see by landing craft loaded with troops buffeting into a boisterous sea with white spray flying. Our first assignment began at 'Piccadilly Circus', half way across the Channel, where the leading assault craft had closed in behind the minesweepers that had been clearing mines from the channels running in towards the beaches for the past thirty-six hours. From there on our task was to lay a series of acetylene gas accumulator lighted navigation buoys (AGAs) at regular intervals astern of the minesweepers to mark the centre of the main swept channel into Arromanches.

Whilst *Scott* had lain in the Solent a small blue box, to which was connected an insignificant copper wire aerial strung to the yardarm, had been brought aboard; only the captain and navigator were instructed in its use. As we moved southwards into the Bay of Seine the navigator called me to the charthouse to be initiated into the mysteries of 'QM'. Two dials on the box, later known as the 'blue gasmeter', provided him with constantly changing numbers which he read off at intervals, using them to plot the ship's position with reference to two sets of numbered hyperbolic curves overprinted on the navigational chart. To me it savoured of pure magic.

At the earliest stages of planning an invasion of north-west Europe it became clear that some type of ship location other than visual would be required to control the extensive pre-invasion minesweeping by day and night within the ebb and flow of the strong tidal streams of the English Channel. The task of the minesweeping force was to establish exact swept channels leading the assault ships and craft infallibly to their assigned beaches.

Even before the War an American engineer, W. J. O'Brien, had been working on a system for locating aircraft using hyperbolic position lines generated by low frequency continuous wave transmissions from two or more fixed stations. Harvey Schwarz, another American and a friend of O'Brien, was working in the early war years as chief engineer of the Decca Record Company in the U.K.; together they developed the idea of electronic fixing in which the Admiralty Signals Establishment became interested.

The system was classified under the code name 'QM' at an early stage and the first successful sea trials were carried out in September 1942 between the Isle of Man and Anglesey using a receiver fitted in a trawler, and two mobile shore transmission stations which provided a single hyperbolic position line. Further highly secret trials followed and Decca began priority production of QM receivers and transmitters, leading to a large scale landing exercise in the Moray Firth employing a master station and two slave stations. 'Decometers', as the receivers were called, fitted onboard ships involved in the exercise, were used to measure the phase differences in two sets of signals emanating from the master and each of the slaves. The decometer readings were plotted on two sets of hyperbolic curves overprinted on the charts. At this stage the Hydrographer of the Navy had been called in for the preparation of Top Secret charts overprinted with hyperbolic lattices to be generated by a master and two slave stations, to be established in southern England in locations which would provide good fixing cover in the approaches to the invasion beaches. The master station was set up near Chichester and the two slaves near Beachy Head in the east and Swanage to the west. The Hydrographic Department surveyed the sites, computed the lattices and prepared the two charts - 'Ile St Marcouf to Cap Marvieux' and 'Cap Marvieux to Dives'. Secrecy was paramount; only two unbriefed persons knew when the operation had begun. In their flat in Dolphin Square Harvey Schwartz and Bill O'Brien, the inventors of this revolutionary method of navigating, had kept their portable receiver running and saw, on 5th June, that the pointers on their decometer had ceased meandering and taken up stable readings, showing that QM had been activated.

As we moved in towards the beaches we could hear a constant rumble of gunfire ashore as the invading infantry spread out like thousands of ants scrambling up over the low sand dunes from their beached assault craft. We recognised the uniquely diverse houses of the region used by Berncastle and Glen for their reconnaissance survey and which we would employ for the survey of the harbour that was so soon to be established as Mulberry B off Arromanches. One of the seaside homes was partially destroyed, whilst smoke billowed from another.

Our first task was to lay a floating beacon to mark the western side of the harbour entrance as a datum point for the sinking of Phoenix to form the western breakwater. Next we located and marked the wreck of the Norwegian minesweeper *Svener* which had been sunk earlier that morning in the approaches to the proposed harbour. We then had further Aga buoys to lay in assigned positions to facilitate navigation in the inshore waters, which became increasingly congested as more and more vessels of every kind arrived to perform their allotted tasks.

By D+2 Lieutenant Glen had positioned and sunk the first of a dozen or so blockships which were to form the eastern breakwater; and Lieutenant Commander Lansdown had arrived in his surveying motor launch to begin the survey of the port, which was developing daily on the plan that had been based upon the reconnaissance survey. Teams from *Scott*, using our surveying boats, augmented Lansdown's sounding work.

Six hundred tons of military stores had been landed at the 'spud' piers, which had been constructed within the eastern part of the port before a great north-easterly gale struck on D plus 13 and brought every activity to a halt for three days. With the boats hoisted we lay to both anchors and watched our bearings, only about three cables under the lee of the western breakwater, as we prayed the Phoenix would withstand the ferocity of the waves that broke continually upon them. A ragged line of figures stood by guardrails on the nearest caisson waving pathetically towards us: whatever their needs, food or warmth, we were powerless to help. Their evacuation from the Phoenix had been frustrated by the onset of the gale. Close westwards of us a destroyer, unprotected by the Phoenix breakwater, dragged rapidly and hopelessly ashore and soon lay wrecked broadside on the rocks.

In the aftermath of the gale the beaches were scattered with wrecked landing craft of every description, including Dukws, one of which we salvaged for use as an extra survey boat. Many of the Aga buoys marking the continually searched channels had dragged from their positions during the gale and these had to be resited until Trinity House vessels, now arriving, could lay larger and more heavily moored navigation buoys as replacements.

Early in July *Scott* sailed westwards to Mulberry A in the Western Assault Area to buoy mark a number of newly sunk wrecks. Contact was made there with Lieutenant Commander Passmore, in his survey launch *Gulnare*, who was urgently in need of stores and assistance as he surveyed the developing port area.

On 6th July *Franklin*, with Egg Irving, now a Commander, in command sailed in to relieve us. Meanwhile the completed survey of the Port of Arromanches had already reached England in Lansdown's hands, to be issued a few days later by the Hydrographic Department as a published chart of a busy port which only six weeks earlier had been an open beach cluttered with German sea defences.

As *Scott* had been either underway or under short notice for steam for five weeks boiler cleaning and minor repairs were necessary so she was ordered to Chatham Dockyard. My wife's job in the Plotting Room of the Citadel now proved its worth. She was able to read signals concerning *Scott*'s movements and, as she worked twenty-four hours on and forty-eight hours off, by taking a day's leave she was enabled to pay a brief visit to Chatham to coincide with our arrival there. A telephone call from Disa at the dockyard gates established contact without any breach of security. So there she was when we arrived back from Arromanches.

Our next mission was to Cherbourg, which had been in the hands of the U.S. Army since D+20. Our main task was to locate and survey suitable sites in the vicinity of Cherbourg for the landing of 'Pluto' (pipeline under the ocean) an ingenious petroleum supply line which was shortly to be laid from huge floating bobbins, each holding seventy miles of flexible pipe, as they were towed across the Channel from the Isle of Wight.

A new form of anti-boat mine had been laid by the enemy at Cherbourg. From a mine laid on the seabed, green buoyant snag lines trailed near the surface ready to foul a passing boat's propellers. This called for a sharp-eyed lookout in the bows of the sounding boats.

On completion of work at Cherbourg *Scott* was ordered by signal to return to Plymouth, but before sailing a countermanding signal came diverting us to Morlaix in Brittany. Unfortunately Disa had only seen the first signal before taking train to Plymouth. At the dockyard gates she was both surprised and angered when the police, after telephoning the ship, told her that *Scott*'s first lieutenant claimed that he was a bachelor! After some confusion it transpired that only U.S.S. *Scott* was in port and Disa dismally embarked in the train for the long and tedious journey back to London. Meanwhile H.M.S. *Scott* was anchoring off Carantec in the extensive estuary of the Morlaix River on 28th August.

The Germans were doggedly holding out in the great naval port of Brest under continual bombardment from U.S. artillery surrounding the fortress city. U-boats, operating from their heavily protected submarine pens, were still a severe menace to the Allied supply lines in the Eastern Atlantic. The siege could be a protracted one as every round of ammunition had to be carried 350 kilometres by road from Cherbourg, diverting vital transport from the United States First and Third Armies which were now thrusting south and east into the heart of France. If ammunition could be landed from ships moored in the Morlaix River, only sixty kilometres east of Brest, the shortening of the supply lines would be dramatic.

The range of the tide at Morlaix is about twelve metres so that the estuary varies from a great expanse of sheltered water to a narrow river channel winding through a waste of mudflats depending on the state of the tide. The plan was to berth Liberty ships at mooring buoys placed in the deep river channel so that their military cargoes could be discharged into a fleet of Dukws to be landed across the mudflats. Our objective therefore was to verify the approach channel southwards through the Baie de Morlaix, where the rocky pinnacled seafloor provides many a hidden danger, and then to delineate exactly the deep river channel within so that the mooring buoys could be precisely sited to provide the maximum number of berths for the ships.

An unexpectedly easy recovery of French triangulation stations, together with the augmentation of our little squadron of three sounding boats by two U.S. Dukws fitted with echo-sounders, enabled the survey to be completed and plotted within a week. This necessitated the ship remaining at anchor in the river for a further few days awaiting the arrival of the mooring craft with the buoys. This brief period turned out to be an oasis of happiness in the wartime desert.

During the search for triangulation stations we had been welcomed everywhere by the local peasantry who, since the Germans' hurried departure, had been virtually leap-frogged by the Americans on their way to Brest. During the waiting period therefore our captain suggested that officers and men might wish to go ashore on either side of the river to meet the French people emerging from their long ordeal.

Even in wartime the engineer officer and I were fortunately carrying our sporting shotguns onboard enabling us to accept the invitation of a farmer on the east shore, a keen 'chasseur' whose gun had long since been confiscated by the Germans, to shoot his partridges. Unmolested for so long, these gamebirds were abundant and were perfectly flushed and retrieved by his old Breton spaniel. Our host had, on the coming of the Germans four years earlier, immured in his farmyard a bottle of Johnnie Walker Black Label to be shared with the first of the 'liberators', whoever they might be, and whenever they should come. We found ourselves in this agreeable rôle as the farmer removed stones from the wall to reveal the long-hidden treasure. The contents provided a superb accompaniment to the 'Fête des Chasseurs' prepared by madame in the farm kitchen, with many a toast in whisky and calvados to the Allies' success and 'La chasse d'avenir'.

Next day Syd Hennessey and I paid a visit to the Chateau Rohou where the elderly Vicomte de Guerdavide lived with his wife and family of girls, where we also met Madame Irvoas and her two daughters, Jeannine and Monique, who had come to visit Carantec from their small farm, Le Moulin Oublié, far up the valley beyond Morlaix. The girls were experiencing for the first time life free from the German imposed curfew and until the mooring craft, H.M.S. *Kirriemoor*, sailed into the river three days later French gaiety held sway, culminating in a joyous party onboard and ending in tears of farewell as our guests descended the gangway to the Dukw waiting to take them ashore.

From now on *Scott* and *Franklin* divided the task of surveying the ports along the north coast of France as each was taken by the First Canadian or the Second British Army; all the facilities were extensively damaged by the departing enemy, blockships were sunk, locks were destroyed and debris bulldozed into the alongside berths. *Franklin* dealt with Dieppe, Le Havre and the River Seine, while *Scott* was to be responsible for Boulogne and Calais, moving our base from Plymouth to Dover. Our work followed to a greater degree the pattern established by our units in North Africa and Italy, where, as soon as the port fell to our forces, we attempted to get an advanced survey party in by road, or along the coast by Dukw.

I was landed at Dieppe on 1st October with an advance party to make my way to Boulogne using a Dukw for the preliminary survey. Our work here was to be of particular importance because no less than sixteen Pluto lines were to be laid across the Channel to their terminal in Boulogne. I found that the Germans had sunk about twenty blockships across the entrance to the inner harbour with many other wrecks littering the Rade Carnot, the outer roadstead.

To facilitate our work we were provided with copies of the largest scale French charts with details in the water areas blocked out to permit the entry of our own work. A basic triangulation was put together by observations from, or into, still existing conspicuous buildings such as lighthouses, church steeples and water towers from which secondary marks around the quays could be fixed. By the time, a week later, that the minesweepers gave clearance for *Scott* and three salvage vessels to anchor in the Rade I had completed the preliminaries and the ship's boats were able to assist the salvage teams in their massive task of harbour clearance.

We remained at Boulogne for the month of October and on one fatal night a westerly gale required that the boats be hoisted whilst we rode out the gale at anchor in the roadstead. As dusk fell we were amazed to see three soldiers in an open service dory making towards us from the shore. The seas were breaking over the craft and when only a couple or so cables distant a wave snuffed out the outboard motor and as the three men struggled to get their oars out the craft drifted rapidly downwind. Securing a lifebelt to the end of a grassline we paid it out astern, but the grasping hands of the soldiers failed by a few feet only to secure the lifebelt and they scudded rapidly and hopelessly into the gloom.

The captain had called away the lifeboat's crew to man *Penguin*, the port survey boat secured at the davit heads. By the time I got to the boatdeck Leading Seaman Peckett, *Penguin*'s coxswain, had got his crew into the boat and Lieutenant Charles Dansie, a young surveying officer who had volunteered and had been briefed by the captain, was climbing in. I gave the order to lower and as the boat reached the waves her experienced crew neatly unhooked the falls, the engine started at a touch, and in moments the headrope was cast off. *Penguin* turned downwind and disappeared into the night.

The Rade Carnot obtains some protection from a long mole running from the western shore before curving north eastwards. To the east the Germans had establishad some form of protection boom, now in considerable disarray with half submerged massive metal buoys and a tangle of wires between them fouling the area. These buoys provided a plethora of targets on the ship's radar and *Penguin* was lost in the clutter, made worse by the considerable sea running. We saw for a while the boat's Aldis signalling lamp searching across the turbulent waters; but then nothing.

It was impossible to take the ship into the tangle of booms in the shallow waters where *Penguin*'s searching light had last been seen. All that could be done was to scan and scan again with radar and binoculars through the long night until dawn revealed nothing but the grey seas breaking on the jumble of rusty red buoys. Only when a shore party searched the eastern beaches was the terrible evidence discovered. Eight bodies, including five of the finest men in our company, and a few broken planks from *Penguin*'s hull, bore testimony to a ghastly collision with the derelict German boom during a desperate attempt to rescue three British soldiers. Thousands had died from enemy action since D-Day, but this tragedy had come upon us from no such cause. We never found out why the soldiers were coming out to *Scott* on such a wild night.

With work completed in Boulogne by the end of October, a detached survey party was sent on by Dukw to Calais where the ship was able to enter a week later. Due to enemy demolition there were no wharves alongside which a vessel could lie, but good berthing was found by breasting the ship off with anchors and lying about fifteen feet off the damaged Gare Maritime.

Nearly a month before Calais fell to our forces on 30th September, a British armoured column had swept on to take Antwerp, perhaps the most important supply base in the whole campaign, but its use was denied as the Germans were still entrenched on the banks of the lower Scheldt River which gives access to the port of Antwerp.

Three lines of blockships had been sunk in the harbour entrance to Ostend which the salvage teams disposed of by massive demolition charges. When *Franklin* was able to enter Ostend, Egg, in his forceful style, sent on one of his survey boats on a tank transporter to Ghent whence it sailed along the canals to Terneuzen, to begin the survey of this important basin on the south bank of the

Scheldt. The glorious assault on Walcheren Island on 1st November by the Canadian Army and Royal Marine Commandos succeeded in removing the Germans from the banks of the Scheldt and the minesweepers immediately moved in to clear the seventy miles of channel from the sea upriver to Antwerp. *Franklin* and *Scott* moved up to Terneuzen at the end of November and together were engaged on wreck location and marking, reinstating the buoyage and sounding the seventy-mile long channel, permitting the arrival in Antwerp of the first convoy of Liberty ships in mid-December when *Scott* sailed for Chatham for boiler cleaning, minor repairs - and Christmas leave!

Early in 1945 *Scott* was ordered to proceed to Brest to work under the orders of Vice-Admiral Thierry d'Argenlieu Chef d'Etat-Major General Adjoint to Amiral Nord in the clearance and rehabilitation of the roadstead and commercial port of Brest.

As we slowly made our way to anchor amid a plethora of wrecks in the outer harbour the sight of this great naval city was staggering in its destruction. Not a single building remained undamaged. The naval dockyard in the Penfeld River and the renowned U-Boat pens, with their protected maintenance workshops and living accommodation, lay in ruins, whilst the whole length of the quays in the Commercial Port east of the river was obstructed by a tangle of fallen cranes and tumbled warehouses. The Americans had put to good use the thousands of tons of ammunition which had been landed across the oyster beds of the Morlaix River.

The rehabilitation of Brest was no longer of major strategic importance to the Allied Armies which, supplied through Antwerp and Dutch ports, had recently repulsed the Germans' last major onslaught in the Ardennes. So caution was exercised in sweeping and salvage work in Brest and the whole of the clearance work proceeded at a more leisurely pace than usual. As each underwater obstruction was discovered it was either demolished by explosives or lifted by salvage craft, after which a pair of survey boats, with a wire drag depth sweep rigged between them, slowly searched to find the least depth remaining.

Long waits for each salvage operation to be completed prompted our captain to suggest that I should make a recce to Morlaix only sixty kilometres distant. Together with a companion, I rode the jeep one wet and stormy winter's day to the village of Pleyber Christ and from there took the winding country road to the Moulin Oublié. Rounding a corner I braked to a halt as a pony and trap came splashing into view. Two figures were huddled on the seat, wrapped in sacking against the downpour. Suddenly - yes - it was the Irvoas girls! Jumping down there were embraces all round as the unattended pony turned to crop the roadside hedge. It was an unforgettable occasion. Jeannine accompanied us in the jeep to Pleyber Christ to stock up with provisions for the night ahead, whilst Monique turned the pony's head for home.

Seated around the log fire at the Moulin Oublié, with the girls in their wonderfully chic homemade dresses, we passed a memorable evening relishing Madame Irvoas' steaming pot au feu, drinking cider from what we came to call 'le pot sans creux', and savouring Monsieur Irvoas' unique home-distilled calvados. What a happy reunion we had that night, hearing the news of the momentous happenings in Brittany since our last visit. We managed a number of visits to the Chateau Rohou and the Moulin Oublié during our six weeks stay in Brest, culminating in a party onboard for our many friends from the Morlaix district, made possible by pressurising our military friends to provide the necessary transport.

On 20th February 1945 we sailed from Brest on final completion of our work for the Allied Naval Commander Expeditionary Forces, Admiral Sir Harold Burroughs, from whom we received the following warm signal which gave all of us onboard tremendous satisfaction:-

> *'Now that you are leaving my sphere of operations I want to express to you and your ship's company my thanks and appreciation for the splendid work that Scott has done in the last nine months since D-Day. I am fully aware of the important part you have played towards the rapid opening of captured ports and I want you all to know that it has not passed unnoticed.*
> *'I wish you good luck and a good leave.*
> *T.O.O. 211745A.February 1945'*

For us the Second Front was over.

FOOTNOTE:- Admiral Sir Bertram Ramsay, who had been Allied Naval Commander from the earliest planning stages of 'Operation Neptune', died tragically in an air accident in January 1945. He was succeeded by Admiral Sir Harold Burroughs.

Chapter VIII

The Post-war Clearance Task

From the end of February until shortly after V-E Day, 6th May 1945, *Scott* was undergoing a much needed refit in Grimsby whilst her company enjoyed well earned leave. I spent the evening of V-E Day with Disa in the nearby Lincolnshire town of Louth where the townsfolk gathered round the impressive church to see the great steeple illuminated by the Royal Engineers with searchlights. It was, of course, a memorable evening – all our troubles seemed over.

It was now time to commence the great postwar clearance of Britain's home waters in which *Scott* was to play a prominent part. To open these seas to peacetime navigation and fishery, thousands of mines had to be swept, hundreds of wartime wrecks had to be located and vast areas in the shallow waters off the south-east coasts had to re-surveyed after five years of wartime neglect of the unstable seabed.

Sailing in mid-May for Plymouth we there embarked fuel, stores and a quantity of surveying beacons required for our work with the Canadian minesweeping flotilla 'M/S 31'. Their job was to sweep clear extensive deep minefields which had been laid four years earlier to trap U-Boats in the Sole Bank area, far out in the Western Approaches to the English Channel. Our job was to mark the limits of the mined areas with survey beacons anchored in 100 fathoms or more, and because of the prevalent overcast weather it was necessary on each occasion of laying the beacons, or relaying them when swept away by gales, to take a departure from the vicinity of the Bishop Rock Lighthouse and run out a measured distance of 100 miles or so by taut-wire. Having laid the beacons we stayed around until a good set of star sights could be obtained at dawn or dusk alongside a beacon. The minesweepers took the whole month of June to clear the area, where but a few mines were proved to have survived four years of Atlantic weather.

The Downs, an extensive anchorage and inshore channel between the Kent Coast and the Goodwin Sands, has always been an unstable area. The Sands themselves, in the shape of a giant lozenge, oscillate about their north/south axis from year to year. What had happened since 1940? *Scott* undertook the re-survey in July 1945, but my chief memory of those days is not of the survey but of the very considerable pressure from politicians on servicemen to vote in the Election in which we lost Winston Churchill as Prime Minister, six years after we had received that electrifying signal 'Winston is back'.

In early August Lieutenant Commander Robin Bill relieved Commander Hennessey, our greatly respected wartime captain, and we moved into the shallow waters off the East Anglian Coast. Many of the offshore sandbanks, such as Scroby Sands on which seals bask at low water, had changed their shape during the war years. As we defined their new limits Trinity House tenders moved in to buoy them.

In this shallow area the search for wrecks was a priority, for every one of the hundreds sunk in wartime was now a potential danger to navigation. To locate wrecks the sonar equipment, developed for hunting U-boats, was used. Running survey lines a mile apart the sonar operator slowly searched ahead from the port beam, through the bows to the starboard beam and back again as the ship steamed slowly ahead. Every time the operator received the 'ping' of a returning echo from a seabed obstruction its bearing was plotted, so that two or more such bearings from different directions would intersect and fix the position of the obstruction.

By the autumn of 1945 a considerable flotilla of wreck disposal vessels had been got together manned by men recently experienced in clearing wrecks from captured harbours. Attempts were made by such vessels to remove the masts and superstructures from dangerous wrecks we had located to increase navigation depths over them. On some occasions it was possible to dig a trench with depth charges laid alongside the wreck into which the wreck could then be overturned by carefully placed explosives.

Whatever methods were used to disperse the wrecks, it was eventually necessary to verify the least depths remaining over them so that the wreck, together with a 'tray' symbol 3_2 showing the swept depth over it, could be precisely charted. We had two methods of sweeping wrecks. If it was thought to be a possible hazard to the survey ship a smaller version of the minesweeper's Oropesa sweep was used. In this system a sweep wire is held to a set depth by the length of towing wire to a metal kite running astern of the ship, whilst its extremity is held by a second otter board which is maintained at its set depth by float wire, at the same time pulling the sweep out on the ship's port or starboard quarter depending on which side the sweep is set. Using the sonar to con the ship safely past the wreck whilst the sweep passed over it, all eyes were on the beflagged torpedo-shaped float which runs in dramatically towards the ship when the sweep wire fouls any part of a wreck. The ship must be rapidly stopped, the sweep recovered, a shorter float wire fitted to reduce the depth of the sweep which is then re-streamed and the operation repeated until the wire runs clear and a least depth over the obstruction is thus established.

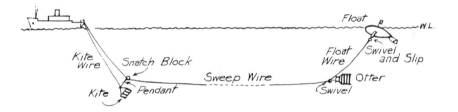

Oropesa Sweep

Once it was clear that the survey ship could pass safely over the wreck, a more precise least depth could be obtained by drift sweeping. To rig such a sweep two marked lowering wires, each with a heavy sinker on the end, are lowered from davits in the eyes of the ship and the after end of the quarterdeck; a light sweep wire runs from the upper deck through leading blocks secured to the weights on the lower ends of the lowering wire sinkers and is kept to a horizontal depth by five lead lines each held by a seaman stationed along the deck. The ship is then taken up tide of the wreck and set broadside to the tidal stream, with the sweep rigged over the upstream side of the ship. By cautious use of the engines, and frequently plotting the ship's position with reference to previously fixed floating marks, the sweep is passed over the wreck. A shout from one of the seamen tending the lead lines that it is growing out from the ship's side denotes a foul on the obstruction and the sweep wire is cast off. It is but a brief task to re-set the sweep and repeat the operation until the sweep runs clear and a precise least depth is obtained.

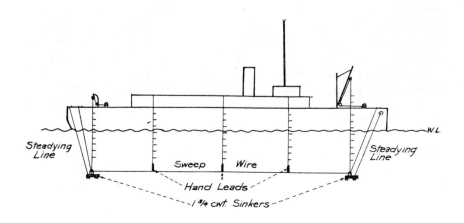

Drift Sweep

With *Scott* working out of Harwich, Lowestoft or Yarmouth the ceaseless sounding and sweeping continued through the winter of 1945/1946, the only respite being at weekends when the long slow railway journey across East Anglia to Liverpool Street Station could be made by those of our company whose turn it was to pay a brief visit 'up the smoke'.

The low-lying coastline of Norfolk is wonderfully illuminated for the surveyor by the soaring Perpendicular church towers; long co-ordinated by the Ordnance Survey, they form the basis for all hydrographic work offshore – Happisburg, Winterton, Corton and many others – how often have I peered through my sextant telescope to reflect their lofty images. Sometimes we had to visit the church towers to intersect with theodolite observations the beflagged floating beacons on the far sea horizon. The vicar was sometimes wary of granting permission to climb the belfry, which had not been regularly visited since the bells were silenced in 1939, so that the stairs and ladders had become dangerous through neglect.

Egg Irving in *Franklin* had returned to the Scheldt in the early months of 1945 to find a Decca chain erected with stations in Belgium and Holland to provide navigation cover in the estuary and river Scheldt as far as Antwerp, whence seaborne cargoes were pouring into North West Europe. He began at once to test the system with reference to the survey marks he had previously established along the extensive dykes on either side of the river. On V-E Day Egg described his officers as 'well satisfied with the equipment and pleased enough to celebrate the end of the War and the success of Decca as a fixing aid.'

This breakthrough encouraged the Decca Company to establish the first commercial navigation chain. Known as the 'English Chain' it comprises a master and three slave stations, each denoted by a colour, in south east and central England to provide navigational cover for ships carrying Decca receivers in the eastern Channel and southern North Sea. Thus I found myself together with Petty Officer 'Friar' Tuck, a surveying recorder, negotiating in a jeep the ploughed fields over which as a boy I had galloped on my pony in pursuit of the Puckeridge Foxhounds. We were in search of Ordnance Survey Stations marked thus Δ on flat stones, eighteen inches to two feet below the surface, where they had been buried and described fifty or more years earlier. Once three of these had been located we were able to co-ordinate the site of the master station near Puckeridge in Hertfordshire. It seemed a strange mixture of old and new technology, searching for a hidden stone with the aid of an ancient diagram to locate the site for a mast from which transmissions were to be made to provide a revolutionary form of navigation.

The English Chain was certainly useful to the sea surveyors engaged in charting the wreck-strewn shallow waters of the southern North Sea. However, the long overland paths traversed by the signals introduced errors which were not acceptable in close survey work; more importantly, the onboard computation and plotting of hyperbolic lattices before computers were carried at sea provided an unacceptable drawback for surveyors.

In August 1951 Admiral Day, the newly appointed Hydrographer of the Navy, in a lecture at the Royal Institution of Chartered Surveyors, mentioned how tiresome hyperbolic co-ordinates were, and how greatly the surveyor's task would be eased if only radio position fixing could be based on the direct measurement of range. Harvey Schwarz and his Engineer, Claud Powell, were at the meeting and went off to develop 'Two Range Decca (2RD),' the finer points of which were discussed by the irrepressible Harvey and the enthusiastic Archie Day in their daily commuter carriage on its way from Meopham to Charing Cross. The master station was to be carried in the survey vessel so that ranges could be directly received from two mobile slave stations located close to the shoreline in positions designed to give circular and easily plottable lattices to cover the survey area.

The first operational 2RD was carried in H.M. Survey Ship *Vidal* under the command of Egg Irving, who used the equipment extensively during 1957-1958 in the West Indies. However, in these early days, the lane numbers had to be closely watched as lock could be lost, particularly around sunset, so it was necessary to lay moored reference beacons against which the system could be regularly checked when working out of sight of land. A notable operation was a successful search for a reported shoal over 100 miles south of Jamaica. Egg's wish to name it 'Decca Shoal' was overridden by the Hydrographer, clinging to the hydrographic tradition which names a shoal after the vessel first reporting it.

By the early sixties 2RD had become the accepted system for offshore surveying which, with the development named 'Lambda' which introduced constant lane number identification, the hydrographer for the first time could operate in any visibilty by day or night. Sea Surveyors had lived through a technical revolution resulting from World War II every bit as radical as that experienced with the introduction of echo-sounding after World War I.

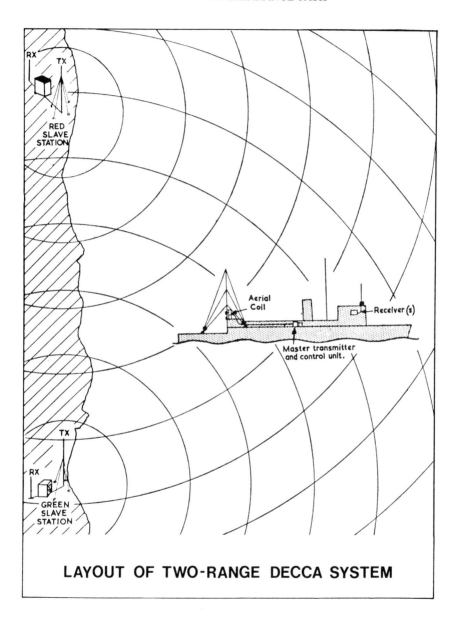

LAYOUT OF TWO-RANGE DECCA SYSTEM

Chapter IX

Back to the East

On the outbreak of war, two of the four Halcyon class minesweepers which had been completed as survey ships, *Jason* and *Gleaner*, were taken over by the general service. The latter, in command of a surveyor, Lieutenant Commander Price, soon distinguished herself by sinking a U-boat in the approaches to the Clyde.

In early 1946 these two vessels were replaced by a single Halcyon class minesweeper which had survived the War, *Sharpshooter*. To this ship I was appointed as first lieutenant to oversee her conversion to a surveying ship, at Green and Silley Weir of London, and by mid-1946 we were on our way to the Far East under the command of Commander Henry Menzies, a gaunt figure with a zest for life and an insatiable enthusiasm for new hobbies. He was a competent surveyor from whom I learnt much during the next four years.

On our way to Singapore we were diverted to Mergui in southern Burma to survey the shallow approaches so that supplies of rice could be brought in to alleviate the hardship currently endured by the people of the Tenasserim coast. Our main tasks, however, were based on Singapore from where we were to conduct surveys on the East Coast of Malaya and in Sarawak.

On arrival in the Naval Base at Singapore the Flag Officer, Malayan Area, requested that surveys of the small East Coast riverine parts of Kuantun and Rompin be given priority so that much needed rice could be shipped in for the natives of a remote area with few roads. It was necessary to complete this work before the onset of the north-east monsoon, so while the ship underwent some minor repairs advance parties were sent north by jeep. In previous years there was no East Coast road, but the Japanese had constructed one. It was little more than a track, whilst the rotting timbers of the many bridges over the sungeis made jeep travel both laborious and at times exciting. Unarmed, we slept happily in our camp beds in a barnlike structure in the village of Rompin, heedless of the posters adorning the walls denoting earlier Communist occupation. Within a few months this was to become a no-go area for Europeans.

Ten years after surveying at Kermaman I was back at the site of our old tidepole in the river. I located with ease our benchmark, which I had cut in a massive boulder, and to which I levelled a newly established tidepole to be read by a couple of tidewatchers concurrently with the reading of a tidepole at Kuantun in order to transfer our previously established datum from Kemaman. Some of the villagers remembered our camp party; they had suffered much since then during the Japanese occupation, and they told me that the District Officer who had organised the building of our atap house in 1936 had been killed by the Japanese as they stormed southwards towards Singapore.

Henry Menzies always believed in testing his surveys with the ship, so we had a thrilling passage in *Sharpshooter* across the shallow Kuantun bar over which the sea was breaking, followed by a 90° turn to starboard into the river. We anchored off the small town of Kuantun dressed overall for the King's Birthday and received onboard His Highness the Sultan of Pahang, a fitting end to our East Coast surveys.

The small State of Brunei in North Borneo comprises land on either side of the Sungei Brunei, the famed stilted village in the river, the town of Brunei and the Sultan's Palace. The river is entered across an extensive bar, the depths over which had not been checked since prewar. This was *Sharpshooter*'s next task, during which a grounding of the vessel on a sandy seabed was soon resolved by the use of kedge anchors, the laying out of which I had already experienced in both *Herald* and *Endeavour*.

Muara Island, on the starboard hand as one enters the river is today, I understand, the centre of a thriving oil industry and it is difficult to believe that a rather stupid surveying recorder whom we sent ashore to erect a mark on the island was lost for twenty-four hours in thick jungle.

Before sailing for Brunei our medical officer was relieved by a stocky young extrovert who came from Combined Operations together with a motorised canoe he had 'liberated' and a number of other diverse items. After a few days at sea the leading stoker in charge of the mess, which was located in close proximity to the Sick Bay, asked me if I could do something about a heavy sack which the doctor had stowed beneath their mess table and required moving every time the mess was scrubbed out. I bustled down to the mess deck and on opening the sewn up sack I was surprised to find a truncated corpse. I confronted the doctor who said that he had bought it from a Chinaman in Singapore, it was heavily injected for preservation, there was no room for it in the Sick Bay and he would be using it for training his junior assistant. He did not take kindly to my order to dispose of his precious body overboard, whilst the stokers expressed some concern that the corpse of a Chinaman had been at their feet as they took their daily meals.

In April we sailed for Sarawak. Much had changed in this beautiful country since the prewar *Herald* days of which I had so many happy memories. During the early war years Sarawak had prospered; oil exported from Miri, rubber and many foodstuffs had been much sought after, so that Rajah Vyner Brooke had been able to make generous financial gifts to the British Government's war effort.

Having no son of his own the ageing Rajah began to think of a successor; either his younger brother or his son Anthony would seem fitting. Meanwhile he drew up a constitution which was announced during a successful week of centenary celebrations in which Malays, Chinese and Dyaks enthusiastically took part.

A Supreme Council was set up by the constitution and Vyner Brooke left the country for a vacation in Australia. Only a single meeting of the Council took place before Sarawak was suddenly overwhelmed by the Japanese who occupied Kuching, the capital, on Christmas Day 1941. Some Europeans escaped over the border into Dutch Borneo and eventually to safety; the remainder were either murdered or imprisoned by the Japanese.

In the early 1930s Tom Harrisson, a young anthropologist, had led an Oxford University Expedition into the Sarawak jungles. Such outsiders were not welcomed by the European establishment in those days, and, in particular, the curator of the Sarawak Museum commented most unfavourably in his Annual Report on the expedition, and particularly upon its leader, who had become intimate with the natives of the hinterland. During the prewar years when he was occupied with setting up 'Mass Observation', a study of British urban communities, Tom never forgot his love for Sarawak and its natives, nor the insults he had received at the hands of the Museum Curator. From the moment the tide of war in the East began to flow in our direction Tom planned and trained to be the first European back into Sarawak. And so it came about that in early 1945 he parachuted into the very heart of Borneo to be welcomed by the Kelabits inhabiting the longhouse at Bario. He was slowly reinforced by air until his unit, named 'Semut' after an indigenous stinging ant, comprised about fifty Australian volunteers and some former employees of the Sarawak Government. Assisted enthusiastically by native headhunters, the men of Semut accounted for the deaths of about 1,000 Japanese soldiers as they penetrated down the rivers to join up with the Australian Army, which landed in Brunei Bay. The campaign ended on 1st September 1945 with surrender of the Japanese in Kuching.

After nearly four years of occupation Sarawak was no longer a prosperous country, and despite a rapturous welcome from the people when he returned to Kuching in April 1946, the Rajah felt that the time had come for the Brooke dynasty to end and for Sarawak to become a British colony. The Council Negri, which included representatives of all the native races and domiciled Europeans, decided by a slender majority to accept the Rajah's proposal which was then made to the British Government and accepted by the Privy Council in London. Annexation to the British Crown took place on 1st July 1946.

The coastal-living Malays and Anthony Brooke, the Rajah's nephew who had twice been nominated as his successor, were dissatisfied with the action which they claimed had been taken hurriedly and clumsily handled. When we arrived in *Sharpshooter* six months after the birth of the new colony we found the people confused and divided, yet they clearly retained much of the friendliness and charm I so vividly remembered from the old days.

The British Government's desire now was to open up their new colony and stimulate trade, so in a country of very few roads our attention was directed towards the improvement of commercial navigation along the rivers. *Herald*, in prewar days, had surveyed the Rajang, Sarawak's greatest river, as far as Sarekei, a small township thirty-five miles from the sea. *Sharpshooter*'s task was now to survey the river for a further thirty-five miles upstream to Sibu, the second largest town in the country and headquarters of the Third Division. There were a great many potential exports from Sibu including rubber, pepper, chillies, timber, charcoal, palm oil, copra, jelutong (the basis of chewing gum), rice and kutch (from mangrove bark, used in tanning).

The river, which was ever busy with prahus coming and going, varies in width from about 200 yards to a mile; for the first half of the passage to Sibu the banks were fringed with a wide band of mangroves and nipah palms, the leaves of the latter being used to thatch the Iban (Sea Dyak) longhouses which, built on high stilts, were to be found at frequent intervals on either side of the river. Later a smaller freshwater mangrove took over and more open country provided space for the rubber gardens of the Foochow Chinese.

Little firm coastline was to be seen on the air photographs with which we had been provided. This dictated that the triangulation supporting the survey would have to be carried upriver by single triangles rather than balanced quadrilaterals, since the labour of clearing mangrove would be disproportionate to the results achieved, whilst there would be a chance to tie in our triangulation to the few Sarawak survey traverse points along the way. Metre-square collapsible canvas covered marks were prepared by the shipwright which could be hung in the mangrove trees beneath which a surveyor could position himself in a folboat to observe the angles to similar marks comprising the triangles.

The ship anchored off Sarikei on 19th April to recover *Herald*'s prewar benchmark and to establish the first of a number of tidal observing camps which would be required to carry the tidal datum upstream. Here we met our first Ibans wandering through the few streets buying necessities from the Chinese stalls. The men were stocky in build, their thick black hair cut to a fringe in front; their throats, their arms and their thighs were tattooed with strange asymmetrical swirling designs. They wore the briefest of loincloths with a parang in its wooden sheath secured with a rope of coconut fibre around their waists, or thrust into the long creel-like baskets which they carried on their backs. Their womenfolk, who we were to encounter later, wore only a sarong and were of comely shape and happy disposition.

The western mooring dolphin off the jetty at Sarikei had been co-ordinated by *Herald* when terminating her prewar survey of the lower Rajang and so, to provide a starting baseline for our own work, a boat's taut-wire machine, such as Berncastle and Glen had used off the Normandy beaches, was used to measure a distance up the first reach of the river to a terminal station established on an accessible firm area of riverbank; the direction to the dolphin was computed from astronomical observations made with theodolite at this terminal.

The captain's ingenuity led us to work out a system that made the best use of all the surveying officers and recorders and our boats, even including the doctor's motor canoe, in order to carry the survey upstream at a rate of one to two miles a day.

Two motor dories were employed, with a surveyor in each, to carry the portable signals upstream to mark the corners of the triangles on either side of the river. Each dory, having hung a mark in the mangroves, steamed up river to a point roughly equal to the width of the river; on arrival at that point each dory signalled to the other in simple code as to whether or not the previous mark on his own side could be seen. If neither dory could see their back marks, positions were adjusted until one of them could do so. If this proved impossible the 'jet-propelled clearing party' travelling in a third dory would be moved in. This party was composed of three parang-wielding Ibans who could clear nipah and mangrove with the speed of light. Then followed one of the two surveying motor boats with a surveying officer onboard and towing a folboat into which he could embark and, with a paddle, station himself by plumb-bob beneath the hanging mark to observe with his sextant the angles to the visible corners of the triangle. Often the operation of adjusting the plumb-line would bring down upon the canoeist a swarm of fiercely biting red ants from which there was no escape.

The observed angles were passed back by radio to the computing team onboard consisting of the captain and navigator, who, having worked out their sums and plotted the ever evolving network of stations, handed to me a field board with which I set off in the second survey boat to sound out the river – fascinating work as the deep channels and the shallow banks emerged on the collector tracing I maintained onboard. Yet another dory collected the marks from downriver which were no longer required, and when these had been refurbished by the shipwright the doctor proudly set out upriver with the new supply for the advanced dories in his motor canoe.

Every two or three days the ship was moved forward into the newly sounded area to anchor nearer the scene of operations. By transferring the port bower anchor, together with its swivel piece, to the $3^1/2$ inch wire towing hawser rove onto the port Oropesa winch, the ship was able to moor head and stern in those narrower parts of the river where there was no room to swing.

Those in the advanced boats often spent their nights as guests in a longhouse, thus avoiding a long upstream trip from the ship in the morning. This was an unusual experience: throughout the night people came and went across the creaking floors of the communal area, gangs left for distant padi fields, groups returned from festivities in other longhouses, unsteadily climbing the notched tree trunk, which led from the prahu landing up to the house. Tuak, a sweet thick alcoholic beverage distilled from rice was always in supply.

My opportunity to spend a night in a longhouse came when Henry Menzies moored the ship off Kampong Leman one afternoon and announced a 'hari raya' (holiday) in honour of the King's Birthday next day. By early evening a raft of about sixty prahus, reaching nearly to the riverbank, was made fast to the gangway with about 300 Dyaks squatting on the quarterdeck in readiness for the ship's film show, in which a newsreel showing the Oxford and Cambridge boat race was always well received with derisive shouts of 'kayu belakang' – or 'paddling the wrong way round'; fortunately we also had a stock of 'Westerns' with plenty of shooting.

As night fell a number of us, including Henry, went ashore for a party in the nearby longhouse. Tuak was liberally served from the outset. We admired the recently acquired stock of smoked Japanese heads hanging from the rafters, and slowly the music began and dancing commenced. Gongs in long wooden troughs, hollow logs and a variety of drums were used to provide the music, whilst the dancing consisted of wild posturings and swirlings by individuals or groups, the imitation of which by the gangling figures of Henry and Charles Scott, our senior watchkeeper, brought shrieks of merriment from the women and children. Time passes quickly when one is under the influence of tuak and first light, announced by the crowing of cockerels and the quarrelling of dogs beneath the longhouse, came all too soon. The weary orchestra fumbled to a finish and our hosts assisted us down the tree trunk and into the prahus for return to the ship and a day's sleep.

Living communally as they did, the Ibans had no conception of privacy and felt free to board the ship at any time and wander where they pleased, a practice we did not oppose. Not one article of any description was stolen during the five weeks it took us to reach Sibu where *Sharpshooter* berthed alongside on 1st July; during this time we estimated we had played host to about 2,000 Ibans.

The sextant triangulation of 253 triangles, which had been referenced to five Sarawak survey points on the way up river, closed in the final point in Sibu within eighty-five feet. The errors were distributable along the thirty-five mile traverse to bring our survey into line with the Survey of Sarawak.

At Sibu we were welcomed by Mr Fisher, the District Officer of the Third Division. He was a tall good-humoured man who had served the Rajah before the War, but being on leave at the time of the Japanese invasion he had been available to be flown in to join Tom Harrisson despite his hatred of flying. With his knowledge of the native peoples and their languages he had acted as the administrator for Semut's drive down the 400 miles of the Rajang river. A few of us joined Fisher in his residence for a curry where we were joined for pre-prandial drinks by an ancient and chiefly Dyak. He tottered on widely bowed legs, his brown torso and face were thin and deeply lined, the latter topped by a small circular hat from which two black and white feathers protruded. He and Fisher had jointly slain a Japanese soldier and once the head had been smoked they decided to share its custody six months apiece. Fisher lifted out the head from behind a settee; the old man averred in a high squeaky voice that not only was that an unworthy place to keep such a trophy, but he was dissatisfied to find that the rice provided in a small basket attached to the head was stale and mouldy. He thought it was high time to bear the head away to his longhouse where it would be treated with the reverence it deserved.

For some time it had been our captain's ambition to have a tame gibbon onboard and this desire had been imparted to the Ibans as we moved up river. Just before we sailed from Sibu a message filtered through that a gibbon awaited delivery in the vicinity of Binatang half way down river to Sarikei.

I have already mentioned Henry's love of shiphandling. He had found that in the rivers when going with the stream the ship almost steered herself around the bends, whilst in the reverse direction canal effect was absent, the current took the wrong bow, and it was necessary to fight her round the bends. When the time came to sail downriver from Sibu a great freshet was running bringing with it huge tree trunks and great islands of vegetation. Henry was delighted and set off downstream at a great speed, sweeping round the bends with the minimum of help from the wheel, including the 120° turn at Leba-an. As we approached Binatang all eyes were on the prahus in search of the gibbon – and, yes, there were four Ibans holding high a young black ape. The river here was narrow so the decision was to anchor by the stern using the kedge anchor and lie to the racing river waters for the transfer. I was sent to the bridge to take charge of the ship, while Henry went to the quarterdeck to receive the animal.

The kedge failed to hold the ship in the strong current and we slowly dragged downstream; only occasionally did I dare to use the engines astern to slow our progress, fearful as I was of fouling the towing hawser. Meanwhile the activities on the quarterdeck seemed unduly protracted; however, at long last a smiling Henry returned to the bridge, blood streaming from one of his fingers, but the ape ('never call it a monkey,' said Henry) was safely belted and on its chain in the cuddy.

Next followed a visit to Singapore for fuel and stores before returning to Sarawak, where a tide-watching party was left on the small uninhabited island of Pulo Lakei near the entrance to the Kuching River in order to transfer a tidal datum established there by *Herald* to the Batang Lupar in the Second Division which was the next river to be surveyed. On arrival next day in the Batang Lupar a tide-watching camp was established on the right bank about a quarter of a mile from a Malay kampong near the entrance to the river. Meanwhile a signal was received from the leading seaman in charge at Pulo Lakei – 'Island swarming at night with giant iguanas stop Request instructions' – 'Carry a torch,' was Henry's laconic reply.

The Batang Lupar posed new problems. It was about two miles wide at its mouth and the streams, apart from brief slack water periods, ran at strengths between two and three and a half knots, making it impossible to use any but the two sounding boats.

Henry had wasted no time during the passage to and from Singapore in training his gibbon and it was already extremely biddable and friendly. It learnt to use the W.C., for peeing at least, whilst hanging by its long arms from the deckhead, although it had not yet learnt to push the flush!

It was arranged that the Governor of the new colony, Sir Charles Arden-Clark, whilst on a tour of the Second Division in his launch, should visit *Sharpshooter* in the Batang Lupar and take luncheon with the captain whilst I joined the A.D.C. to make a foursome. Henry was delighted at the opportunity to show off the gibbon, which was restricted to the starboard side of the cuddy by its belt and chain. After lunch, when seated in armchairs to take coffee, I noticed that the gibbon, hanging by its arms from the deckhead, was fascinated by the plume of feathers on the Governor's hat, on the table beside him, which was being gently agitated by an overhead fan. Suddenly, at the end of its tether, the gibbon aimed a copious jet towards the ornate head gear. The effort fell slightly short of target but never have I seen a vice-regal visit so abruptly concluded as the coxswain and quartermaster were rapidly assembled to pipe the 'Still' for the Governor's departure.

On return from a brief visit by the ship to Kuching I was despatched with Petty Officer Slater, the coxswain, in a surveying motor-boat to see how the tide-watchers were faring. At the tidepole among the mangroves we found a crude notice affixed to a tree – 'Gon Kampong back soon, Abang.' Within five minutes, on nearing the hour, a young Malay carrying the 'Record of Tide Readings' book emerged from the soggy pathway. He was taken aback when he saw us but nevertheless composed himself sufficiently to record the hourly tidepole reading before we started to question him as to the whereabouts of the leading seaman and his two fellow tide-watchers. He indicated haltingly that as 'Charlie' was getting married to an upriver Dyak woman the whole party had gone for the celebrations, leaving him in charge of the tidepole. Informing the ship by radio of these surprising developments we set out upriver against a strong ebbing current. In time the first longhouses appeared, deserted except for a few old men and women who waved onwards whither the young people had gone to celebrate. After three or four hours of travelling we heard a distant cacophony of gongs, drums and the human voice which led us eventually into a backwater and to a longhouse alive with activity and merriment. Seldom have two uninvited guests been so unwelcome at a wedding party. Refusing offers of roast pig and foaming tuak we arrested the three absentee tide-watchers, dressed in sarongs, their heads bedecked with flowers, whilst the young bride clung to Stoker Charlie Ledger weeping copiously. It was dark long before we reached the ship with our deflated captives who were charged on arrival with being absent from their place of duty, perhaps a less serious crime than desertion which could equally have met the case.

Charles Ledger, a 'hostilities only' rating, had, like a number of others onboard, been keenly awaiting news of his discharge. As a former Yorkshire miner he had received priority, and orders to arrange an immediate passage for him to U.K. had been received onboard during the recent visit to Kuching. There were some sad days in the river when daily the young bride and her mother arrived alongside by prahu and were allowed to converse with Charles, who was confined to the ship, from the quarterdeck. Meanwhile messages between the ship and the authorities in Kuching elicited the fact that a marriage of this nature was not recognisable in law, and the hope must be that, as Ledger returned to the coalface, his Dyak bride found a more suitable husband to provide for her in the jungles of Sarawak.

There was no particular task for the doctor in the survey of the Batang Lupar so he spent most of his days lying on the bridge chart table enduring the daily increasing pain as a Dyak tattooist tap-tapped with a hand-held needle to impose a native tattoo on his shoulder. Only tots of brandy brought to him by his fellow Idlers enabled him to see the work completed.

During visits to Kuching I stayed once again with my old friend 'Shot' Spurway, back in his former job as chief forestry officer after $3^1/_2$ years imprisonment by the Japanese in a camp near the capital. Whilst enjoying black curried eggs at a night market Shot introduced me to the Chinese stallholder who had risked his life daily to bring food supplies to the starving European prisoners.

Tom Harrisson was also in town, having become curator of the Museum and thus the immediate successor to the man who had accused him of being uncouth and irresponsible fifteen years earlier. Tom usually had visitors from up country: Kenyans, Kelabits or Punans exotically attired for the capital. Tom loved them all and much fun was to be had at his house. In the Museum I had seen an insignificant little bone plug which was used in Kelabit family planning. Normally it plugged a small hole bored in the underside of the base of the penis, but when removed during sexual intercourse the open aperture formed an efficient by-pass. I asked Tom if he were so fitted but only a broad smile came in answer. We young officers were intrigued.

When *Sharpshooter* had sailed from England in May 1946 we were told that we should be away for a limited period until we were relieved by *Dampier*, the first of four Bay Class frigates which, with war ended, were being completed as survey ships. At long last news of *Dampier's* completion was received and we realised that with luck we should be home a few days before Christmas after eighteen months' absence.

There was, however, one last task to be tackled. Port Swettenham, the port serving the capital of Malaya, Kuala Lumpur, was now quite inadequate for post-war trade and plans had been drawn up for the establishment of extensive wharves in the closely adjacent North Klang Strait. The Strait was bordered with a wide and ancient mangrove forest. Here the scale of the survey for the port development was large, necessitating a second order triangulation to be carried through the swamps where 'jet propelled clearers' were unavailable. So we had to clear lanes ourselves up to half a mile in length; many days were spent either up to our waists in water or kneedeep in mud as we hacked away at the iron-hard mangrove trees with an assortment of axes, choppers and parangs, nightly re-sharpened by the shipwright. Eventually the sightlines were clear, platforms were built above the mud to facilitate theodolite observations, the triangulation was balanced and plotted and the work of sounding North Klang Strait completed.

Henry had found a good home for his gibbon with friends in Singapore, and for the long voyage home he turned his attention to rug-making, devising his own pattern of a bluish grey Dyak tattoo on a brown skin background. By the time we reached Chatham a magnificent and unusual hearth rug adorned the cuddy. In front of the bridge the ship carried a great wooden carved and gaudily painted 'Kenyalang', the mythical bird of good omen of the Borneo jungles, to remind us, had that been necessary, of our life among the Ibans of Sarawak.

Chapter X

Shore Jobs

Early in 1948 I received my first shore appointment to the Hydrographic Department of the Admiralty as Officer in Charge of Notices to Mariners. Apart from the Chart Printing Factory, which had been prudently built at Taunton in the West Country just prior to the War, the whole Department, comprising chart compilation and maintenance, the Tidal and Sailing Direction branches and a large section devoted to aircharts for the Fleet Air Arm, had been moved at the War's end from Bath to Cricklewood. The building provided had been built as a 'shadow' Admiralty which could have been used if the main building were destroyed by enemy action. It was totally unsuitable for a chart compilation office, which requires extensive draughting rooms easily supervised by a senior draughtsman. It was composed of numerous hutch-like offices from one of which the Hydrographer himself, Vice Admiral Sir Guy Wyatt, happier on the bridge of his ship than at a desk, looked out upon a dismal coal yard. Worst of all, the precious fair charts sent to the Admiralty by many famous explorers and dedicated seamen over the past 200 years were housed in damp basements liable to flooding.

A patient courier went daily by van to Paddington with his 'baskets' of chart compilation drawings to travel onwards by the Great Western Railway to Taunton; later in the day he returned by the same route, his baskets loaded with chart proofs from the factory to be checked by the cartographers. Mistakes were always made 'at the other end'.

It seems odd to me that, although one is almost certain as a naval officer to serve for periods within the Admiralty or Royal Dockyards, one is taught absolutely nothing, in the course of an exhaustive training, about civil servants or their organisation; all is uniquely directed to the provision of an efficient

79

seagoing officer. So the first few weeks in the Office provided for me a completely new experience – dealing with civil servants instead of sailors – and there are differences! Happily there served for many years at Cricklewood, and later within the Department at Whitehall, a remarkable clerical officer, Mrs. Chris Auckland, who was in charge of the Secretariat. She took compassion on newly-joined naval officers, instructing them in the mysteries of files, dockets, jackets and clerical routines; many of us are indebted to her over the years.

Cartographers had been founder members of the Institute of Professional Civil Servants when it was formed in 1919. They were university graduates who directed the cartographic draughtsmen in the several geographic sections devoted to chart making. Since 1935 Mr G. B. Stigant had held the post of Superintending Cartographer and Assistant Superintendent of Charts. The Superintendent was a surveying captain; Stigant had seen many such come and go over the years.

'Stiggy' was a surprise to me for he bore little resemblance to my pre-conceived idea of a senior civil servant. He went out of his way to befriend me. He told me tales of eccentric surveying officers whom he had served with in his youth, and he appeared to have absorbed some of that eccentricity himself as he reminisced somewhat frenetically in a high staccato voice. He instructed me in the ways of professional civil servants and introduced me to them. I found that they were every bit as dedicated to the compiling of charts as we were to making surveys. Stiggy had many outside interests; he enrolled me as a fellow member of the Anthropological Society, and took me to conversaziones and performances of Noh at the London Japan Society; he spoke and wrote Japanese tolerably well although he had never visited that land. Despite these deviations he had a clear and concise mind when it came to charts. He explained that the most important criteria by which the value of a chart is judged are its accuracy, adequacy and clarity, and accordingly constant reference to these three principles forms the best practical guide during chart compilation. He regarded the chart as the link between the surveyor and the navigator. The cartographer's problem, similar to that of the surveyor's, was how to show best within the borders of the chart, by means of symbols and abbreviations, those things which are of primary importance to the navigator.

Stigant first revealed these concepts in a lecture delivered to the Fourth International Hydrographic Conference in Monaco in April 1937. The salient points of this lecture have recently been reprinted in the 'Fifty Years Ago' column in the *International Hydrographic Review* for January 1988.

My task of preparing the daily Notices to Mariners was a full time one. Each day thirty or forty Hydrographic Notes or letters from merchant ship captains, harbourmasters, naval navigating officers or yachtsmen flopped into my 'In' tray in their respective jackets; each described some physical change affecting the charts – a new shoal found, a lighthouse discontinued, a navigation buoy withdrawn. My job was to decide which were of pressing navigational importance and which could be sent to the appropriate geographical section for incorporation in the next revision of the affected chart. For those requiring immediate promulgation exact plotting was necessary and the preparation of an unambiguous Notice in the standard format for printing and distribution to Admiralty chart users worldwide. It was essential to check and proof read with full concentration; nevertheless small mistakes inevitably crept into the published Notices, each of which was uncannily spotted by Rear Admiral Baron van Asbeck, the Netherlands Hydrographer. His letters to my chief led sometimes to a stern rebuke. We christened the Baron the 'Long Stop' who never failed to play his part in this particular game.

The sanctity of jackets was brought home to me one day when Chris Auckland, visiting my office, noticed jacket H1320/48, torn asunder, lying in my wastepaper basket. 'Good Heavens! You can't do that!' she said. Only God, it seemed, could exorcise a jacket. My predecessor in the post had, before returning thankfully to sea, proposed at some length in a virgin jacket a considerable reorganisation within the Notices to Mariners set-up, which would have provided me with much additional work. A few less committed persons had written supporting minutes but I believed that the matter should be quietly disposed of. However that was not to be, as Chris 'kept me back after school' while she retyped the proposal and the minute sheets and I forged the signatures and reconstituted the jacket. Many years later, as Assistant Hydrographer, I was looking into some matter concerning Notices to Mariners the details of which were presented to me in a jacket over an inch thick, its torn covers held together with tape – it was H1320/48, the jacket that might never have been. The proposed re-organisation had, however, never come about!

As has been described, learning the arts of hydrographic surveying depended on one's senior officers, how competent they were themselves and how much they were prepared to help the beginner. A number of middle-ranking officers, including myself, had been pressing for some time for the establishment of a modest hydrographic school. This came about in the middle of 1948, but to our surprise the Surveying Training Unit to be established in the R.N. Barracks, Chatham, was to be for the training of surveying recorders, not officers. I was placed in charge and also became responsible for the drafting appointments of the 200 or so surveying recorders.

I was not unhappy to allow another to replace me on the N to Ms treadmill and make my way to Chatham to take up my appointment in the Barracks. My little empire was fragmented – a room high up in the Training Block, a cubby-hutch built onto the Drafting Office and, moored in the Medway, the oldest surveying motor boat still afloat, in which my assistant, Petty Officer Slater, former Coxswain of *Sharpshooter*, taught boat sounding to our initial class of six ordinary seamen. For transport about my domain I was provided with a bicycle which had seen better days. On my second morning when pedalling rapidly down from the Training Block to the Drafting Office a stentorian 'Halt – that Officer!' came from the burly Commodore of the Barracks. 'Who are you, racing round the parade ground in bicycle clips?' I informed him of my new posting, of which he was clearly unaware, and that my unprepossessing cycle was my official transport. He gave me a dismissive 'Humph' and shrugged his shoulders in a gesture of unbelief.

My barrack duties included a day's stint once weekly as Duty Commanding Officer, which began when morning 'Colours' were hoisted at the mast in front of the Wardroom Block. The guard and band required for this ceremony set out some ten minutes earlier marching from the furthest end of the Barracks. If it was raining heavily it was my responsiblity to cancel the guard and band, if drizzling to order them to don greatcoats. The Commodore's Residence was hard by and he usually attended the ceremony half hidden by a bank of laurel bushes. How fickle the Medway weather was! If the sailors set off in sunshine it would quite likely be drizzling by the time they reached the mast: on the other hand if I cancelled their departure because of rain the sun could be shining by the time the colours were hoisted. I seldom got it right and I could see from the Commodore's demeanour that he had doubts about my judgment as he peered skywards in mock surprise.

However, Commodore Eccles' bark was far worse than his bite. He was a holder of the Judo Black Belt and he played eastern music on a large brass tray on guest nights, and even looked favourably on my little school as it began to take shape.

By July 1949 we had drafted to surveying ships the first four shore-trained third class surveying recorders, and were engaged on training the second class of six, when I received orders to join H.M.S. *Owen*, the third of the Bay Class frigates then being completed as surveying ships.

Chapter XI

The Persian Gulf

'Chiefie' Kelly, our popular engineer officer in *Sharpshooter*, who had been standing by *Owen* completing as a surveying vessel since the beginning of 1949, was joined in May by Lieutenant Hatfield who was to be the navigator.

In his first letter of proceedings Hatfield reported that he had visited George Wilson's boatyard at Sunbury-on-Thames to inspect two new-construction twenty-nine-foot surveying motor boats being completed for the ship, and he witnessed onboard tests of new type Welwyn McLaughlan davits fitted to receive them. Although the new boats retained the Kitchen rudder, so useful in surveying work, the coxswain's position had been moved amidships to allow a more spacious area aft for the observers, the echo sounder and the plotting table. In addition to the sounding boats two surf boats were supplied to replace the cumbersome whalers as seaboats. They had been designed by Camper Nicholson at the request of Admiral Wyatt and proved excellent sloop-rigged sailing boats capable of being beached in quite difficult surf conditions. These boats remained as the standard seaboats in survey ships for over twenty years.

Petty Officer Slater accompanied me from the Training Unit as coxswain in *Owen* when I was appointed first lieutenant and we only awaited Henry Menzies' arrival to take command at the end of July to complete a team of four old *Sharpshooters*. Commander Menzies had been representing the Hydrographer in Whitehall, a necessary appointment since the Hydrographer himself had been banished to Cricklewood, but he was delighted to be going back to sea.

By the end of September the ship had been commissioned, the necessary trials had been completed, and we sailed for a number of boisterous 'shake down' surveys off the Hebrides and St. Kilda before arriving at Plymouth to prepare for final departure for the Persian Gulf.

In Plymouth we received the unwelcome news that we were to take with us under tow a motor fishing vessel for the Persian Navy; nicknamed *Minnie*, she was to give us a troublesome passage. After passing the Breakwater on 11th October 1949 we streamed the tow on 150 fathoms of three-and-a-half-inch wire rope. By the time we reached Gibraltar it was clear that *Minnie* was sensitive to the slightest sea and in winds in excess of force five speed had to be reduced to less than four knots. Inexperienced as we were as towmasters, we managed to get a single turn of the towing hawser around the ship's starboard propeller when hauling *Minnie* alongside prior to entering Gibraltar. At first it seemed a simple task to hang the bight of hawser and send down a diver to clear the screw, but, as so often happens in such cases, it proved much more difficult. As we had been expecting to be on our way into harbour quite soon our captain had not informed Gibraltar of the cause of our delay. Meanwhile the Flag Officer, Gibraltar, who had been watching our efforts through his telescope, sent a signal inviting Henry to lunch, so that he had to come clean in signalling his inability to accept.

Throughout our difficulties, which were not resolved until the early afternoon, a Spanish salvage tug circled us like a vulture, frequently heaving lines towards us which we were at pains to disregard.

The transit of the Suez Canal was made without incident with *Minnie* secured alongside, but by the time we reached the southern end of the Red Sea our speed was down to two-and-a-half knots in a force eight headwind. *Minnie* was plunging heavily even at that speed and by the time we entered Aden she was lolling from side to side like a drunkard, with fifteen tons of seawater in her hull.

Repairs in the local shipyard were required, but two hours before sailing the tug bringing *Minnie* alongside had too much way on and carried her under the ship's forward flare, thus dismasting her. The shattered mast was recovered from the harbour and provided the shipwrights with an interesting scarfing job on the final leg of this tedious voyage. So much had *Minnie* suffered in heavy sea that Henry decided that before delivering her to Khorramshahr we should go to Basra to carry out repairs and make the little vessel shipshape once more. This was a wise decision for, as dawn broke off the Shatt al Arab, *Minnie* was seen to be badly down by the head, floundering in rough seas. It was necessary to tow her across the bar into calmer water before pumps could be placed onboard. A spare cylinder liner had broken adrift from its lashings fracturing a fire main inlet which had to be plugged before proceeding up river with *Minnie* alongside.

It took two weeks to make *Minnie* seaworthy again and to clean her up and paint her. However, when we put a crew aboard and she sailed with us in company for final presentation to the Persian Navy in Khorramshahr she looked quite a proud little vessel. Thankfully we turned her over to her new owners and sailed, with a considerable feeling of relief, for Christmas in Bahrein.

Henry's latest hobby, which he had pursued in the cuddy on the long voyage out, had been the building of a model steam locomotive. Whilst at Basra he had been able to further his current enthusiasm by joining the night train from Baghdad to Basra, travelling on the footplate. I met the train as it steamed into Basra station and saw my captain climbing down from the great locomotive: he was grinning widely and his hair was tousled, he looked like a badly made-up nigger minstrel, but he had got steam out of his system and was ready to begin work on a model hydrofoil.

Over a century before our arrival in the Gulf, Great Britain had signed truces with a number of sheikhs who ruled territories on the so-called Trucial Coast stretching from Muscat in the east along the southern shore of the Persian Gulf to Qatar in the west, an extensive peninsula running northwards from the Arabian shore. To the north-west of Qatar lies the island sheikhdom of Bahrein where the United Kingdom maintained a modest naval establishment housing the headquarters of the Senior Naval Officer, Persian Gulf. The Political Resident with responsibility for Britain's relationships with the Trucial States, Sir Rupert Hay, had his residence within the naval compound on the shores of the Khor Khaliya, which provided an anchorage for naval vessels. Sir Rupert was represented in each of the sheikhdoms by a political agent who advised as to how the states could be defended and developed. Christmas time 1949 gave the officers their first introduction to Sir Rupert and Lady Hay, for they held open house at the Residency every evening between 6.00 and 8.00 p.m. Here we met people of many diverse interests travelling through Bahrein; oilmen, sheikhs' advisers and Arabian travellers.

One of the pleasures of naval service for officers east of Suez in those days was the provision of courteous Goanese stewards and cooks, the latter providing perpetual curry for those who enjoyed it. The Goans were permitted to bring onboard with them a boy whose sole daily duty was to prepare curry paste by grinding chillies, herbs and spices with a rough stone rolling pin upon a coarse stone platter. The Goanese were Catholics as was our navigating officer.

Peter Stent, our paymaster, was by choice serving in his third survey ship; although an early riser he was not at his best at breakfast time, hiding himself behind a month-old newspaper as he awaited his bacon and eggs. On Christmas morning he and I were early in our respective chairs at opposite ends of the table, but no response came from the pantry when we rang for service. I pulled down the hatch but only the curry boy was to be seen about his daily pounding. 'Where are the stewards?' I asked. 'All gone mess,' said he. We hurried to the cooks' and stewards' messroom to rout them out – not a Goan to be seen. It was only when the Officer of the Day came into the wardroom that he told us the navigator had, at an early hour, rounded up every Goan onboard and taken them ashore in the motor cutter to attend morning Mass in Manama. As the Goan's divisional officer Peter Stent was not amused, and it took a little time after the return of the Catholic church party before that harmony expected during the festive season could be recaptured.

New Year's Eve was a joyous time. Henry Menzies was promoted to Captain's rank and this was happily celebrated.

Soon after the War Petroleum Development (Qatar) was formed in association with the Iraq Petroleum Company to develop an oilfield which had been located at the southern end of the Qatar peninsula in 1940. Although the discovery dictated that the wells were drilled on the western side of the peninsula, the shallow reef-encumbered offshore waters in that area made it necessary to pipe the crude oil to the east coast. At Umm Said depths of sixty feet or so, close to shore, were found in water sheltered from the north by the extensive Fasht al Arif reef, enabling tankers to load whilst moored to buoys.

H.M.S. *Challenger* had arrived in this area towards the end of 1946 to spend two winter seasons charting northwards from Umm Said as far as Doha, which allowed the oil company to buoy a long and circuitous approach channel into the new terminal. The intricacies of the offshore islands and reefs eastwards from Qatar, largely uncharted, together with information that searches for offshore oil were to be made in Qatar's complex territorial waters, had persuaded the Hydrographer to send two of his ships to the region in the winter season 1949/1950. *Dalrymple*, unhampered by a tow, had arrived much earlier than *Owen* in the Gulf and was at work east of Qatar where we joined her in the New Year.

To my delight our former *Endeavour* captain, Buck Baker, was now in command of *Dalrymple*. When we all left the old ship in 1943 Buck, seeking the most active service, became Senior Naval Officer, Aegean, on the British-held island of Leros. There he gained the D.S.O. for his leadership in harassing the German forces.

Eventually the enemy overran the island in a fierce onslaught and Baker was transported with his fellow prisoners across Europe in a cattle truck to the naval camp Marlag 0 near Bremen. Here, for a time, he acted as Senior British Officer; with his forthright personality he stood up to his German captors and got away with it, refusing to speak or understand their 'horrible language'.

As the Allied forces closed in towards the War's end the Germans decided to march the prisoners north-eastwards 150 miles to Lübeck. Buck was in charge on this miserable trek and managed to keep everyone together, the only losses being three killed by mistaken strafing by Allied aircraft. Happily, on arrival near Lübeck the prisoners were liberated by the Eleventh Armoured Division on the day before V-E Day.

Petroleum Development (Qatar) believed that they had obtained the rights to prospect throughout Qatar and its waters from Emir Ali, the sheikh. Towards the end of 1949 the Company accused Superior Oil and the International Marine Oil Company of usurping these rights; accordingly, early in 1950 an Arbitration Court was established in the somewhat rundown capital Doha, under the chairmanship of Lord Radcliffe. In April he handed down an award in favour of Superior Oil and International Marine, so quite a scramble of prospecting began in the areas where we were engaged in surveying for the charts which would so clearly be required.

Charles Grattan, D.S.C. and Bar, a highly competent if didactic surveyor with a gallant war record, was Buck Baker's first lieutenant. He had already served in the Gulf in *Challenger* and was thus able without difficulty to continue her triangulation along the coast from the vicinity of Doha northwards a further thirty miles or so to Ras Lafan, the northeast headland of Qatar, to provide control for the offshore work being undertaken by the two ships.

On joining company with *Dalrymple* it was necessary for the captains to confer and divide the work between them. Whilst the sea areas eastwards towards the small island, Jazirat Halul, were to be sounded out by the ships, Charles Grattan was to be in charge of a large camp party composed of officers and surveying recorders from both ships, with jeep transport to progress the triangulation across inhospitable wastes of sand and boulders.

Charles was a hard taskmaster and in his forthright way demanded the minimum closing errors from the young surveyors' theodolite observations within every triangle.

Shamals, strong north-westerly storms, which are a feature of wintertime in the Gulf and may blow for several days, often hindered our work, although the triangulation teams were usually able to continue. Each evening Charles mustered his four junior officers in the plotting tent, where, in the light of a pressure lantern, he studied the day's observations critically.

Petty Officer Slater and I, before we left the Survey Training Unit in Chatham, had arranged to appoint the brightest of our first four graduates to *Owen*, and now young Brown was ashore with the camp party anxious to learn as much as he could, including how to drive a jeep. One night he reversed inadvertently into the plotting tent sending Charles and his assistants sprawling under the collapsed canvas and then, in his confusion, repeated the action as the officers were scrambling to their feet. Onboard *Owen* I was called to the radio telephone to hear Charles spluttering with rage as he demanded that Brown should be withdrawn from the camp by boat at dawn. I pointed out that a severe shamal was blowing and that it might be several days before a boat could be sent inshore. Petty Officer Slater arrived three days later to collect the errant recorder. 'No – you're not taking young Brown away, he's one of the best recorders we've got here,' was Grattan's surprising welcome. That was the only commendation Slater and I were ever to receive concerning our first four graduates from the Surveying Training Unit.

H.M. Ships passing through Aden on their way to the Persian Gulf in those days embarked a dozen or so Somali ratings together with their 'tindal'. Their main purpose was to assist with the ship's maintenance during the torrid summer months; in our case they were extremely useful onboard when so many of our men were absent in boats and camp parties. Our tindal, who claimed that he had assembled his Somalis from his own tribesmen, was a jolly rotund fellow who, until the day I ordered him to land with me as an interpreter on a visit to the Bedu, spoke expansively of his flocks of sheep and herds of camel. However, when I informed him that, lacking transport, we might have to ride camels his eyes rolled apprehensively. Fortunately for the tindal a jeep was available, for I do not believe he had ever backed a camel nor travelled far from the souks of Aden. He began to resume his normal happy countenance as we bumped across the desert to meet the minor sheikh who headed the Bedu tribe in northern Qatar.

The sheikh welcomed us on the flat roof of his house built of locally made bricks. From there we could see two donkeys, cunningly harnessed, hoisting water in goatskins from a deep well. This water was then channelled to irrigate a sizeable vegetable garden, some date palms and even a small orange grove.

After the second cup of coffee I broached the question of the loss of our survey marks and was able to point to a practical example – a dilapidated tent nearby shored up with survey poles and patched with black and red flags. After protracted discussion it was finally agreed that the sheikh would impose stricter control over his tribe if we, in turn, sent our doctor ashore to set up a clinic for his people for two or three weeks. That we were in some way involved with the oil waiting for exploitation beneath the adjacent seas had facilitated an agreement, for the sheikh informed me that, as he was related to the Sheikh of Qatar, he must soon travel to Doha to voice his claim for a part of the revenue already so confidently expected.

Surgeon Lieutenant Copperstone was Maltese by birth and one of four compatriots who had recently joined the Royal Navy. Shortly before he was due to set up his clinic in the desert one of our stewards, Ferrera, had become somewhat unbalanced, one of his peculiarities being evident at breakfast time when, with the bacon and eggs, he handed each officer a chit with racing tips for an unknown and distant race meeting. I went to the captain and suggested we should take Ferrera to Bahrein for a passage home to Goa.

'We can't waste two days Number One. Tell the doctor to keep his eye on him until we next go to Bahrein for stores.'

'But the doctor is going ashore to-day to set up the Bedu clinic,' said I.

'Excellent,' said Henry, 'He can take Ferrera as his steward.'

The doctor was provided with a tent, camping gear and two sleeping bags; as he descended into the boat alongside to take him ashore he said to me, 'Don't worry , Number One, I'll look after Ferrera.' Then came Ferrera with his kit, hurrying aft along the deck, pausing before manning the boat only to say to me, 'Don't worry, Sir, I'll look after the doctor.' So the two men, each believing he was in charge of the other, set off for a fortnight in the wilderness. The clinic was a success, and certainly Ferrera was no worse when he finally sailed for home.

Sometimes in the evenings in harbour the doctor would perform incredible acts of thought transference. When he was sent from the wardroom, and well out of hearing, the assembled officers thought up a chain of simple tasks for him to perform such as filling a glass with water from a jug, then offering it to a selected officer. On entering Copperstone would hold the wrist of one of our number who, together with the rest of us, concentrated on the task to be performed. To our amazement he would then carry out the routine step by step in a series of jerky movements. On other occasions we would, in his absence, scatter a pack of cards face downwards on the dining table, noting the positions of two of them. The doctor's hand, when he entered the room where all of us were visualizing the position of the pair, would hover over the pack and quite suddenly fall unerringly first on one and then the other of the cards. One night, to trick Copperstone, we merely concentrated our minds on the Queen of Spades and the Ace of Diamonds without sighting them. It took him a long time, sweating profusely, before he was able to turn them up. This was the nearest I ever saw to a miracle.

The doctor's unusual gifts were much in demand when we entertained visitors but after only two routines he was so exhausted that he retired to his bunk and fell into a heavy sleep, missing what little social life we were enjoying.

The Sheikh of Qatar, Emir Ali, had been indisposed when we first arrived off the coast, but in due course our captain was bidden to lunch at the palace in Doha. Henry had noted that sheikhs, when calling, took with them a retinue and he decided to do likewise, so he and I wore swords and medals, and two petty officers, armed with curved naval cutlasses (still on issue) accompanied us. Joined by the political agent, our little party proceeded to the palace, where in a room draped with carpets, we gathered on our haunches around a massive circular brass tray on which had been placed a roast lamb on a bed of saffron rice. The sheikh would, from time to time, tear off succulent morsels for Henry, while his minions did likewise for the remainder of our party. Occasionally, hard boiled curried eggs, stuffed within the beast's stomach, were strewn among the guests, who soon learnt to mould the rice into suitable mouthfuls with their fingers. It was a memorable meal, concluded with two cups of Arab coffee which cleansed the greasy palate. Contrary to common Western belief, the sheep's eye was not dispensed, nor have I ever seen this practice followed.

As yet, Two Range Decca as an electronic fixing aid for surveying operations was at the drawing board stage, so that ship sounding out of sight of land still relied upon visual fixing using moored beacons. Rather than setting up a floating triangulation, as had been the practice in the past, it was decided that owing to the prevalence of shamal winds, which often wrecked or displaced the beacons, they would be laid in transit lines from an inshore datum beacon fixed by theodolite observations from the shore triangulation. Thereafter taut wire was used to measure the intervals between the beacons in the line stretching twenty to twenty-five miles to seaward. These beflagged floating marks were then used to fix the ship, with sextants and station pointers, as she proceeded along sounding lines parallel to the beacons. The method was similar to that used for laying the Channel Mine Barrage ten years earlier.

Every few days it was necessary to weigh the beacons and relay the line some six miles further along the coast. Two beacon teams were employed, using both port and starboard derricks on the forecastle alternately. A high standard of seamanship was achieved which allowed beacon work to continue even during severe shamals.

At the end of April 1950 the last beacon was weighed, the camp parties were embarked, a visit to Basra was made for fuel and *Owen* sailed for Cyprus.

Disa and our two small boys, who had been visiting relatives in South Africa whilst I was in the Gulf, had managed, in these difficult postwar years, to get two seats on a charter flight from Johannesburg to Haifa, calling at Nicosia. The aircraft was an old DC 3, piloted by a white-haired German, said to be a survivor of von Richthofen's Air Circus. He flew low over jungle and desert, landing for the nights at remote African airfields. They survived this perilous journey and were there on the quay to welcome the ship as we berthed beneath the castle walls in Famagusta.

The survey task in Cyprus was to continue the work begun by *Challenger* along the north coast with happy weekends spent off Kyrenia. We rented a traditional house on Nicosia Road where we shared the bedrooms and courtyard with a host of nesting swallows. Although the Cyprus troubles had begun, we received nothing but friendship and courtesy from the people of Kyrenia. We enjoyed the wine of the country and the kebabs sold nightly from stalls which advertised their presence on the streets with their appetising aroma. This was a blissful period for us, culminating on the morning of the first of June when the captain ordered the quartermaster to 'Send the Commander to see me.'

I had been promoted. In those days one assumed the new rank immediately, so that it was necessary for me to receive a new appointment. I was to get my first surveying command – H.M.S. *Scott*, based in Chatham for surveys in Home Waters. Disa and the boys flew home to open up our little house in Wigmore and I followed by troopship with the exciting prospect of a home command and settled family life.

Chapter XII

Challenger – My First Surveying Command

Rear Admiral Day had relieved Vice Admiral Sir Guy Wyatt as Hydrographer of the Navy early in 1950 and at once arranged to move his personal office back into the Admiralty Building, changing his view of a coal yard to that of the Mall and the statue of Captain Cook. He left an Assistant Hydrographer at Cricklewood and by July 1950 that post was held by Captain Baker who had returned from the Persian Gulf.

It was to him that I had to report on return to U.K., anxious of course to know how much leave I could expect before taking command of H.M.S. *Scott*. I was to receive a sharp shock.

Challenger had set off in May on a two-and-a-half-year world voyage with scientists embarked and was now, after two cruises in the north-west Atlantic, lying in Bermuda. Her captain had been invalided home and her first lieutenant, not a surveying specialist, was said to be at loggerheads with the chief scientist. In ten days' time I was to fly to Bermuda to take command – dreams of home service and family life were shattered on the instant.

Recovering from this bombshell I rallied sufficiently to plead with Buck that, if I had to accept this pier-head jump, then I should take with me a surveying officer to replace the first lieutenant who was said to be so unsympathetic to scientists. So it was that I met Lieutenant Commander Geoff Simeon at the BOAC check-in near Victoria Station one afternoon in early July 1950, and we flew out together to take over *Challenger* in Bermuda.

Challenger has, since the 1870s, been an honoured name in oceanographic and surveying circles. With a surveying captain, Nares, and a team of scientists headed by Dr. Wyville Thomson, the ship set out in December 1872 to circle the world in three years. During this voyage investigations were made of physical conditions in the deep sea in the great ocean basins with regard to water temperature and circulation, the morphology of the ocean floor and the nature of the deposits lying thereon.

An expedition of this nature would not have gained lasting fame had not the results been carefully prepared and published. After the voyage ended in 1876 Sir Wyville Thomson set up an office in Edinburgh for this purpose, and there, under his direction, Sir John Murray, who had been his deputy during the voyage, commenced compiling the fifty volumes of the now famous '*Challenger* Reports' which, with the co-operation of many European scientists, were eventually published by the end of the century. They form the very basis for all studies concerned with the oceans from the time of their publication to the present day. Although the current expedition was far less ambitious, I was acutely aware of the need to make the voyage a scientific success.

As we motored across the island towards the Naval Base in Bermuda, Geoff and I wondered what we would find. Our first view of the ship in the greyness of dawn was not reassuring; her white hull was streaked with red rust, halyards bowed out in the wind, the decks were cluttered and she appeared dejected.

My steward welcomed me, and during a bath and a good breakfast I decided that the first thing I should do was to send for the chief scientist, whilst Geoff Simeon took over the ship from the first lieutenant whose departure was imminent.

Dr. Tom Gaskell had been represented to me as somewhat of an ogre, so that when a cheery-faced, plain-clothed figure appeared at my cabin door I thought it must be the canteen manager. Tom roared with laughter at this assumption as we sat down over cups of coffee to discuss the situation. Tom's enthusiasm was absolute and by midday I was fully aware of what the ship was trying to achieve and I had found a friend for life.

The cruise had been planned to achieve a very considerable amount of sounding in the three great oceans, as well as carrying out searches for a number of shoals reported in such areas, particularly in the latter years of the war when thousands of ships were running their echo-sounding machines – many of the operators interpreting their sounders correctly, while others 'discovered' shoals that never existed.

It had been arranged that a party of scientists from the Department of Geodesy and Geophysics, Cambridge, should embark to explore the structure of the ocean bed itself. This was to be done by seismic refraction methods already in use on land, but recently adapted by Cambridge scientists for use from a ship at sea with over 2,600 fathoms of water separating her from the ocean bed. To carry out such experiments a ship must be fitted with special apparatus.

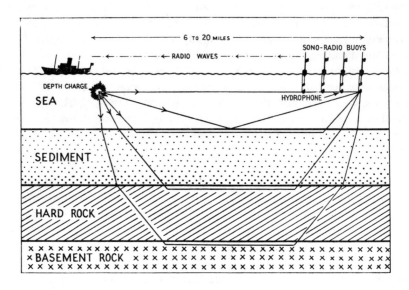

Seismic refraction at sea

A comparatively flat area of the ocean bed having been found, four sono radio buoys are laid about half a mile apart. Each buoy has a hydrophone slung beneath it in the water and within the buoy itself is a receiver and transmitter wireless set, with batteries. An aerial is carried on the buoy's mast. Having laid the buoys, the ship moves off to a distance of eight miles or so and fires a depth charge. This forms a source of sound which travels out in all directions in the sea. One path of sound travels horizontally through the water to the hydrophones below the buoys, whence it returns to the ship as a radio signal. An accurate timing device in the ship records the time of firing the depth charge and the returning signal. The speed of sound in sea water is known (5,000 feet per second) so that a range of the buoys has now been found. Other paths of sound lead towards the sea-bed and then horizontally through the layer of sediment. As this sound passes beneath the buoys it can be picked up through the water by the hydrophone and again a signal is sent to the ship. The depth of water both beneath the buoys and beneath the ship has been found with the sounding machine, and the time of passage of sound from the ship to the sea-bed and from the sea-bed to the buoy hydrophone can be calculated. These time intervals are subtracted from the total time for the passage of sound, the resulting time being that taken by the sound to pass horizontally through the sediment layer for a distance of eight miles, so that the speed of sound in the sediment layer has been discovered. Other paths of sound pass through the sediment to the harder, more compressed layers beneath, in which sound travels more quickly. The time of passage of sound through these lower layers is also obtained, and a speed of sound for these layers found. When the speed of sound in a material is known then geophysicists get a pretty good idea of the type of rock forming this material, relating it to their experiences on land, where borings can be made and samples of the material inspected after measuring the speed of sound by seismic methods.

By carrying out these seismic refraction experiments at a number of increasing ranges from the sono buoys, and knowing the speed of sound in the material forming the layers, the vertical thickness of the layers may be measured. Thus a picture is built up of the types of material which form the layers of the earth's crust beneath the oceans, and the thickness of these layers.

Tom Gaskell and John Swallow, our two scientists from Cambridge, were both outstanding in their way, although completely different in outlook. Tom was hard-working in the extreme when he had work to do, but when his experiments were complete and his records made up he would enjoy life as few others can; his enthusiasm for every new project was unbounded and carried others along with him. Whenever one did anything with Tom he made it seem really worthwhile doing. He was an inveterate sightseer in the scientific field or any other: as the voyage went on his cabin became fuller and fuller of souvenirs which he picked up at every port of call. John Swallow was serious, never happier than when he was working on the results of his experiments, and intensely interested in all forms of science and in Natural History. John could relax, however, and when he started mixing highballs a good evening lay ahead.

Only a few days were available in Bermuda to get to know the ship and her company before we sailed for my first cruise. It was to be an exciting one. We steered northward over the Great Newfoundland Bank and on into the North Atlantic. We were intending to stay at sea as long as possible to carry out investigations before returning to Bermuda for fuel. This is a risky business in a low-powered ship in the hurricane season, and after steaming southwards for some days on our way back to Bermuda a hurricane warning was received. Before the war, the first a ship often knew about a hurricane was the rapid falling of the barometer and the presence of an ominous calm. By the late 1940s, at the suspicion of a circular storm forming in the hurricane breeding area, which lies eastward of the West Indies, United States aircraft searched for and located the storm, which, if it proved to be a hurricane, was given a girl's name and assumed a personality. The storm was followed daily by the patrol 'planes, which often flew boldly through the storm, fixing its position and estimating its course and speed, until the hurricane entered the mainland of the United States or petered out in the North Atlantic. Such storms usually set out in a north-westerly direction and if they did not reach the mainland turned slowly northward and then north-eastward, when they were said to have 'recurved'. Bermuda often found itself in the hurricane area at the time of recurving.

Some ships have passed right through the centre of a hurricane, experiencing winds of well over 100 miles an hour and mountainous seas; such ships' captains have often lived to tell the tale, usually with much understatement, one feels, when reading these accounts in the meteorological journals: but well-found vessels have gone to the bottom on meeting a hurricane or a typhoon at sea, often as a result of a giant wave pouring down the funnel, as the ship is tossed wildly in a confused and towering sea. So it is well to avoid these circular storms, and this is difficult of accomplishment in a low-speed ship.

On this occasion the hurricane was reported coming northwards between Bermuda and the coast of the United States. Her name was Doris. A little later she was reported to be recurving and to be moving in a north-easterly direction. *Challenger* was just south of the Grand Banks and the navigator and I decided to head due westwards and later southwards towards Bermuda, getting round behind Doris. As the next twelve hours wore on the feeling of ominous calm became gradually apparent, and by evening, as the ship sailed westwards into the setting sun, it was unmistakable. Cirrus clouds stretched in wispy bands right across the sky, and lower cumulus clouds cast leaden shadows on the glassy surface of the gently heaving sea. A flock of storm petrels fluttered in the wake of the ship, which was flanked by the waves caused by the ship's bow rippling outwards on either quarter as far as the eye could see. Those on the bridge were not surprised therefore when a signal was passed up which said that the last report of Doris's movements had been in error and that in fact she was still proceeding northwards. A simple sum in relative velocity showed that ship and hurricane would eventually meet. The course was altered to the south-east and *Challenger* began to run a little faster, at her maximum speed of about ten knots.

For two or three days *Challenger* hustled south-eastwards and was by now approaching the latitude of Bermuda, and she began edging to the westward in heavy seas in Doris's wake. About this time the wardroom invented a game called 'Ships and Hurricanes'. It was played on a squared board with the goal, Bermuda, in the left-hand bottom corner. One player, representing the ship, dodged this way and that, being countered in turn by the hurricane, the other player. A thrown dice gave the number of squares which could be moved. When I visited the wardroom to play the game, I was depressed by the number of times that the hurricane was able to keep the ship from reaching Bermuda until the fuel, represented by a certain number of dice throws, ran out. The game seemed more and more like the efforts being made on the bridge to reach our haven – a tiny speck in a vast ocean defended by a hurricane; and when a second hurricane was reported and she too was represented by a counter on the game board, my visits to the wardroom abruptly ceased.

The second hurricane, Effie, was travelling northwards towards Bermuda at a steady ten knots and a course alteration was required by *Challenger* to come into Bermuda from the south. About 150 miles short of the island Effie came to a halt, and Bermuda signalled that conditions were unsuitable for a ship to enter through the reefs owing to strong winds and high seas .

Challenger's fuel was now very low owing to the great amount of dodging this way and that, and now Effie's action in pulling up seemed almost human in its malevolence. The waves were very high as the ship steamed slowly into them, playing for time. The small party on the bridge gazed upwards with awe at the oncoming wavetops towering above them.

At this point I sent a signal describing our plight to the Commander-in-Chief of the Station, who was at the time visiting a South American port in his flagship: there was nothing that he could do, but before a hurricane caught *Challenger* without fuel and toppled her over it seemed that someone should be told. The C.-in-C.'s reply, which simply said, 'Good Luck', produced quicker results than many a longer operational message. Almost at once Effie began to move northwards, and as signals reporting this movement came in *Challenger* moved slowly forwards in her wake. Effie's influence gradually cleared from Bermuda and *Challenger* steamed in on the very last of her fuel. The beach felt good that night as the men stepped ashore for a 'run'.

Chapter XIII

The Pacific

Passing through the Panama Canal in October 1950, *Challenger* sailed northward in the Pacific towards San Diego. For the last five days' steaming before reaching San Diego the 'deep scattering layer', as it is called, was seen at dawn and dusk on the echo-sounding machine. This is a common phenomenon in the oceans and appears on the echo-sounder as a false sea-bed echo. The layer spends the day at about 200 fathoms, ascending steadily through the water at sunset until it has reached a depth of 20 fathoms or so, where it spends the night, whence it returns just before sunrise to 200 fathoms. The layer may be caused by countless millions of tiny animal plankton forms, hard-shelled, and known as euphausids. These animals, which with many similar types abound in the oceans, are known to migrate towards the sea surface at nightfall, but the echoes seen on the sounding machine may be coming from the vast numbers of fish which live in the deep ocean and are feeding on the migrating plankton: such fish have air bladders and may be a cause of the echoes being reflected. This may be the answer, possibly combined with other, unthought-of, factors and as one watches the unbroken layer hour after hour on the sounding machine one thinks of the wealth of life within the oceans.

At San Diego a brief visit was paid to the Scripps Institute of Oceanography, a Department of the University of California. From here, under the leadership of Dr. Revelle, the Director, four great oceanographic expeditions had sailed out into the Pacific since the close of the war. At Scripps the recent scattering layer records were being discussed and one of their biologists investigating the cause of this layer suggested that *Challenger* should take one of his depressors, which, attached to a plankton net, would keep it at a constant depth as it was towed through the layer to capture specimens of the plankton. The depressor was of brass, heavy, and of an intriguing curvaceous shape. The inventor said that the inspiration had come to him when contemplating his attractive secretary.

Three months were spent working off the British Columbia coast, based on the naval harbour of Esquimalt. On one occasion for two ot three days the ship lay at anchor in Heater Harbour, a little fjord-like anchorage on the east coast of Kunghit Island at the southern end of the Queen Charlotte Islands. Deer abounded here and could often be seen on the beaches apparently feeding on seaweed. Small parties of the ship's company would land to try to get fresh venison, and on such occasions were warned not to enter the bush. Thick forests of sitka, Douglas fir and hemlock came right down to the water's edge and beneath these stately trees lay a jumble of fallen trunks and boughs, rotting stumps and thick undergrowth.

One evening, when the boat went to collect four stokers who had been ashore on such an expedition, only two of the men were on the beach. The others were said to have entered the woods and had not been seen again. Until dusk cries of 'Hope' and 'Abel', the names of the missing pair, rang out from searchers along the shore.

Although snow lay on the ground the afternoon had been mild and these hunters from the boiler-room were lightly clad. The wind increased in the night, snow was falling and the temperature was well below zero. All thoughts onboard were with the two lost in the Canadian forests, and it was long before dawn when the first men were 'wetting tea' in the galley and preparing to land as search parties. A full gale was blowing when over forty men, with the first lieutenant in charge, were landed to search the woods. By noon he was back onboard to report that the woods were so thick that he was in danger of losing members of the search party. Without a compass one lost all sense of direction in these forests, and what was needed was a number of small parties, each in charge of a leader with a compass.

The lost stoker mechanics had landed on a peninsula on the north side of the harbour, the northern shore of which looks out across a broad channel between Kunghit Island and Graham Island, the next land to the northward. This shore was searched by boat, while small parties, keeping only a few yards from their leader, fought their way across the peninsula at maximum speeds of about 400 yards an hour, so tangled and matted was the undergrowth and so frequent and deep were the potholes left by old decayed tree stumps.

The second day ended without results and by now all onboard were seriously worried as to whether their two shipmates would survive a second night, ill clad as they were in light overalls, with freezing temperatures, high winds and falling snow.

There is on Kunghit Island an abandoned whaling station, shown on the charts. It lies on the north coast of the island but considerably to the west of the limit of the north shore already searched by boat. On the third day it was decided to send a boat to the old whaling station, in the hope that the wanderers had found shelter there.

At about noon the wireless operator ran into my cabin. A message had been received from the boat by R/T – Hope and Abel had been found.

The first lieutenant had been in charge, and as soon as he landed on the ruined jetty at the whaling station he saw footprints in the snow and called out the now familiar names. A thin answering cry came from one of the tumbledown huts, and there, too cold and weary to stagger out to meet their rescuers, were the lost men.

They spent about a week in the sick bay and after a painful interview with the captain, who took the odd view that they had been absent over leave for two days, told their messmates of their experiences. They had entered the woods for only a few yards before losing their sense of direction. They spent the first night huddled under a fallen tree, scared by the howling of the wolves; as no wolves are known in these islands, it must have been the ship's siren that they heard, sounded at intervals to assist them to locate the ship. The pair were interviewed on the ship's internal broadcasting system. When asked if they had considered eating berries to nourish themselves, Hope replied: 'No – I gets my food at the shop on the corner.' So answered a Cockney after being lost in the Canadian backwoods.

Among other places visited in British Columbia was Port Simpson in the extreme north. This is a fine but little-used anchorage, with a township inhabited by Indians of the Tsimpsean tribe. A Hudson Bay Company store was run by two white men, and one or two other white families lived close about the store in wooden frame houses. A white minister served a somewhat difficult flock.

The men of *Challenger* enjoyed this place and quickly made friends among the Indians, who arranged dancing and games in the local hall almost nightly. There were no other amenities in Port Simpson except the 'diner', which consisted of the living room of a house with 'B.C.Diner' painted on the front door; within this room was a wood-burning stove which was always red-hot, and coffee was brought from the back room to the customers. Outside all was crisp and crunchy with snow.

A 'Sacred Concert' in the village hall was the highlight of the ship's visit. A silver band played hymns and sacred songs, sometimes on their own and sometimes accompanying soloists or mixed choruses. Many of the hymns were dedicated to the men of the ship, and finally an elderly Indian woman dedicated 'Into Battle' to the ship herself, somewhat inappropriate for unarmed and peace-loving *Challenger*. A small band of beautiful young Indian girls hung over the rails of the balcony, but the Chairman whispered into my ear that at least two of them had been run out of town for moral lapses and should not now be gracing such a solemn occasion. As the evening came to an end a fine painted wooden paddle was presented by the Indians to the ship. This paddle had magic qualities – if the ship broke down or ran short of fuel, no matter how far from land, the magic paddle could be used to take her to port. This was a source of comfort to the engineer officer for the rest of the voyage.

It will be recalled that as a boy I had heard tales of the N.W. Coast of British Columbia from Admiral Learmonth who had commanded *Egeria* when he was surveying there back in 1908. Whilst at Port Simpson I heard that Sam Bennett, an old Indian who had acted as Captain Learmonth's local pilot, was still living nearby, so a meeting was arranged in Sam's wooden house by the shore. He had been blind for many years, but he remembered the happenings in the old days in *Egeria* and described them as if they had occurred yesterday. He told us where to find his Bible and guided us to an old ship's company photograph still between the pages. There was Captain Learmonth, the officers grouped around him in their old-fashioned small-topped uniform caps, the men ranged behind them. The inevitable small dog lay on the deck in front of the group, and at one side proudly stood Sam Bennett, the local pilot.

Things have changed little in many ways in the routine of a surveyor's day. Sam described the early start in the mornings, the boats going off from the ship in all directions, the climbs through the woods, the clearing of the hilltops, the erection of flags and the long hours spent around the theodolites. In those days, as now, the ship's doctor found time heavy on his hands as the fit men manned the boats or climbed the hills, and Sam Bennett told how he had taken the doctor deer-hunting. He described how he had led him unerringly to a fine coast deer, the breathless minute as the doctor took aim, and how he had skinned and carved up the deer, packing it in its own skin and carrying it onboard on his back.

Coming south from Port Simpson the ship travelled down the fjord-like passage between Vancouver Island and the mainland, which at its narrowest part passes through Seymour Narrows. This passage was made more hazardous by Ripple Rock, a submerged danger in mid-channel, with strong tidal streams swirling past it. A vessel of *Challenger*'s modest power had to wait for slack water to make the passage between the hidden rock and the steep mountainside on the port side. I was committed to this route, unaware that the high land was obscuring the approach from the south of a vast raft of logs being shepherded northwards through the narrows by two tiny tugs. It was a thrilling few minutes as we squeezed through between the logs and the precipitous shore.

Many years later Ripple Rock, on which a Canadian surveying ship had once foundered, was removed by drilling a tunnel from the shore to place a massive charge in the very heart of the rock. Seismologists throughout North America were alerted to take advantage of this unique explosion. Navigation of Seymour Narrows must now be a very tame affair.

Whilst navigating the inner route the ship spent a night at Alert Bay, a trading port on one of the small islands lying in the channel; a fine forest of Indian totem poles and a processing works for turning herrings into fertiliser were the two most prominent features of this little place. There was also, of course, a beer parlour, and it was here that the petty officer steward and three shipmates made arrangements to get some herring. When the boat went off to the ship that night at midnight, all that had to be done was to take the boat underneath a chute which overhung the water, and their new-found friend, who worked in the herring factory, would release a small quantity of herring. As the evening drew on, the idea seemed a very excellent one to the four petty officers, and they thought how much the whole ship's company, from the 'Old Man' downwards, would enjoy their meal of fresh herring. They collected a number of cardboard beer cartons to carry the fish.

The coxswain of the boat seemed strangely unenthusiastic and the P.O.s had to assert their authority to make him take his boat under the chute. The new-found friend had also indulged in the parlour and having once released the stream of herring he was unable to stem it, despite the shouting of those below this fishy waterfall. It poured into the open compartments of the boat to a depth of two feet or more before the coxswain could cast off and get clear. When the boat reached the gangway, the officer of the day could hardly believe his eyes, nor could I, roused from my sleep by the shouting and argument which accompanied the inefficient methods the petty officers were employing to bring the fish up the gangway in the slippery cardboard cartons, which were collapsing and showering herring in every direction. The bowman stood disconsolately in the forepeak, knee deep in herring, while he held the boat's bows into the ship's side.

THE PACIFIC

It was a difficult morning for the first lieutenant, who had to forget the fresh herrings he had enjoyed for breakfast when he confronted the four petty officers and ordered them to scrub out the boat which hung miserably at the davits, so covered with fish scales that she appeared to be under snow.

Christmas 1950 was spent in Victoria, where this festival is celebrated in the old-fashioned way. Trees are easy to get from the woods and on Christmas Eve everyone is out visiting everyone else, carrying gifts.

A 'friend' of the ship put a personal advertisement in the local paper to the effect that *Challenger*, whose badge was a challenging stag, wished to carry a pair of antlers on the fore side of her bridge. There are many hunters in British Columbia and a new and better pair of antlers replaces from time to time the pair hanging in the front hall. The relegated pair goes into a back room. Hunters' wives could hardly believe their eyes when they read of the opportunity to be honourably rid of their junk. For a week around Christmas time, with the spirit of giving in the air, every car and every van that pulled up on the quay alongside carried a load of antlers.

With a fine pair of caribou horns in front of the bridge, with every member of the ship's company possessing a pair of antlers, and with a huge stuffed stag's head over Tom Gaskell's bunk, the ship sailed southwards towards the islands of Hawaii.

The pilot who boarded the ship off Pearl Harbour was just what one might have expected. Instead of the drab figure who boards a ship for this purpose in most parts of the world, he was colourfully dressed in a gay aloha shirt, palms and hula girls entwining themselves against an orange background. He wore a cap more suited to a jockey than a man of the sea and leapt from his fast-moving launch with the agility of a trapeze artist. Once on the bridge he said, 'Let's go, Captain,' and soon the ship was steaming at her best speed through the man-made passage in the coral reef that leads into the extensive lagoons which now form the greatest naval base in the Pacific.

My first task was to call upon the U.S. Admiral commanding the Hawaiian area and so I landed in full white uniform, buttoned close up below the chin, as British naval tradition demands. On this warm day I envied the Admiral in his open-necked khaki uniform shirt and his short sleeves as he sat at his desk. 'Sit down and relax, Captain,' said he, 'why, you sure look all trussed up in that outfit.' His statement set the pattern for the remainder of a very relaxed visit to my first Pacific island. How long I had wanted to enter the Pacific, and now I began to succumb to its charms, leading to a nostalgia from which I have never recovered.

Fine weather endured for some days after leaving Pearl Harbour, and the ship's philosophers, refreshed by their scientific and social contacts in Honolulu, turned to their seismic experiments with renewed vigour. The course was northwards for Adak, a U.S. naval base in the Aleutians, and after a week or so the weather grew more stormy daily until the ship passed through the chain of the Aleutian Islands in a gale of great ferocity, cold northerly winds shrieking in the rigging and over the top of the open bridge where the officer of the watch huddled in his corner. He peered over the windbreak at the cold white scene of countless breaking seas joined by wind-blown streaks of foam which stretched away on either hand to the snow-covered mountains of rugged aspect. Two or three Black-footed Albatross, still attendant upon the ship, were sweeping across this seascape like leaves in the gale, the only dark-coloured objects in a grey-white scene.

Although the country was bleak and snowbound the U.S. Naval hospitality made up for everything, the few days spent at Adak passing quickly, and once again the ship was at sea on her way to Japan.

Day after day, week after week, as the ship sailed in the North Pacific the sky was overcast, the visibility was down to a mile or so and winds of gale force kept the seas high and the ship's motion violent. Ocean sounding was all that could be done, although water temperatures and samples at depth were taken with the reversing water bottles whenever the weather moderated. The sono buoys lay snugly in their stowage and the scientists cursed their luck and once again went over their records made on calmer days.

There was one activity, however, which never ceased by day and that was the watching of birds. Except in the tropics one cannot sail for long unaccompanied by seabirds. In the more temperate zones there are always birds in attendance or to be seen flying past from time to time. At regular intervals the birds in sight were logged and, as the cruise progressed, subarctic, subtropical and tropical avian communities were encountered. There are many seabirds which, unlike the coast-loving gulls, spend the whole of their lives, except for the nesting season, at sea far from land. Such are the Black-footed and Laysan Albatross which attended the ship throughout her time in the North Pacific, although they never followed *Challenger* west of the Nanpo Shoto Islands which lie in a chain running southwards from the vicinity of Tokyo Bay. The Black-footed Albatross were very numerous and very inquisitive. They clustered daily about the wooden float which supported the small charge that the scientists drifted astern. The explosion sent a sound signal to the sea-bed; the difference in time between the returning echo and a second return provided evidence of the thickness of the ocean-floor sediment. Despite considerable patience in waiting for the birds to lose interest in the float, it was sometimes necessary to fire the charge while they still clustered round and inevitable casualties resulted.

Oceanic birds can be regarded as telltales for the changes of temperature, and hence ocean current boundaries; thus systematic watching of birds while travelling across the oceans forms a useful type of oceanographic observing. It is pleasing to watch the petrels as they skim endlessly and effortlessly between and over the wave crests to windward of the ship and to try and pick out this or that peculiarity of colour or profile which will serve to identify the species. Alexander's 'Birds of the Ocean', well thumbed and whitened with salt spray, lay to hand on the bridge chart table.

One day in the North Pacific, when the ship was about 250 miles eastward of the coast of the main Japanese Island of Honshu, an albatross of unfamiliar appearance circled the ship and settled upon the water, folding its long wings, which, so graceful when the bird is in the air, appear unwieldy and out of proportion as it gathers them to it after landing. The bird was white above and below but with brown wings and a white back, and, most noticeable, a yellow-tinged head and neck. There was no doubt in the observers' minds that this must be the Steller's Albatross, named after Behring's naturalist. John Swallow was sent for with his camera, but before he was on deck the bird had taken wing, waddling at first across the surface of the sea, wiggling its stern in a most laughable manner. But once the last wave top was cleared the legs were snugged away, the wings set, and the bird became at once a thing of effortless beauty as it sailed into the mist.

Experience with albatross told the watchers it would probably return again to the vicinity of the ship, so Swallow stood by with his camera, and two hours later the bird was sighted coming in low over the wave tops. This time the bird circled the ship again and again, never very near, but close enough for John with his telescopic lens; his photos show sufficient evidence for ornithologists to say that *Challenger* had undoubtedly sighted this rare bird. The story goes that the Japanese fishermen had been in the habit of killing these birds while they were at their nests on the Izu Islands. Here they were easily caught, for they need a long run to become airborne. Their downy feathers brought a good price in Japan in those days for use as stuffing for pillows and mattresses. Hearing that legislation was being prepared to protect these birds the fishermen struck first and eliminated them once and for all, it was thought, from the face of the earth. Happily, some years after our sighting the American ornithologist, Oliver Austin, found a small breeding colony on a remote island off Japan.

The hundreds of fishing and other small craft met during the day's steaming through the Inland Sea to reach Kure, on the island of Honshu, made us aware how much Japan is dependent upon fisheries and how much inter-island traffic is required for the everyday running of the country. Kure is a former naval base; the shipyards and the giant graving docks, then fouled with wreckage, bore witness to the former greatness of this port where Japan's largest battleships were once built.

Tom Gaskell, the inveterate sightseer, was soon active in Japan and he, Swallow and I crossed the Inland Sea in a local ferry boat for a few days' holiday at the watering spa of Dogo, near Matsuyama, the capital of the Island of Shikoku. Here we lived in the luxury of a small Japanese hotel, being truly waited upon hand and foot. The duty of one small girl was simply to turn our slippers, discarded at the bedroom door, in a direction suitable for stepping into when moving off again. Each morning was spent in the hot sulphur bath, where fellow bathers carried out their daily ablutions around the edges of the tank which fell away so that the soapy water drained clear of the bath and a fresh pannikin was taken from the bath itself, wherein a number of patrons were wallowing in the well-nigh boiling water, constantly added to from a pipe jutting from the side of the bath. Rest rooms were provided in the vicinity of the baths where the bather could relax in a kimono, sipping the small cups of tea and watching the coming and going in the busy little shopping street that ran beneath the windows.

Our evenings were enlivened by the company of geishas, summoned as a matter of course from the local geisha house by the hotel manager. The geisha's duty is to look attractive, tell stories, play parlour games and assist her temporary employer to raise his rice and sake to his mouth. How well established was the comfort of the male in Japan in those days! It would be pleasant indeed if, benighted at the Railway Hotel in one of Britain's drearier Midland towns, the traveller could summon a decorative companion and pay her some trifling sum per hour to amuse him while he took his high tea in the Commercial Room.

One day Tom took a party with him to Hiroshima, where, from the roof garden of a seven-storied departmental store which had surprisingly survived the blast of the atomic bomb, they looked down upon the dwarf city that had sprung up over the whole area so recently laid waste. At the supposed centre of the devastated area a few small stalls existed for the sale of photographs of the scenes of horror and the human wreckage which the bomb had left behind. There were also more material relics on sale, such as bricks and roof tiles, showing signs of scorching from the heat of the blast. Tom was surprised when I declined to buy one of these to add to my souvenirs, while he himself bought two tiles, the glazing of which was blackened and had air bubbles beneath its surface. At sea again, Tom came to the cuddy with a tile saying that he still thought I should have one and he had bought this one for me; he knew that I would regret forever having failed to get one in Hiroshima. This tile survived the buffetings of the remainder of the voyage in my cabin, but although it had come intact through the holocaust, it was fractured into a dozen pieces with ease by our three-year-old son a few days after it had been set upon a shelf at home.

From Japan the ship sailed southwards into the warmer weather, encountering upon her way a most rugged sea-bed topography, mountain ranges interspersed with extensive plains. The sounding and seismic work went forward steadily with the better weather. Hour after hour the deep sounder was running, the 'ping' of the outgoing signal ringing and reverberating from the loudspeaker on the bridge. There were few places on deck where this could not be heard and the metallic and regular sound formed the background to every shipboard activity.

A brief pause at Manus off the coast of New Guinea was made to take in fuel from the Royal Australian naval base; then onwards again and southward past New Caledonia to Auckland in New Zealand where the ship was taken in hand for refit, for half of her world voyage was now over and she had encountered weeks of rugged weather.

Challenger was in New Zealand for seven weeks. It is, above all else, a hospitable country and invitations were showered upon the officers and men to stay on farms and sheep stations. Nearly the whole company went for such country holidays and all made friends. The author was invited to Te Aute Station in the prosperous sheep-farming district of Hawke's Bay in the North Island. This station was owned by an old New Zealand family, the Williams, whose great-grandfather was an officer in the Royal Navy, forsaking the life to become one of the first Christian missionaries to settle in New Zealand. His son, also a missionary, was bidden by the Maoris of Hawke's Bay to travel from Otaki on the West Coast on foot and by canoe through the precipitous gorge and turbulent waters of the Manawatu River to bring his religious teaching to them. In Hawke's Bay, over 100 years ago, he founded a school which became the famous Maori College of Te Aute, where many great leaders have been educated.

It was now springtime, and all was green, except the golden willows, delicate and beautiful, by the creeks. The lines of macrocarpa trees forming the windbreaks showed dark against the lush and vivid grass of the paddocks and the rounded, rumpled hills beyond.

The whole country was uniformly dotted with sheep and their lambs, and across every acre, twice each day, rode the shepherds on their rough, unshod horses to see that all was well with newborn lambs and mothers. Their teams of dogs followed the riders, alert for a command to head or drive away the sheep. With one of these shepherds I rode, a sailor on horseback, my ship forgotten. Sailing the sea seemed a dull business when compared with these happy spring days on the sunny hills. For the first time during the voyage the ship seemed unimportant, the return to sea a dreaded undertaking. But the stocky Maori tractor driver, the Maori boys fishing for eels in the creek, the carved village meeting houses and the students at the college, all were reminiscent of the Pacific, calling one back. Slowly the mood of discontent passed – there was yet so much to be seen in that great ocean.

I was asked to talk to the college boys about charting the seas. The headmaster welcomed me with the news that he had been a prisoner of war in Germany with Buck Baker, and thus knew something of naval surveyors. During the lecture I nearly committed a *faux pas*, but checked myself just in time. I had been about to refer to the discovery of New Zealand by Captain Cook when I became aware of the dusky faces of those whose ancestors had reached the Land of the Long White Cloud some hundreds of years before Captain Cook set sail. The real discoverers were depicted on the red-ochre pillars of the school hall where the boys were gathered; curvilinear carvings showed them with lolling tongues, three-fingered hands and flashing eyes of pawa shell.

The half-way break was soon over and the ship was at sea again investigating the shoals on the western side of the Kermadec Trench and the depths of the great trench itself.

The waters about New Zealand are a delight to the watcher of ocean birds. The ship was usually attended by at least half-a-dozen Wandering Albatross in their various plumages, ranging from the scruffy brown youngster, through the brown and white spotted 'leopard stage' to the magnificent old birds almost white from wing tip to wing tip. There is also, in fewer numbers, the smaller dapper Black-browed Albatross and the black and brown Giant Petrel who tries, without success, to emulate the soaring albatross – but where they have grace the petrel is ungainly, its wings being short and broad rather than long and tapering. Other types of petrel abound, the most striking being the Cape Pigeon with its wings spotted white on black, like a domino, and the small Cook Petrel which reveals in its cartwheeling flight an underwing surface of startling whiteness edged with black. As the ship journeyed northwards the birds became fewer until quite suddenly one morning, in latitude about twenty-five degrees south, *Challenger's* men realised that they had seen their last Wandering Albatross and not a bird moved in an empty sky. Later that day a white flash against the distant blue above proclaimed the flight of the first Tropic Bird and the ship passed into a new avian world; that of the Boatswain Bird, as the sailors call the Tropic Bird, of the Booby which crashes clumsily onboard at nights, and the stately Frigate Bird which sails slowly above the atolls waiting for the Boobies to return from fishing, when he will swoop from above them, instilling such fear that they cast up their food to be caught in mid-air by the attacker.

As we sailed in through the coral reefs which form the harbour of Suva, in Fiji, this was for nearly all the company their first visit to the islands of the South Pacific. The ship berthed on the King's Wharf and we smelled the rich sweet copra which had been unloaded from the schooners and lay in untidy heaps or in sacks alongside. The schooners themselves were loading mixed cargoes and in their rigging were small blackboards upon which were chalked the times at which each vessel would depart for romantic sounding destinations – Rotuma, Katafanga. Levuka, Taveuni, Lakemba.

Challenger's arrival in Suva coincided with the festivities being arranged by the Fijians to honour the Governor on his departure from the islands. These included the formal and colourful kava ceremony and dances, known loosely as 'meke', by large parties of men and women. Such ceremonies may pall after many years of life in the islands, but to see them for the first time is a thrill indeed. The leisured skill with which the group seated around the kava bowl make the precious mixture from the roots of the yanggona shrub, the drawing and the re-drawing of the hibiscus fibre through the kava to extract pieces of solid matter, the rustle of the leaves which form the green and brown skirts of the men, the hollow rhythmic clap and the grunts which issue from the seated elders to denote satisfaction with the words of their upstanding spokesman, all these are but the preliminaries to the reverent serving of the kava. Before the mixing of the kava was started, a grass rope embellished with cowrie shells was led from the bowl itself to the feet of the Guest of Honour, who was served first. The other guests, seated within a green arbour, were served next. I was among these and watched the inscrutable faces of the seasoned kava drinkers for any indication of the taste I might expect, pleasant or ill. The 'bilo', or cup, in which the yanggona is served is made from the lower half of a coconut shell, highly polished; it is smooth to the touch. Soon I was draining the brown-coloured liquid. Its taste is hard to define; unattractive at first to the European palate, it soon grows on one, for it leaves a sharp clean taste in the mouth. It is drunk by Europeans and Fijians alike in the mid-morning in many of the offices in Suva.

As I came off the ship next day onto the wharf an old Fijian in khaki shorts offered me kava. Feeling that I was now a hardened kava drinker I readily consented to enter the temporary shelter where, I found, this old man made kava for the workers upon the wharf. The old man's offering was contained not in a smooth well-worn kava bowl, wrought from a solid tree trunk, but in the rusty interior of a battered half kerosene tin. A chipped plastic bowl floated upon the surface, and soon this was in my hands. Fijians are nature's gentlemen, so I had been told, and thus there was no turning back unless I risked giving offence. Luckily yanggona should be drunk at a single draught and soon I was throwing back the little empty bowl and clapping my appreciation. But my friend did not end his generosity here, for every time I left the ship after this, whether dressed in plain clothes or in full uniform with sword, and to the shrill of the boatswain's pipe, to call upon His Excellency, nature's own gentleman tottered out with his rusty offering of kava, and the crew paused on deck to watch the skipper in his embarrassment.

If the formal dancing of mekes on the green turf of Fiji was thrilling, the impromptu dancing at Rotuma was the real thing – the South Sea Island dancing I had dreamt about for years. The anchorage at Rotuma is exposed, and so after landing the stores, which had been carried from Fiji, the ship weighed anchor and steamed to the bay known as Foviung Emua at the eastern end of the island. There the boats were lowered and, after dark, on a night of perfect calm and white moonlight, the keels grated gently on the coral shore and a party landed to find two trucks waiting in the dark shadows of the palms to take them on the rough road which wound between low lava-stone walls to the village. Doctor Evans, the Administrator, was the only European living on the island and with him we sat down beneath a palm-leaf canopy that had been rapidly constructed in front of the General Store. The orchestra consisted of men seated around a pile of rolled grass mats upon which they beat a vigorous rhythm with short sticks. The dancers were arranged in a rectangle, forty-two of them in rows of six, three men and three women in each row. As the dances progressed without pause the front row would from time to time turn and go to form the rear rank and the second row of dancers moved forward into the limelight. The whole dancing team sang continuously. Clad in bright red and white lava-lavas, wearing the traditional grass skirts, with red fruits of the pandanus tree in their hair, the dancers made an active and all absorbing scene. They went on and on; the rhythm changed from slow to fast; men and women now began to come forward singly or in pairs to form some particular variation of their own, hips swinging, arms moving, knees bending with acrobatic agility. Sweat poured from foreheads and formed in beads upon bronze chests, but still the ranks kept coming forward as the music, now enlivened with an electric guitar, became more and more insistent. The ship, the sea, the distant homecoming, all were forgotten by the sailors as they watched, utterly absorbed, wishing this Rotuman night to go on for ever.

At last the music stopped, as abruptly as it had started three hours before. The singing ceased and the dancers sank where they were to the ground. A moment's complete silence reigned and then Dr. Evans leant over to me and whispered that a few words were now expected. I rose, and speaking slowly through the government clerk, who interpreted, I thanked the people of Rotuma for this glorious evening. Never had I seen dancing equal to it nor a setting so lovely, for the moon was now above the mountainous little island that lay in the sea but half a mile from the village. These utterings, as they were interpreted, were hailed with appreciative mumblings from the exhausted dancers and the Rotumans who were sitting round them. Then an elderly male dancer spoke to the interpreter, who turned to me. 'They ask if you have talcum powder with you,' he said. I looked baffled, and the interpreter explained that to sprinkle such scented powder upon the dancers at this stage would be the highest praise that the ship could have showered upon them. Surprised, I recovered myself and said that next time I came to Rotuma I would bring such a gift from Fiji instead of the Public Works Department water tanks that I had brought on this occasion. This caused a roar of applause and the speeches were over.

Hours later the sailors reached the coral beach to embark. The sleepy boat keepers who had been waiting on the shore were surprised to see their messmates, grass skirts about their waists and leis about their necks, being farewelled by the girls of Rotuma as if they had been Rotumans themselves going out on a journey to the world beyond the reef.

Chapter XIV

Atolls

At the time of *Challenger*'s visit Funafuti was one of nine coral atolls forming a British colony – the Ellice Islands. To-day this group forms the Republic of Tuvalu. Funafuti is a classic coral atoll and shaped like a pear. The lagoon is thirteen miles long in the north and south direction and nine miles from east to west. It is about twenty-five fathoms deep and is surrounded by a thin line of reef which is broken here and there, mostly upon the leeward or western side; such channels permit vessels to navigate from the deep ocean outside to a safe and secure anchorage within. Time and the battering of the waves on the reefs have thrown sufficient coral debris above sea level to enable floating coconuts and other seeds to establish themselves as trees and bushes, from which organic matter has in turn fallen to form soil upon which Man, travelling south-eastward into the Pacific some 2,000 years ago, was able to settle.

There was one village on Funafuti, and that lay on the main island of Fongafale, which is about seven miles long but only about 500 yards across at its widest part from the lagoon to the white breakers pounding the eastern shore. The cooking huts were situated along the shore of the lagoon, and the houses, widely spaced, among the tall coconut palms behind them.

Challenger spent the night anchored precariously on a shallow spit outside the lagoon, for it was inadvisable to navigate the narrow channels through the reefs until the sun was well up in the sky, illuminating the amber-coloured coral flats and the pale green of the shallows, between which the ship had to pass in the deep blue water, turning this way and that as the channel twisted its way into the safety of the lagoon. Once inside the atoll the run across to the village was simple enough, and even before the slip was knocked from the cable a little party were seen in their boat well on their way from the village to board the ship.

It is always an exciting moment for the sailor when he makes his first contact with people he has not visited before. The boat brought Chief Clerk Kofe, the assistant medical practitioner, and the island's only policeman. There were no Europeans in the Ellice Islands at this time and the Gilbertese District Officer was far away on the other side of the world studying at Oxford University. The Chief Clerk was now making his official call in true Colonial tradition, neatly attired in his white duck suit.

Whilst Kofe took tea with me and spoke of the activities in their little-visited territory, the policeman on deck was subjected to many questions. The supply officer was interested to know whether there was much crime in such an isolated community of 350 souls, and asked the policeman if there were any prisoners in gaol. 'Yes, we have one man in prison,' he replied. 'What for?' asked the paymaster, to which the policeman replied in one short word, common enough in a sailor's vocabulary but not looked upon as a crime in itself in the western world.

This was by no means the first visit to Funafuti of a ship carrying enquiring scientists, for between 1896 and 1900 a series of expeditions had reached this atoll under the auspices of the Royal Society's Coral Reef Committee; at first they had come in the naval surveying ship *Penguin* and later in a number of other craft to make deep borings below the islands around the lagoon. Darwin's theory of atoll construction was being challenged at this time. He believed that the atolls had begun their life as fringing reefs about the coast of high islands, which having been raised up by volcanic action from the deep ocean floor had for millions of years been sinking slowly back into the earth's crust. As the highest peaks had at last sunk beneath sea level there remained a void at the centre of the reef where food for the polyp was scarce and which became a lagoon floored with coral debris. Murray, who had been on the earlier *Challenger* expedition, suggested that the atolls were formed by coral growing on clay-like sediments covering submerged seamounts, which lay at a depth less than 200 feet below the sea surface, enabling the shallow reef-building corals to grow, for at greater depths these polyps cannot remain alive. In Darwin's theory they are presumed to continue growing upwards on a platform of dead and dying coral.

The Coral Reef Committee during their various visits to Funafuti made a series of borings, the most successful of which had reached a depth of 1,114 feet on the main island, not far from the village. Borings to any great depth within the lagoon itself had proved technically too difficult.

Analysis of the cores obtained from these borings showed coral rock of a shallow water type to their greatest depths. At first this seemed to support Darwin's theory, for if Murray was correct rock other than limestone would have been encountered at comparatively shallow depths. The borings were, however, near the seaward edge of the whole atoll structure, and followers of the new theory claimed that such borings were almost entirely through the talus or slope of coral debris which was being constantly broken from the edge of the reef by the unceasing pounding of the breakers. Such material would certainly fall down the steep slopes towards the ocean floor and would form a sort of coral rubbish dump to great depths.

What was needed to clinch either theory was a boring in the centre of the lagoon, a wildly expensive and technically difficult task. However, the seismic apparatus in *Challenger* was well suited for this work, for it had been used successfully to measure the thickness of the sediment layers upon the floor of the ocean and could be used similarly in the lagoon at Funafuti to measure the thickness of the coral limestone, overlying something harder. The technique was similar to that which the ship had used at sea, but within the lagoon she lay at anchor using her photographic device to record the times of the returning sound signals from the floor of the lagoon initiated by the firing of charges from the ship's boats at varying distances from the anchored ship. These returning signals were picked up by the sono-buoy hydrophones, the buoys themselves being anchored on a line between the ship and the distant boat.

I went ashore to see the village and to tell the people of Funafuti what was happening. An old man remembered the coming of the scientists of the Coral Investigation Committee fifty years before, and he led Dr. Gaskell to the site of the deep borehole, the mouth of the hole being still visible but choked with vegetation. Apart from the native magistrate, who was absent from the island, there were two other personalities to call upon – the pastor, and the keeper of the Government Store, Mr. Reher, who sold cloth and bicycles and other commodities whenever they became available to him on the occasional visits of the government store-carrying ship. The pastor was away working on his taro patch and the visitors must sit down while he was sent for. As we waited, the pastor's daughters gave us green coconuts so that we might drink the refreshing, cold liquid which such immature nuts contain. Like many London Mission Society pastors, he was a Samoan, massive of build and cheerful of nature. He invited the '*Challengers*' to his church the following Sunday, a service that everyone on the island attended and where the singing was vigorous. The church at Funafuti has two floors, the main part of the chapel being upstairs. Women with very small children stay below, but the remainder of the little ones sit at the front of the congregation, girls on one side and boys upon the other. There they are under the eyes of two elder sidesmen who, from time to time throughout the service, walk among them to distribute a hearty bare-footed kick to those who are misbehaving.

The pastor had a blind brother who played the harmonium in church and was led to the meeting house in the evenings during *Challenger*'s visit so that he might play for the hulas which were danced in the intervals between the Ellice Island dances. The women and girls invited the sailors to hula with them, much of this dance here being done in a crouching position known in physical training parlance as a 'full knees bend', and somewhat painful to untrained Europeans. A hissing noise between the teeth is emitted by both dancers from time to time.

The local dances were performed by a line of seven or eight, male and female, and consisted of numerous actions which became more vigorous as the rhythm gathered momentum, accompanied by the banging of sticks upon upturned boxes. Eventually the dancers were exhausted and they sank to the mat-strewn floor for a brief respite before the singing and the insistent thumping started again. I asked an elder what these activities portrayed, imagining that the actors were re-living great battles or canoe voyages from their distant past. The elder replied, without much conviction, that they were Bible stories, but failed to put a satisfactory name to any of these.

On the last night in the meeting-house at Funafuti, when all were utterly exhausted after taking part in the many action dances, the island girls began to lay a great quantity of shell ornaments, necklaces, belts and hat bands as well as hats and fans at my feet, where I sat with one or two of the kaubures, or members of the Island Council; it seemed that the presentation would never end as more and more girls appeared and re-appeared loaded with gifts. There were enough of these articles for every one of the ship's company to carry away some memento of the glorious days and nights they had spent at Funafuti among its charming and happy people.

There was time for much sport as well as science. A cricket match, an outrigger canoe race and a sailing race were all contested between the islanders and the sailors. The sailing boats at Funafuti are of European design, doubtless introduced into the island by some long-forgotten District Officer. There were about fifteen of these boats, all built on Funafuti, and as well as taking a dozen or so of a crew they carry a great deal of canvas. On the British Sovereign's Birthday and on Boxing Day a sailing race was always held on the spacious waters of the lagoon. Such a race was now arranged, *Challenger*'s own surf boat taking part. These races are started in a novel manner. The prevailing wind blows over the village from the east and across the lagoon; the boats, fully loaded, with whole families forming enthusiastic sailing crews, are lined up off the village beach; the sails are fully rigged and filled while one member of the crew, knee deep in the water, holds the boat's stern. At the word 'GO' each thrusts off his boat and leaps in and the whole fleet is quickly running before the wind in a spectacular and even start.

While the scientists and their naval assistants became daily more suntanned during long days exploding charges from the boat, I took a party away in the small motor skiff to collect living shells and seaweeds around the perimeter reefs of the atoll. This had been requested by the Museum and the University in Auckland and proved a fascinating occupation. Different islands around the atoll had to be visited so that the various molluscae and algae might be sampled, both inside and outside the lagoon, to windward and to leeward of the reef, for each had its own environment.

To cross the lagoon on these expeditions might take two hours and the small palm-clad islet for which the party were bound would be below the horizon for many miles of the voyage. It sometimes appeared to the medical officer, Leading Sick Berth Attendant Soulsby, and me that we were bound westward into the open Pacific in our inadequate craft; but slowly the palms on our objective would creep up over the horizon, and an hour or so later we anchored off the reef and waded through the shallows to the glaring white coral beach beneath the towering trees in which beautiful White Terns fluttered like pigeons or sat regarding the intruders with one small black-ringed eye. The collectors then split up and walked the reefs, finding frequent treasures. Shells there were of many types, and small coraline weeds of brilliant green and red hues. Gradually, the saltwater and formalin containing jars onboard became full of specimens. At Fongafale the assistance of the children was obtained, for they knew where to find the shells, which they required for the making of necklaces and hatbands. I went with Reher, the storekeeper, on an expedition along the shore in search of living cowries. It was low water at dark midnight as Reher flashed a torch beneath the large overhanging coral boulders for he knew where the cowries would be, clinging like great slugs to the underside of the rocks. He guided me on as they filled the specimen bottles, his gentle voice barely audible above the sound of the breakers on the seaward side of the island a few hundred yards away.

Although *Challenger* was at Funafuti only about a fortnight, her men became a part of the place; they spent their evenings in the scattered, palm-thatched homes along the main street, while Tom and I, at the invitation of Chief Clerk Kofe, occupied the empty District Officer's house for a night or two and imagined ourselves administering these lovely atolls. It was a sad moment when the ship's boat left the wharf for the last time, carefully steering between the children splashing in the water and leaping from the jetty into the sea ahead of her. Reher's big straw hat and the massive figure of the pastor could be seen above the group that stood watching on the wharf till the ship had weighed and turned to the westward.

Nukufetau was the next of the group visited, sixty miles to the north, and it appeared over the horizon at first like the two masts of a ship, which resolved themselves into towering trees as the island gradually took shape. As at Funafuti, the ship was able to anchor within the lagoon, which is enclosed by an almost perfect rectangle of reefs and low islands, with the village situated at the south-west corner.

A ship had been lost on the northern part of this atoll some months previously and it was our task to fix the island by star sights ashore, using the theodolite, as the wreck enquiry had thrown some doubt as to the position of Nukufetau. The scientists were delighted to visit another atoll similar in construction to Funafuti, and they were soon at work verifying the doubtful points that still remained.

Here there was no convenient wharf and, except at high tide, those landing had to disembark from the ship's boats at the edge of the reef and either wade or be pushed in a narrow canoe across the half mile of shallows to the village. A tried and trusted surveying recorder, Jimmy Greenshields, was landed to find a suitable location for the taking of the sights and to find accommodation for the party who would be observing throughout the night, and therefore must live ashore. When I landed next day everything was in perfect order. The brass plate marking the observation post had already been cemented in position in the open space below the court house, while camp beds and mosquito nets had been set up within; the chronometer which was to play such a vital part in the sight-taking was ticking away snugly in its case alongside the radio to be used for the time signals, and now playing Hawaiian music to the delight of the considerable crowd that had taken up its position around the entrance to the palm-thatched court house. Staff had been taken on and consisted of massive, bronzed Toma, who was busy in a nearby cooking hut preparing a meal of roast chicken and taros for the party, and a girl of extremely comely appearance, with a flowered garland in her hair, who was sweeping the bare ground around the observation spot with a sort of hand besom made of the mid-ribs of coconut leaves. A small group of chickens lay tethered and a sucking pig secured by one hind leg was close by. Almost at once on the arrival of the surveying party some of the crowd began an impromptu dance while the remainder made way for them, and soon the dancers were screaming with delight as I walked among them scattering talcum powder. On this occasion I had come prepared.

Shortly after sunset on the second night ashore it became necessary to signal off to the ship to send a battery in by boat, and the shore party set out wading to the edge of the reef to meet it. There was a strong north-easterly breeze blowing straight from the ship towards the village, and as we felt our way in the darkness of the cloudy night we could see the lights of the motor skiff appearing and disappearing as she rose and fell on the waves. We were unaware that a fleet of unlit sailing canoes was bearing down upon us, homeward bound before the wind. As we neared the breakers at the reef's edge we saw first one and then another of the canoes, and there we stood, now waist deep in the water, shouting to make our presence known as they swept past on either side. It was a tense moment for the waders as the canoes came in, for those sailing them did not notice us in the general excitement of coming through the breakers, and it was lucky that we were not run down. The greater part of the island's population had spent the afternoon onboard buying, at the ship's canteen, chocolates, tinned fruit, cigarettes and, of course, talcum powder.

The inevitable dance took place in the meeting house on the last night ashore, a party of youngsters being employed throughout the evening alternately erecting the thatch screens on the windward side of the building, for it was a wild night, and taking them down again as the dancers called for air after their exertions. When we returned to the court house in the early hours Greenshields was absent, but by morning he was with us again. It was months afterwards before the events of this night reached my ears. As the paymaster had been told, sleeping with someone other than one's husband or wife was a punishable offence in the Ellice group, and the attractive girl who had been laid on to sweep the court house was in fact such a prisoner carrying out her daily tasks. The missing recorder had fallen for the girl and had asked the jailer if he might release her on the night of the dance. This he had absolutely refused to do, fearing retribution from the kaubares; however, he saw no harm in locking the sailor up with the prisoner for the night, releasing him again as dawn crept over the island.

The scientists had finished their work in the lagoon, the surveyors were content with their sights, farewells were said once again, a frequent and oft-recurring duty on this voyage, and the ship sailed out and away for Manus in the Admiralty Islands, 2,000 miles to the west.

Tom Gaskell and John Swallow turned to their mass of seismic records – long, narrow sheets of paper with long steady lines, here and there violently interrupted, showing the vital time of returning sound waves from the floor of the lagoon. There was much drawing of graphs in the chartroom, making of computations, gloom as pieces of scientific evidence failed to fit in, excitement and renewed efforts when the data began to dovetail like pieces of a jigsaw to form the picture of the atoll structure.

Doctor Gaskell has described this work in scientific papers and has voiced his propositions at learned symposia with a wealth of detail which baffles the layman, but a few weeks after the visit to the Ellice Islands he gave the *Challengers*, in an article in the ship's magazine, a simple account of the results of these experiments. At Funafuti, he said, they had found a depth of 1,800 feet of rock in which the velocity of sound was 6,000-8,000 feet per second, such a velocity being much as one would expect in coral limestone. Below this lay material with a velocity of sound of 12,000 feet per second, which could either be hard limestone or volcanic rock. To clear up the matter he had carried the explosions in Nukufetau right up to the edge of the reef and these showed that the border between these two layers fell rapidly away as the perimeter was reached, which gave a picture of a supposed volcanic hump within the heart of the atoll structure. Deeper again, an even harder material was located, probably the true volcanic core of the original volcano that had formed the island.

Thus, on the seismic evidence obtained by *Challenger*, it would seem that as the coral cannot live at a depth greater than 200 feet below the surface of the ocean, the atolls forming the Ellice Group are being built up gradually upon old, sinking volcanoes as Darwin had proposed. As Gaskell and Swallow concluded that there was 2,500 feet of coral below Nukufetau, a considerably greater depth than that under Funafuti, it would seem that while Funafuti still remained an island about 500 feet high, Nukufetau as a volcanic island had passed from the face of the oceans.

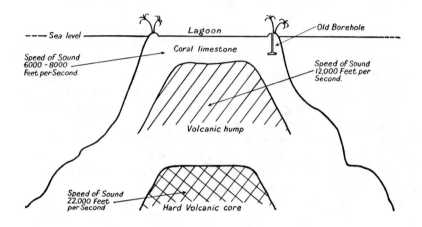

Structure of Funafuti Atoll as deduced from seismic experiments

H.M.S. *Herald*, circa 1930. (Photograph, Abraham, Devonport)

Sextant and Station Pointers.

Taut Wire Measuring Gear.

H.M.S. *Endeavour* in Grand Harbour, Malta, circa 1934.

Lieutenant Ritchie and A. B. Proctor in their Fiat Truck, Italy 1943. (John Worsley, War Artist, National Maritime Museum, London)

H.M.S. *Scott* in her War Paint, 1944

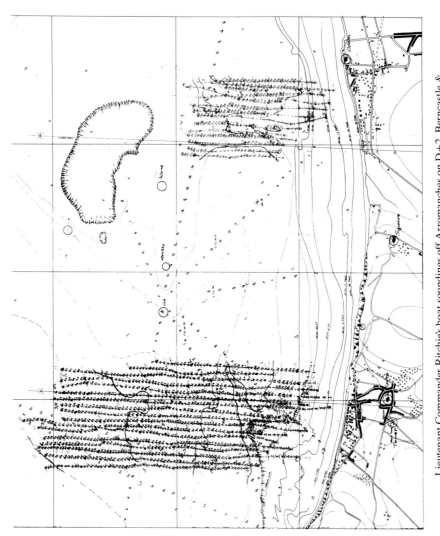

Lieutenant Commander Ritchie's boat soundings off Arromanches on D+2. Berncastle & Glen's 1943 soundings are seen as a star; on these the Port of Arromanches was planned.

Return from a fishing trip. H.M.S. *Owen*, Persian Gulf 1950. P. O. Slater, Lt. Cdr. Ritchie, Captain Henry Menzies and the Motor Boat E.R.A.

H.M.S. *Challenger*. Arriving at Suva, Fiji, 1951.

H.M.N.Z.S. *Lachlan* at Apia, 1954. (Photograph, The Aerial Mapping Company of Hastings, Van Ash)

Cabaret at the Navy Ball, Wellington, New Zealand, 1955.

Fijians preparing Kava in a Somerset garden, July 1962.

Relaxed Polynesian/Worried Impresario.

Mid-Atlantic Concert, H.M.S. *Vidal*, 1963.

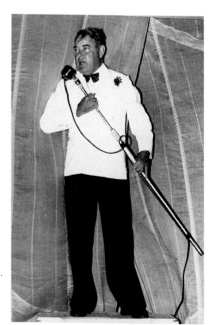

H.M.S. *Vidal* moored in the Neva abreast the Admiralty Building, Leningrad, September 1964.

H.M.S. *Vidal*'s Regatta in Man of War Bay, Tobago, June 1965. The Captain urging his centipede crew to victory.

The Hydrographer, accompanied by Captain Hall, his Assistant, calling on Commodore Bailey, H.M.S. *Drake*, before inspecting the Hydrographic School, March 1966. Commander Richard Campbell, C.O. of the School, at the wheel of his Lagonda.

Mrs. Ritchie launching the Coastal Survey ship H.M.S. *Beagle* at the Yard of Brooke Marine Limited on 7 September 1967. (Photograph, Ford Jenkins, Lowestoft)

A Wild West welcome for the Hydrographer at Taunton Station before the 1968 Christmas Party at the Civil Service Club. (Photograph, Jack Beale, Taunton)

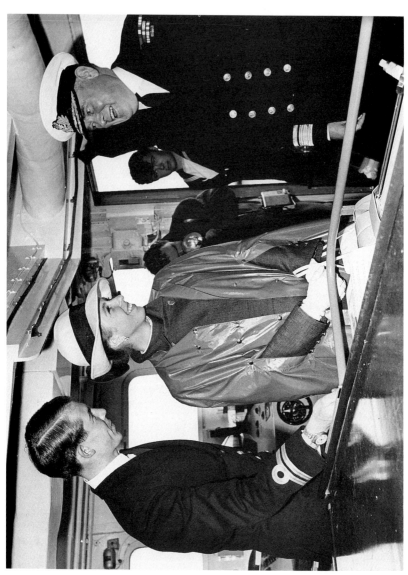

Princess Anne onboard H.M.S. *Hecate* with Rear Admiral Ritchie and Lieutenant Lancaster-Williams at the Fleet Review in Torbay, July 1969. (Photograph, *Western Morning News*)

Rear Admiral Ritchie's last days at sea. H.M.S. *Hydra* wearing his Flag in the Malacca Strait, January 1971.

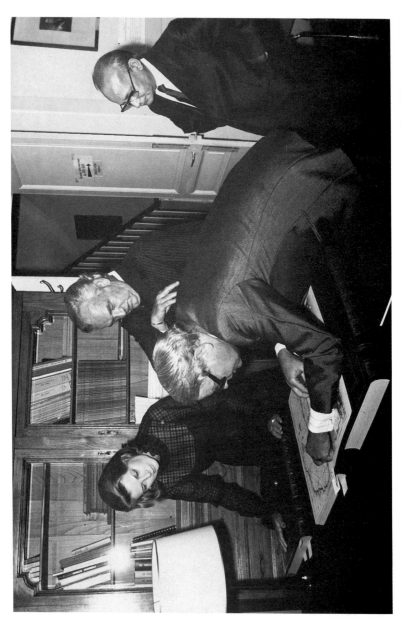

Their Serene Highnesses Prince Rainier and Princess Grace with the President and fellow Director, Rear Admiral Kapoor, examining van Keulen's charts in the I.H.B.

Dinner onboard Soviet Survey Ship *Bellinghausen* during 11th I.H. Conference, May 1977. Captain Ivanovich Mitin, Chief of Black Sea Fleet Hydrographic Service; Lieutenant Commander Mark Miliavko, Ship's Oceanographer (Interpreter); Rear Admiral Ritchie; Captain Viktor Faleev, Chief of Charts and Publications Division, Soviet Hydrographic Office.

'Ready for the Road'
— Trinidad Carnival

Edmund Hart 'North American Indians' 1976

The Mavericks 1980 'Space Encounter' (Band of the Year)

Chapter XV

The Deepest Depths

On the way south from Japan to New Zealand Dr. Gaskell had said that he wished to carry out one of his seismic experiments in a deep trench in order to find out something of the structure of the sea-floor in such an area. Accordingly, as the ship moved into the Marianas Trench between Guam and Ulithi, John Swallow was active with the seismic gear, using it purely as a reflection or sounding machine to record the time of the double passage of sound from the small charge he exploded until it returned as an echo from the sea-bed to his hydrophone, thus giving him the depth. The soundings rapidly increased and soon Swallow was reporting over 5,000 fathoms and finally 5,663 fathoms.

This was an exciting report, for it was known to be nearly as deep as any sounding so far recorded, but unfortunately it was about 1,000 fathoms beyond the scope of the deep echo-sounder at this time. However, using the taut-wire machine, with 140 pounds of scrap iron attached to the end of the wire, as a sounding machine, a depth of 5,899 fathoms was recorded. This was a new depth record for the world.

The history of deep sounding in the ocean is not a long one. It was during Lord Mulgrave's expedition to the Arctic in 1773 that some of the earliest attempts at deep sounding were made, the greatest depth being 683 fathoms, whence a sample of sediment was obtained.

In 1817-1818 Sir John Ross, during a voyage to Baffin Bay, made some deep sea soundings using a 'deep sea clam' on the end of his rope which brought up several pounds of greenish mud from his deepest sounding of 1,050 fathoms.

Sir James Clark Ross led an expedition to the Antarctic in the ships *Erebus* and *Terror* in the years 1839–1843, during which time he really started systematic deep sea sounding. He had a line 3,600 fathoms long which he allowed to run out from a large reel fitted in one of the ship's boats. The line was marked every 100 fathoms and while the line ran out the time was noted as each mark left the reel. When the time interval between two marks appreciably lengthened, the weight at the line's end was assumed to have reached the bottom and the amount run out taken to indicate the depth. The procedure was necessarily one for calm weather and this restricted the number of successful casts made in the open sea; however, the first 'abysmal' soundings, as the oceanographic textbooks call them, were thus obtained to a depth of 2,425 fathoms.

One of the early snags of deep sounding was that a heavy weight was needed to take the line down, but to recover such a weight with the bottom sample adhering to it a very bulky line was required. There was in the United States Navy at this time the now famous officer, Lieutenant Maury, who had produced numerous wind and current charts and Sailing Directions for mariners. Working under him was a Midshipman Brooke, who about the year 1859 constructed an apparatus which took a sample of the sea-bed and then detached the bulk of the heavy weight that had taken it down, leaving only a light tube, inside which the sample was retained, to be hauled back to the surface. This invention speeded up the sounding of the oceans and in 1854 Maury was able to make the first bathymetric chart of the North Atlantic. This apparatus, modified by Lieutenant Baillie, Royal Navy, and named after him, was still in use in the 1950s.

The earlier *Challenger* Expedition is said to have carried wire for sounding purposes, but for some reason this was not used, and the method of using marked rope and time intervals was employed for taking the many ocean soundings that this vessel made. Her deepest for the voyage was 4,500 fathoms, recorded in the Marianas Trench where we too found our deepest sounding referred to above.

The U.S.S. *Tuscarora* was also at sea employed upon oceanographic work at the time of the *Challenger* Expedition and it was from her decks that piano wire was first used for sounding great depths. With this wire she recorded 4,655 fathoms in the Kuril Trench north east of Japan.

The first ship to sound at a greater depth then 5,000 fathoms was the British surveying vessel *Penguin* in 1895. Her captain was Andrew Balfour, who had been a sub-lieutenant in *Challenger* during the Expedition and, ever since, had been fired with enthusiasm to find a great depth. He took two soundings with piano wire on a steam-sounding machine which had by then come into use; these soundings were taken in the Kermadec Trench, in the South Pacific, north-east of New Zealand. On the first occasion the wire parted, as so often happens, while the Baillie rod was being hauled to the surface. As the rod is comparatively light, the parting of the wire is not readily apparent and it is only as the hours pass that the surveyors, constantly feeling the wire, begin to suspect that the worst has happened, for it takes over four hours to haul in the sampler from 5,000 fathoms. It took Andrew Balfour far longer, for when he recorded a sounding of 5,155 fathoms he insisted that, to avoid parting the wire again, watches of two seamen at a time hove in the whole five miles by using the manual handles on the machine, so that no undue strain of an unfeeling steam engine would be imparted to the thin wire as the ship rolled in the heavy swell. He never left the winch himself throughout the whole long day, and thankfully and excitedly he ladled the sediment from the sampler onto a plate he had kept beside him in readiness for this supreme moment.

The German ship *Planet* shifted the scene of greatest depth once again to the northern hemisphere – in the Philippine Trench close eastward of the islands which give it the name. And here some years later the Dutch vessel *Willebord Snellius* subsequently found 5,539 fathoms, using early audio-frequency sounding methods.

The U.S.S. *Ramapo* moved the scene once more to the Japan Trench with 5,673 fathoms, using audio-frequency methods, but the German *Emden*, returning to the Philippine Trench, found just a few more fathoms to make it 5,686.

This was the state of great depth sounding when World War II came. At the close of the Pacific War the United States was once again to take the lead in the friendly rivalry of deep ocean discovery. Dr. H.H. Hess, a university professor, had studied the shape of the ocean floor for many years and had produced the best bathymetric chart of the North Pacific available before the war. Like so many others of his calling, he joined the Services and his knowledge of the sea took him into the Navy, where he eventually commanded a large fleet oiler, the U.S.S. *Cape Johnson*. Commander Hess's crew was composed of Reserves and he had no difficulty in persuading them that it was normal in the Navy to carry out standard oceanographic observations as the vessel proceeded upon her naval duties across the oceans. Thus this ship was able to add much to the knowledge of oceanography and eventually sounded with her echo-sounding machine in the Philippine Trench, recording there a depth of 5,740 fathoms, now known as the 'Cape Johnson Depth', from which the Danish research ship *Galathea* later dredged up forms of life including small sea anemones, a number of worms and some living bacteria.

The scene of the greatest depth having once again shifted to the Marianas Trench, we were determined to make a survey of the deep area and to get a sample of sediment from the depths. During the visit to New Zealand the ship enjoyed great assistance from knowledgeable technicians in the Royal New Zealand Dockyard at Devonport, who managed to boost the echo-sounder to record at the greatest depths: here also extra wire for the sounding machine was obtained.

It was an exciting time as *Challenger* steamed back into the trench on the way northwards from Manus to Japan, for on this occasion she was not restricted to spot soundings here and there; enthusiasm rose as the water became deeper and deeper, and still the officer with headphones sitting before the sounder could hear the small answering signal returning from the depths first eight, then slowly nine, ten, eleven, twelve and finally fourteen seconds after the metallic sound of the outgoing signal had been heard – for such is the time the sound takes to reach the sea-bed and return from 5,900 fathoms.

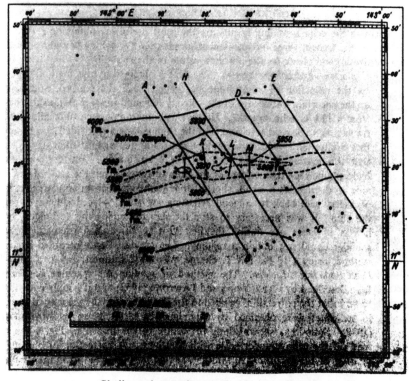

Challenger's soundings in the Marianas Trench

Sounding lines were run at right angles to the east-west axis of the trench, thus obtaining profiles across this giant crack on the surface of the globe. Such trenches do not have spectacular slopes as one might find in a canyon on land, but descend slowly and steadily to meet in a small flat expanse at the bottom from which the echo returns more clearly than from any other part. On completion of the mapping it appeared that there was a considerable area of a depth greater than 5,900 fathoms and that a sounding of 5,940 fathoms existed. But the 6,000 fathom barrier remained inviolate.

A sample from the trench was obtained with the Baillie rod after three attempts. It is difficult when using the steam-sounding machine in such depths to know just when the sampler has reached the bottom, and during the short delay between realising this and the application of the brake to stop more wire running out, a certain amount will have coiled itself on the sea-floor beside the sampler. When the winch begins to heave, these coils become kinks, and often, perhaps hours later when the sample seems to be almost on deck, the wire finally parts at the kink and the six-hour task has to be done all over again. This difficulty was finally overcome by laying up the whole of the last 100 fathoms of piano wire within a piece of rope which obviated the kinking as the superfluous wire coiled onto the sea-bed six and three-quarters land miles below.

Excitement on deck was tense when, at long last, the ceaseless chugging of the winch was slowed and Petty Officer Greenshields grasped the rope and hauled in hand-over-hand. Even before the sampler could be clearly sighted a brown cloud was seen spreading from it, indicating that the rod must contain a sample of what the surveyor has termed 'red clay', the deposit of the great depths.

Very considerable areas of the ocean floor are composed of ooze formed by countless millions of skeletons of microscopic and macroscopic plankton which have lived a brief life near the sea's surface and, having died there, sunk slowly to form this deposit. At greater depths than 3,000 fathoms or so the calcarious plankton are no more and only the skeletons of silicate forms remain, for the calcarious forms have been eroded away during their long slow fall and have become once again an integral part of sea water. The silicate forms continue unscathed to the great depths, where are found the skeletons of diatoms (the plants), and radiolarians (the animals), that, with red volcanic dust which has fallen upon the sea surface miles above, form the really deep ocean deposits.

Such a sample now lay secure in a pickle jar, and this I took home with me when I left the ship a month later. Back in London, I made my way to that striking building of many turrets which houses the British Museum of Natural

History in the Cromwell Road. It was the first of many visits to this treasure house, and I was taking the cherished deep-bottom sample to Dr. J. D. H. Wiseman, an expert in such matters. A guide took me from the main hall, where stuffed elephants stood with oversized statues of Darwin and Huxley, down to the cellars beneath. Here we passed along a maze of corridors lined with racks on which were stacked spare or forgotten stuffed animals, their horns, their hoofs, their heads and their bones, like some nightmare Aladdin's cave. At last the guide reached a locked door on which he rapped with a conspiratorial air, and we were admitted to Dr. Wiseman's presence.

The small pickle jar looked insignificant as it was placed upon the table among many other jars of more imposing size and content, but Dr. Wiseman's enthusiasm made up for this, and soon he and his companions were inspecting the sample through microscopes, searching for the skeletons of the planktonic animals and plants that it contained, which had once floated near the blue surface of the far-away Pacific Oean.

When using the echo-sounder in the Trench we had actually recorded a deepest sounding of 5,960 fathoms (10,900 metres) in position 11° 19′N 142° 15′E. This sounding was repeatedly made using earphones to hear the return of the signal as the stylus passed across the graduated depth scale, whilst the timing of the speed of the echo-sounding machine, a necessary part of the process, was made with a hand-held stopwatch. For these reasons I considered it prudent to subtract one scale division of 20 fathoms when officially reporting a new greatest depth of 5940 fathoms (10,863 metres). With hindsight this caution on my part appears to have been a mistake.

In 1957 I provided Professor C. V. Udintsev of the Soviet Union with our sounding data from the Marianas Trench, which he then visited in his research vessel *Vityaz*. He subsequently reported that he had found depths of more than 11,000 metres.

In January 1960 Jacques Piccard and Lieutenant Don Walsh of the United States Navy descended in the bathyscaphe *Trieste* to the floor of the Challenger Deep, recording a depth of 10,900 metres on their depth gauge.

Later Dr. Robert L. Fisher of Scripps Institute of Oceanography visited the vicinity of Challenger Deep on a number of occasions. In 1962 with the Proa Expedition in M.V. *Spencer F. Baird*, using the advanced precision depth recorders with stable electrical frequency sources by then available, Fisher recorded a greatest depth of 10,915 metres.

In 1984 the Japanese Hydrographer reported a greatest depth of 10,924 metres as having been recorded by the survey vessel *Takuyo*, using a multi-beam echo-sounder during a sounding run of about 500 miles in the vicinity of the Challenger Deep.

All the soundings referred to above have been corrected for sound velocity in the water column to give true depth, either by the use of various tables available, or by temperature and salinity measurements obtained at depth in the area concerned.

When one takes into account the great technical advances since 1951, the *Challenger* measurement made with our crude methods agrees very creditably with those of Fisher (1962) and the Japanese (1984).

Chapter XVI

S.O.B.

The Hydrographer, recognising that eighteen months' absence from my family after a 'pier head jump' on my return from the Persian Gulf involved some hardship, sent out Commander Ashton to relieve me when the ship berthed at Kure in November 1951.

Bill Ashton is the only surveyor of the old *Endeavour* team, who were scattered across the Mediterranean when the ship paid off in Suez in 1943, whom I have not yet mentioned. With his extrovert character and his buoyant attitude to life he was well suited to his appointment to the staff of Commodore Sullivan of the United States Navy's salvage team clearing the port of Naples. Bill subsequently worked with the United States Navy in other west coast Italian ports as they came into Allied hands, receiving the United States Bronze Star for his fine work. He often boasted that he was the only surveyor to have employed four 'Hydrographers', for that was how Commodore Sullivan had categorised the swarthy bare-footed Neapolitan boatmen enlisted to assist Bill with his work.

Back in London I found myself appointed to take over as Superintendent of the small Oceanographic Branch at Cricklewood headed by Dr. Jack Carruthers. Thus I came to work with a unique personality in the oceanographic world.

Before the war Jack was on the staff of the Fisheries Research Laboratory at Lowestoft where he had become the expert on water movements, and hence the temperature and salinity patterns, in the English Channel and southern North Sea. He took an active part in the meetings of the International Council for the Exploration of the Sea, where his practical approach was valued and where he met many European oceanographers, including a number of Germans, whose language he spoke.

On the outbreak of war he was appointed to the Hydrographic Department, where his wide knowledge of oceanographic literature enabled him to lay his hands on recorded information on such subjects as water movements, temperature layering, sediments and wave heights, all vital to naval operations worldwide. Towards the War's end he greatly assisted the Hydrographer, still Sir John Edgell who had despatched me to the *Herald* in 1936, with the lengthy preparations he was making for the peacetime foundation of a National Institute of Oceanography.

When hostilities ceased in north-west Europe Jack Carruthers was sent to Germany as part of a small team from the Hydrographic Department to re-activate the German hydrographic and oceanographic potential. Dr. Böhecke, who expected little from the victors, was both surprised and delighted when his old friend Jack Carruthers, who had located the German research vessel *Börgen*, sailed into Flensberg in June 1945.

Jack's prewar knowledge of German oceanography, coupled with his great energy, enabled him and his British assistants to gather together the great mass of instruments and technical books that had been dispersed during the war as far afield as a remote village in Bavaria. From the ashes of former observatories and institutes Dr. Carruthers was largely responsible for the establishment of the new Deutsches Hydrographisches Institut (D.H.I.) in Hamburg, with Dr. Böhecke as its first Director.

Admiral Day and Dr George Deacon, the first Director of the National Institute of Oceanography (N.I.O.), which had been established at Wormley in Surrey, had decided between them that the Navy should now maintain a small practical Oceanographic Branch concerned largely with the collection and presentation of seasonal temperature layer depth data and sea-floor characteristics, both of which are vital elements in anti-submarine warfare. The new Branch would maintain a liaison with the N.I.O. and other appropriate scientific bodies within the U.K. in furtherance of these objectives; berths for scientists could be provided onboard H.M. surveying ships when suitable cruises were arranged. Jack Carruthers accepted a post as an Assistant Director at the N.I.O. to be taken up when I had relieved him.

This was to be no week-long turnover period such as was customary in the Service, for Jack was walled in by his personal oceanographic library acquired over many years. This not only comprised hundreds of books, but also thousands of scientific papers sent to him by their authors worldwide. Dr Jack and his glamorous secretary, Georgie Woodman, were vigorously engaged daily for six months indexing and packing this material while I fretted, unable yet to take over my new job, my office or my secretary.

During this frustrating period, however, I learnt much from Carruthers as I accompanied him to conferences, symposia and scientific meetings and the convivial evenings which sometimes followed if Jack had his way. It was a new world to me, and Jack was generous with his introductions to many oceanographers who subsequently helped me in my work.

Dr. Carruthers was a big bulky man and during the delivery of a scientific paper before an audience, let us say on sea-bed sedimentation, one might imagine that he was asleep as he reclined deeply in his seat, his eyes closed; but no sooner had the speaker concluded his dissertation than Jack would rise cumbersomely to his feet to congratulate him warmly on the erudition and breadth of his paper but had he not, perhaps, overlooked the very relevant paper by Schott 'Geographie der Indischen und Stillen Ozeans' delivered in Hamburg in 1935, or Laing's important thesis on sediments resulting from the Meteor Expedition of 1925-1927? The speaker, who would probably have to admit such oversights, would receive within a few days one of Dr. Jack's well-known, but barely legible, postcards setting out in his bold hand details of a number of references relevant to the paper.

At long last Dr. Carruthers led a small fleet of heavily laden trucks carrying his library across London and on into Surrey, and I was able to assume the duties of S.O.B., an acronym which my fellow officers interpreted in a less complimentary way than I had envisaged.

In October 1952 I joined Wynford Vaughan-Thomas, the B.B.C. commentator, onboard *Challenger*; she had arrived in Portsmouth at the end of her three-year voyage around the world. It was an enjoyable day for me, meeting again the officers, scientists and crew members with whom I had sailed so blithely across the Pacific. I found myself back again in Tom Gaskell's cabin, sitting on the bunk beneath the huge red deer head from Vancouver Island and hemmed in by Tom's countless curios, while he took over the microphone to recount with gusto his endless experiences on the voyage.

Challenger made some further sounding and seismic cruises in the eastern North Atlantic in the spring and summer of 1953 with Dr. M.N. Hill and John Swallow before being finally paid off and sold for scrap. An article in the *Times* then described some of the activities of the ship during her long life of twenty-five years. This resulted in Tom Burns, of the publishers Hollis and Carter, arriving in my office at Cricklewood one day when I was busy dealing with some of the many data received from *Challenger*. He proposed that I should write a book about the old ship and offered attractive advance royalties. I had no experience as a writer, and I was already preparing to sail, with my family, to take over the recently formed Hydrographic Service of the New Zealand Navy. Tom was insistent, so I went to seek advice from Captain Clarke, the Naval Public Relations Officer in Whitehall. 'Of course you'll take it on, young man,' said he. 'When I retire I will have great difficulty in finding a publisher for my memoirs – you'll already have a publisher.' Taking this as an order I accepted the offer from Hollis and Carter and, before sailing in the *Rangitiki* for New Zealand, I had photocopies made of all *Challenger*'s Letters of Proceedings and provided myself with several thick pads of paper. With the advance royalties we bought a washing machine to take with us.

Chapter XVII

New Zealand

Tradition has it that in the tenth century Kupe, on a fishing expedition in his canoe, was blown far to the south-west from his island in central Polynesia and came to a mountainous land, heavily afforested and inhabited only by birds, many of them flightless. In time he managed to return to his homeland bearing a message for his people – 'I found a great land covered with high mists in Tiritiri-o-te-moana, the open sea that lies to the south.'

These words passed from one generation to the next, and in the fourteenth century overpopulation and strife in the homelands led to a number of large canoes, manned by men and women and well supplied, following Kupe's sailing directions to the great south land.

The Maoris had no need of charts; once they had sailed a strange coast directions for returning thither were handed down as folklore.

It was only when Europeans came to New Zealand that it became necessary to lay down the outlines of the coast and the depths in the channels on parchment so that others could follow. Abel Tasman was the first navigator to do this when he visited a part of the west coast in 1642. However, it was Captain James Cook who, having spent only a few brief months off the coast of New Zealand in H.M.S. *Endeavour*, can be said to have charted New Zealand. His remarkable outline of the whole coast appeared first on a chart dated 1772, published in the Admiralty's official account of Cook's first Pacific voyage.

Two French naval officers, Duperrey and Dumont d'Urville, made surveys of parts of the New Zealand coast in the early decades of the nineteenth century, their charts appearing in the 'Atlas Hydrographique'.

The Royal Navy, under pressure from the increasing number of British settlers, returned in the middle of the century to improve the charts. Captain

Lort Stokes in the paddler *Acheron*, and Commander Byron Drury in the brig *Pandora*, achieved the first detailed surveys around the coasts, whilst port plans were prepared by early harbourmasters.

The next Royal Navy contribution came at the turn of the century when the steam and sail survey ship *Penguin* spent five years charting the approaches to Auckland and Wellington, and parts of the east coast lying between.

The last time a Royal Navy survey ship had worked in New Zealand waters was from 1937-1939 when Captain Guy Wyatt commanded *Endeavour* off the north east coast. On the outbreak of war the ship was sailed to Singapore where I took up her story earlier.

With the ending of World War II there was a clamour from shipping companies, shipmasters and harbourmasters in New Zealand for the resumption of the Royal Navy's prewar survey work. The Admiralty saw things differently now that the Royal New Zealand Navy had come of age after five years of maritime warfare; they would lend surveying officers, but the New Zealand Navy Board would have to find a vessel.

Fortunately Australia had a River Class frigate named *Lachlan* which had been fitted out as an armed survey vessel and now lay unused at Fremantle. The Royal Australian Navy was prepared to lend *Lachlan* to the Royal New Zealand Navy.

Admiral Wyatt, now Hydrographer of the Navy, selected Commander Sharpey-Schafer, who had served with him in New Zealand, to command *Lachlan* and to establish a modest hydrographic office in Wellington.

Sharpey-Schafer was a man of great energy. He arrived in New Zealand in advance of the ship and was able to advise the Chief of Naval Staff when the latter called a meeting of Government Departments and other authorities having an interest in safe navigation. This was the first meeting of the National Hydrographic Committee, which annually sets the priorities for the coming year's surveys.

Cook and Foveaux Straits were the first priorities and Sharpey-Schafer hurried north to meet *Lachlan* when she arrived in Auckland from Sydney on 2nd November 1949. He had already discussed with Devonport Dockyard how the ship was to be converted for peacetime surveying. In fourteen days the guns were removed; a spacious chartroom was built and fitted out with a massive chart table and stowages for the many instruments; a captain's cabin was built on B deck, and beacon stowages constructed. Ready for sea, *Lachlan* sailed away southwards to one of the most boisterous surveying grounds on this earth.

Commander Lowry R.N. relieved Sharpey-Schafer in June 1952. I took over from Lowry as *Lachlan*'s third commanding officer on the New Zealand Station in March 1954.

Most of the senior appointments in the New Zealand Navy at that time were held by Royal Navy officers on loan service. Commodore Sir Charles Madden was the Chief of Naval Staff to whom I was responsible for developing the Surveying Service and the Hydrographic Office. He was a lively man with a twinkle in his eye and a fine sense of humour.

For the administration of the ship I was responsible to Captain Maurice Hardie R.N., the Naval Officer in Charge Auckland (NOCA). He was a more serious character, dedicated to the correct procedure when dealing with official correspondence, in which he instructed me when he came onboard soon after my arrival. He expressed pained surprise when he saw my 'Too Difficult' tray which I was in the habit of using in addition to 'In' and 'Out' boxes. He gave me another tip – 'When a New Zealander says ''She'll be right'' you can assume things will go wrong,' said he.

The more senior surveying officers were also from the R.N., whilst the juniors were learning their trade. The ship's company included a number of ratings who had transferred from the R.N., whilst the majority of the junior engine room ratings in *Lachlan* were Maoris.

I took over the surveying from Lowry some miles north of Pencarrow Point, working onwards along the east coast to Cape Kidnappers. This task was comparatively simple because liaison with the Lands and Survey Department was close. Their surveyors had cleared selected triangulation stations on the coastal hills, and erected new beacons upon them, so that they could be used for fixing the ship by sextant and station pointers.

Northwards from Cape Kidnappers things became more complex as the vast Hawke's Bay opened out, the coastline receding westwards and the 100 fathom line extending eastwards so that much of the continental shelf lay out of sight of land.

These difficulties had been foreseen and our Marconi Radiolocater was fitted with a ranging panel developed for us by the Department of Industrial and Scientific Research. This panel increased the scale of a particular section of the radar scan, enabling ranges of up to ten miles or so to be taken of small targets with an accuracy of ± 10 yards. The Dockyard had made a number of special radar reflectors to fix to floating beacons which we laid out in taut-wire controlled lines across the Bay, much as we had done in *Owen* in the Persian Gulf.

This method of fixing the ship by radar ranges reduced dramatically the number of beacons required, and allowed ship sounding to go ahead in low visibility and through the night. Much of the northern part of the Bay was sounded by sailing on circular courses controlled by keeping the radar range constant from the well-defined southern tip of Mahia Peninsula, whilst ranging with the panel on the next beacon ahead. Some vessels entering Hawke's Bay from the north-east bound for Napier clearly found it baffling to meet a ship which was constantly changing course, even though we were displaying our surveying signals and lights.

Weekends in Napier gave way to those at Gisborne as we worked northwards. One Saturday a party of us went to Gisborne races and backed a horse named *Lachlan* in the last race. It came in a poor second. While we were having a final drink beside our car I noticed *Lachlan*'s jockey, Campbell, getting into his vehicle nearby; handing him a glass of whisky I informed him that we didn't like to see *Lachlan* in second place. He answered that he was not aware that the ship was in port or he would have done better. 'She'll be right in a fortnight's time at Hastings,' said he.

Ignoring Captain Hardie's advice, I informed the ship's company in my 'Weekly Bulletin' that I had received this tip from the jockey, and as the ship was in Wellington on the day in question everyone was able to place a wager for the 3.30 at Hastings at the nearest T.A.B. I sent a telegram to Campbell care of the Jockey's Room – 'Ride hard the ship is watching you.' Sure enough *Lachlan* romped home at 12 to 1 and my reputation as a tipster soared. I looked forward to a close association with jockey Campbell, but the end of the story is very sad; Campbell was tipped over the rails and killed during a race six weeks later.

Whenever *Lachlan* was in Auckland for more than a few days I hurried south to Wellington to supervise the work in the Hydrographic Office. Compilation of N.Z. charts from the fair sheets sent in from the ship and the motor launches was in the good hands of George Thorn and Ray Evins, both formerly employed in the Hydrographic Department at Cricklewood, whilst C.P.O. Long, who had been in *Endeavour* with Captain Wyatt, ran the office and took charge of the archives.

The charts were beautifully printed by the Government Printer. Hill shading enhanced by a green land tint realistically portrayed the crumpled hills and folded valleys which derived, so the early discoverers believed, from the writhings of the great fish, which the puckish god Maui had hauled from the deep, when his brothers began to carve it up. Thoughts of how hill shading would fit in with computer-assisted cartography were far from our minds in the early 1950s.

As our confidence grew in the seagoing capability of our two motor launches off these stormy shores they were employed more and more on their own in command of lieutenants. It seemed to me that they deserved names rather than numbers and so, with the permission of the Naval Board, I commissioned them as *Takapu* and *Tarapunga*, the Maori words for the gannet, so numerous on Cape Kidnappers, and a ubiquitous small New Zealand gull – both as sparkling white as I hoped our launches would always remain.

There was one major anomaly to be resolved in Wellington; the Marine Department continued to publish and control Notices to Mariners, which announce changes affecting charts. As the catalogue of N.Z. charts steadily expanded it became increasingly necessary for the Hydrographic Office to publish the N to M corrections. After lengthy discussions this transfer was agreed upon and thenceforward the Hydrographic Office was in control of its own affairs and could hold its head high among fellow members of the International Hydrographic Organisation, which New Zealand had joined five years earlier.

We found for ourselves a small but friendly house at Eastbourne on the shores of Port Nicholson across the water from Wellington. Beside the front door grew a pohutukawa tree which bore crimson blooms at Christmas time; a stony beach sloped a few yards down to the sea where we could bathe or fish, except when a southerly gale brought fearful breakers to our doorstep; nearby on a shingle strand fishermen set and hauled seine nets and our boys joined the excited throng as they captured the splashing slithery fish; across the village street behind the house a track led over the first range of hills to Butterfly Creek, where we experienced our first simple adventures of camping in the bush. We were very happy at Eastbourne.

Like all naval vessels *Lachlan* had to undergo an annual inspection, a half day in harbour devoted to an examination for cleanliness and correct stowage, followed by an afternoon at sea when various manoeuvres and emergencies were exercised. On the day before our 1954 inspection Captain Hardie came onboard to discuss with me how he and his staff would conduct affairs on the morrow. As he left my cabin he glanced towards my desk. 'I see you still have that irresponsible tray,' said he.

As NOCA would be signing the ship's books at my desk during the inspection to leave my 'Too Difficult' tray on display could be perceived as an act of insolence. I hid it in my wardrobe. This cowardice seemed justified when, a few weeks later, I received a glowing Inspection Report from NOCA, beginning *'In my wide experience as an Inspecting Officer of destroyers, frigates and smaller vessels, I have seldom come across a ship which had a better claim to be described as clean, happy and efficient.'*

The Hydrographic Committee had decided in 1953 that the charts of Western Samoa, an island territory which had been mandated to New Zealand at the close of World War I, were much in need of modernisation. There was a lively export trade from the port of Apia including copra, bananas and cocoa, much of which was carried by sea to New Zealand. Accordingly a three-year programme of surveys in the Apolima Strait between the two main islands of Upolu and Savai'i and the waters along the north coast of Upolu eastwards to Apia was assigned to *Lachlan.* I was happy enough to spend six weeks each winter in the heartland of Polynesia.

A party from the N.Z. Lands and Survey Department had made a traverse around the island of Upolu in 1953 to co-ordinate a number of coastal survey stations, including the great white churches of the London Mission Society, which provided superb surveying marks along the coastline. Under contract, Mr Van Asch of Hastings brought his aircraft to Samoa and made an air photo survey, from which we were able to assemble mosaics to provide us with the coastline.

There were about 100,000 Samoans on the two islands at that time, living in villages of thatched fales, whilst about 3,000 part-Samoans of German descent, providing the entrepreneurial skills, lived in and around Apia in well-found timber houses.

Captain Jones, the harbourmaster, had spent his life trading amongst the islands. He was a genial and forthright character who welcomed us each weekend to the port of Apia where, with the assistance of his launch, we moored to a buoy. Leaving the Officer of the Day and the Duty Part of the Watch onboard, we were soon all ashore for the weekend, unmindful that as the ship swung to the prevailing wind her stern would be but a few yards from the visible remains of a German warship wrecked on the reef in the disastrous hurricane of 1889.

We made many friends among the part-Samoans, with whom we spent delectable days on distant beaches and danced the nights away in their houses around town. The Samoan dance is the sivasiva which begins with delicate swaying and gentle hand movements, a woman and perhaps two men participating. Bent at the knees and the groin, the dancers move their feet only slightly to the rhythm of drum and guitar; as the tempo increases all manner of antics may be performed with heads and arms.

High above the town on the slopes of Mount Vaea lived the New Zealand High Commissioner in Robert Louis Stevenson's old house, Vailima. Many an evening I planned to climb to the peak of Mount Vaea to observe the sunrise and scan the immortal words on the writer's grave. To my abiding regret the revels of the night never left me in good enough shape to tackle the steep and muddy track at first light.

Two of our greatest friends were Peter Plowman, an Australian, long since settled in Western Samoa, and his dear wife Aggie, a vivacious and generous part-Samoan. Peter was the Minister in Government responsible for marine affairs and in his quiet, deliberate way he supported us in all our efforts to improve the charts of Western Samoa.

During the first two years of my visits to Apia, the Plowmans lived on the east side of the harbour where we were welcome at any time. During my last visit they were building a house below Vailima which they named *Lachlan* in our honour.

During our 1955 visit to Apia a Guard of Honour, impeccably turned out in white uniforms, was provided for the dawn service at the War Memorial on Anzac Day. On completion of the ceremony the Guard marched smartly along Beach Road to the Returned Servicemen's Association clubhouse near the landing stage. On arrival arms were piled, webbing equipment unbuckled and the sailors sat down four to a table on each of which two unlabelled bottles of rum were placed, together with four glasses. The chairman of the club then offered me the first tot; it hit the back of my throat like a flaming arrow and I made a rapid departure for my boat.

An hour or so later we were aware, even from the ship, of some considerable commotion at the R.S.A. and a strong patrol was rapidly landed. Some sailors were wallowing in the harbour having fallen from the club windows a few feet above the water; others were wandering aimlessly in Beach Road, to the fascination of a crowd of Samoan boys, whilst two of our men had staggered into the bush behind the town.

It was an hour or more before all the members of the erstwhile immaculate Guard had been rounded up and carried back onboard. I was furious and next day demanded an enquiry by the Club Committee. It transpired that a cask of Australian rum had been shipped in specially for the refreshment of my crew on this important day. Unfortunately, the Samoan barman, more used to serving beer, had failed to read a label tacked onto the rum barrel which stated that in bottling off the spirit it should be broken down ten parts of water to one of rum.

On Christmas Eve 1955 I was called from my home in Eastbourne to meet the Chief of Naval Staff, now Commodore McBeath, in Navy Office. The staff were already on leave and we sat alone in his room, a wall map of the Pacific behind him. He had something of extreme secrecy to discuss.

It appeared that Anthony Eden, the British Prime Minister, had been in communication with Sidney Holland, his opposite number in New Zealand, concerning the United Kingdom's plans to test their hydrogen bombs in the Line Islands, a series of British possessions on the Equator 3,000 miles across the Pacific from New Zealand. It was proposed to set up a base on Christmas Island and select an uninhabited island as the target over which it was planned to release the bombs. No British survey ship was available in the Pacific, the time schedule was tight, and so Eden had requested that *Lachlan* should carry out the necessary surveys.

This was at a time when, disillusioned by the United States' postwar reluctance to exchange nuclear data with the U.K., the latter had decided to go it alone in developing nuclear weapons. Hence the secrecy, and even a visit to Pearl Harbour for fuel must be avoided by *Lachlan*. The Line Islands were nine days' steaming from Suva. 'Where,' asked C.N.S., 'will you obtain fuel for the return passage?' At that moment his head moved as he glanced at his notes, revealing to me on the wall map the island of Tahiti. Here was an opportunity to visit that happy isle. The Commodore readily agreed to ask the French Navy to make fuel available in Papeete.

I was to sail away quietly from Auckland as soon as Christmas leave was over on 17th January, and call at Suva to embark Lieutenant Commander Paton, an R.N. surveying officer, and Captain Wadsworth, a Royal Engineer officer, who would both be fully briefed in U.K.

Just before leaving the office C.N.S. informed me that there was a single resident New Zealand planter on Christmas Island in charge of 200 Gilbertese employed in cutting copra. I would have to invent a cover story before I met him.

Having picked up the British officers at Suva we set out across the Pacific. I had plenty of time to study the instructions they had brought with them, and to devise my story. Aware that the International Geophysical Year was to begin in July 1957, and that radio-sonde equipment was to be installed at a number of remote places before that date, a solution occurred to me. The landing of heavy vehicles on which such equipment would be mounted would require sounding the approach to the wharf and studies of the terrain.

Captain Cook had landed on the island on Christmas Day 1777, having sent the boats to sound out an anchorage under the lee of 'Cook Island' which straddles the entrance to the lagoon.

Over the long years the island has been occupied by a number of copra traders including the French rogue priest Father Rougier. It was he who gave the name 'London' to a small settlement on the north side of the lagoon, and 'Paris' to an even smaller village on the south side.

There had been some United States Airforce activity during the Second World War, when minimal dredging had been carried out to permit barge access to a jetty which was built at London. More importantly for me, a New Zealand survey team had done some triangulation in the early days of the war, and Paton brought with him the co-ordinates of stations at London and Paris which provided us with a reliable baseline to start from.

Our job was to carry out a large scale survey of the lagoon, its approaches and the anchorages off the west end of the island, for there was a great deal of equipment to be brought in by sea when 2,000 servicemen began to arrive in three to four months' time in preparation for Operation 'Grapple' about eight months later.

With the ship safely anchored to the west of Cook Island, I went ashore to call on the resident planter, who accepted my cover story and offered the use of his jeep. (Much later when John Paton returned for 'Grapple' the planter told him that *Lachlan*'s captain was an inveterate liar.)

Having read Captain Cook's account of the great haul of fish his men made at Christmas Island, I had encouraged my sailors, always keen for fresh food, to try their luck. On my return to the ship a number of the crew were engaged on the quarterdeck in gutting a great catch of fine-looking fish they had caught off the reef from the ship's whaler.

Just as this task was being completed two Gilbertese, who had come off in their canoe to visit the ship, mounted the gangway. As their heads came level with the deck their eyes widened in astonishment and their jaws sagged. 'You eat?' they asked, and on receiving an affirmative reply they cried out. 'All men die!' The paymaster, a loan officer from the R.N., was a stickler for 'going by the book' and assured me that he had already boiled a fish together with a sixpence. As the latter remained untarnished it was, according to the Victualling Manual, perfectly safe to eat. Convinced as I was by the two Gilbertese, I ordered the whole catch to be thrown overboard, to the accompaniment of much grumbling from the sailors, and complaints from the paymaster that his professional advice had been ignored.

Next day the planter assured me that these fish are indeed quite deadly. He sent a party of Gilbertese to catch some edible species.

A large camp party was established at London near the landing place where the two sounding boats were based and a tidewatch was established. Each morning at 0700 the boats came out to the ship, were fuelled, collected the surveying officers, including myself, and began the day's work of ferrying the observers to the various stations which had to be established to extend the triangulation from the London-Paris baseline to control the whole area to be surveyed. The theodolite observers had to work through the noon heat of the tropic day, unsheltered except for a surveying umbrella, and a few prickly trees in or under which red-footed and blue-faced boobies panted on their nests.

As the ship was to remain at anchor, six Maori stokers were available to form 'Party Rugged' to work under Captain Wadsworth's direction. His task was to obtain ten-pound soil samples to a depth of a foot, bagged and tagged with reference to their position on his plan of the 160 square miles of the island. With a single jeep it was a formidable task; he set out each day with his Maoris onboard, dropping them off in pairs, each with a spade and suitably tagged sacks, to collect sand in an area allocated to them. Their orders were to make their way back on foot to the camp at London, taking the samples with them, while Wadsworth in the jeep ranged to far distant locations thirty or more miles from camp.

The triangulated stations and sounding marks around the lagoon and along the west coast were beflagged, the plotting sheet was made, the sounding crews got to work and in fourteen scorching days the survey was complete. A bar sweep, suspended from two boats, was used to find the least depth in the vital channel into the lagoon.

On our last night, the Gilbertese labourers and their families were brought off to the ship for a film show and, of course, a visit to the ship's canteen. As it was a moonlight night of extremely low tide our Maoris deemed it propitious for crawfishing on the reef. And so it proved to be; they brought back enough fine specimens to feed the whole ship's company. They had found Captain Wadsworth's soil probe (a fine rapier with a pressure gauge fitted in the handle) a most useful tool for dislodging the crustaceans. Unfortunately, on their return this precious instrument, which had been lent to Wadsworth by no less a man than his Colonel-in-Chief, was badly bent; he was inconsolable until the engineer officer, with infinite skill and patience, restored it to its former elegance.

At dawn we were on our way to the target island, Malden, named after a lieutenant whom Captain Byron had sent ashore from the *Blonde* when he discovered it in 1825.

About 360 miles south of Christmas Island we found this barren uninhabited island, about fifteen miles in circumference with, at its western end, the collapsed buildings of a former phosphate company which had abandoned the island, apparently hurriedly, in 1927.

The island is fringed with a narrow reef and a steep pebble beach about fifteen feet in height. We came to anchor as close as we dared to the western extremity of the island in ninety-three fathoms. This was safe enough as long as the prevailing easterly wind endured, but had it veered to the west we should have swung onto the reef, so a buoy with a two-and-a-half inch wire buoy rope was prepared, and the vessel kept up steam in case we had to cut and run.

At first glance the boat channel through the reef looked navigable until, observing from the bridge of the ship, we noted that at irregular intervals a great swell would break over the reef and surge through the channel.

We laid a well-anchored buoy at the entrance and led from it a floating grass line along the 100-yard channel to a holdfast at the top of the beach. Landing parties with securely tied lifebelts, together with their gear, manned a whaler which was towed to the entrance buoy where each man grabbed the grassline. Sitting in the stern and staring to seaward the man in charge would, when he deemed it safe, cry 'Go', whereupon every member of the crew pulled on the rope with all his might, hand over hand, until the boat was safely beached. A few mistakes in timing were made and from the decks of the ship a terrifying spectacle was observed as the boat was overturned on her way by a giant wave, and the men and their gear were scattered high on the beach. We were lucky indeed not to have any serious casualties.

There was a good deal of gear to be landed. Only a simple hydrographic survey of the anchorage was required, and a means of locating the boat channel. It was decided to measure a straight baseline along the crest of the beach and mark with large wooden tripod beacons the terminals and a midway point to serve as sounding marks and, later, as navigation beacons for operation 'Grapple's' seaborne units to land the mass of monitoring equipment to be set up on Malden.

There was a requirement to fix the position of the island but I was unwilling to see a theodolite, chronometer and chronograph, expensive items, cast up on the beach. However, as the island was so low we were able to command an all round sea horizon from the bridge, where on three cloudless nights a team were able to observe morning and evening stars.

All went well: the capstan was man enough to lift ninety-three fathoms of chain cable and we were on our way after four days at Malden, and one day ahead of time for our arrival in Papeete.

Lachlan approached Tahiti from the north as *Challenger* had done eighty years earlier. At the time of our visit there was as yet no airport, communication with metropolitan France being maintained by the monthly visits of the Messageries Maritimes steamers which brought a few tourists and quantities of red wine.

Mr. Spry, *Challenger*'s engineer officer, wrote a book about the expedition of 1872-1876 and I use his words to describe our approach –

> *'We came in sight of Tahiti and the outlying island of Morea, and, as we neared, could be seen very plainly the singular zig-zag outline, precipitous crags, and crater-like depressions of every shade of blue, grey, and purple, broken into every conceivable fantastic shape, with deep, dark, mysterious gorges, showing almost black by contrast with the surrounding brightness; while in the foreground, stretching away from the base to the shore, is a forest of tropical trees, with the huts and houses of the town peeping out between them. We entered the lovely harbour of Papeete, which is surrounded by coral reefs, forming a most safe and pleasant haven of rest after thirty days at sea.'*

For our arrival alongside I quote the words of one of *Lachlan*'s men writing in the 'Weekly Bulletin', a newsheet I produced onboard to keep the crew in touch with our activities.

> *'As we neared the main jetty and commenced tying up we were welcomed by the sound of natives singing their traditional songs of greeting. A group of musicians enthralled us with music of an island rhythm such as we had never heard before. To complete our welcome and to convey their feeling of friendship a beautiful Tahitian maiden began to demonstrate a blood-heating papeo, a native hula requiring extreme ability at manipulating the abdominal muscles. The moment the gangway was lowered three dusky Tahitian girls skipped aboard with armfuls of floral leis which were freely distributed and placed around our necks along with the traditional kiss of welcome. All the*

while the music was increasing in tempo giving everyone the feeling of being thoroughly welcome.'

Freddie Devenish, the British Consul, was soon onboard, a bulky figure in an immaculately laundered, if somewhat crumpled, tropical suit, doffing his panama hat as he stepped over the gangway. He had lots of plans, including one for a welcoming party at the Consulate that evening.

The Consulate, an ornately carved wooden building presented by Queen Pomare to Queen Victoria, stood among trees near the seafront. The party was a sailor's dream; there were many pretty women and girls with flowered and scented couronnes upon their heads, from which cascaded long black hair to their waists over boldly patterned pareos. One of these women was Princess Turia, a descendant of the Pomare dynasty, who informed me that I should be staying at her house at Paea, a dozen or so miles down the coast.

Life there was idyllic, lazing on the coral beach and bathing in the limpid water whilst entertained by Turia's young nephews with guitar and drums; fishing from canoes on the reef at night; and on one occasion enjoying roast sucking pig, cooked in an earth oven by the nephews, accompanied by copious draughts of red wine.

Early one morning Freddie arrived in his ancient motor car, clearly agitated; I must return with him to Papeete for there were problems with my sailors. At the Consulate the Consul and I were seated at a table and two pretty girls were ushered in. They began at once to gesticulate and gabble in the Tahitian patois which Freddie translated for my benefit. It appeared that two sailors from *Lachlan* had escorted these girls for three evenings but on each occasion had consumed so much Hinano beer that they had been unable to offer the normal courtesies.

The Consul's fear was that *Lachlan*'s men might sail away leaving behind them a sullied reputation. Many a time I had 'cleared lower deck' to congratulate or to castigate the ship's company; this was quite a novel opportunity which, going onboard and climbing into uniform, I seized with relish. New Zealanders' virility must not be left in question.

On Sundays it was the custom for many Tahitians to circle the island by car or bus along the perimeter road. Turia and I were able to rendezvous with Freddie and others at Quinn's Tahitian Hut at 10.00 a.m. where we were joined by worshippers emerging from the nearby cathedral. A makeshift band was already picking up the rhythm, rousing a few revellers from the previous night who still slumbered beneath the tables.

Many happy flower-bedecked parties were on the road. We admired the giant Benedictine bottle which suitably serves as a tomb for the last King of Tahiti on Point Venus; we bathed in an icy pool below a towering waterfall; we picnicked on a grassy headland and watched the fishermen on the reef casting with their long bamboo rods just as Captain Cook's artists had depicted them; only when we visited a massive stone marae in dark woodland shade, where human sacrifices once took place, did our chattering companions fall silent, and some shed a few tears.

Too soon the day of departure came. All our new-found friends were on the wharf, placing about our shoulders the leis of scented flowers they had woven overnight. These beautiful gifts gave but fleeting pleasure, for they were to be cast into the sea as the ship passed through the reef to the open sea if we were to ensure our return to this happy isle.

The long voyage back to Fiji gave us ample time to complete the drawing of our surveys of Christmas and Malden Islands. We paused only for a few hours off remote Palmerston Atoll where the Marsters clan, which had peopled the atoll for a century, exchanged with us two live turtles for some essential commodities. The turtles could have been a problem but, as usual, we had six Fijian sailors with us who soon had the animals butchered and dressed for the galley.

From Suva Paton and Wadsworth flew to U.K., taking with them the surveys. An R.A.F. transport plane came to Fiji to embark the several tons of bagged soil samples for study at the British Army's research laboratories in England.

Only as we sailed on towards New Zealand did a long tendril from the ship's grapevine reach my ears to reveal that a great proportion of the samples that the stokers had collected under Captain Wadsworth's direction had been bagged up a few hundred yards from the camp site on Christmas Island. The Maoris had soon realised that throughout the island a thin layer of fine sand overlaid coarse coral fragments. Why then carry heavy sacks of such uniform material for four or five miles, with little shade in the heat of an equatorial day, when it could be found in abundance in the vicinity of the wharf?

I was at first much agitated by this news, but a few hours' thought convinced me that there was no useful action I could now take. As *Lachlan*'s Christmas Island surveys were later loudly praised by no less a man than Lord Louis Mountbatten, the First Sea Lord, clearly our Maoris had made a sound diagnosis.

Soon after leaving Suva on our way north to Samoa in June 1956 I received a signal informing me that the motor vessel *Vasu* was in danger of sinking, so we worked *Lachlan* up to full speed and set course for her position, which was only a little off our track to Apia. A few hours later we received a message that the crew were abandoning ship.

R.N.Z.A.F. Sunderland flying boats from Lauthala Bay, Fiji, sighted the boats next morning and remained circling until *Lachlan* arrived about noon to embark the captain and crew, none the worse for a night in the boats.

Whilst examining the flotsam which was all that remained from *Vasu* a large bag of mail was spotted. In a letter to me Captain Darling of *Vasu*, thanking us for the rescue, added, '*as a result of conversations with residents of Apia I am surprised at the amount of trouble saved by the alertness of the men who recognised and reported the floating mail bag and your care in retrieving same.*'

During the 1956 visit for Samoan surveys the ship paid a visit to Motautu, on the north coast of Savai'i, to carry out a reconnaissance to assess how much blasting would be required to make a deep-water passage through the reef into this natural harbour.

We were there on the last day of June, when festivities to raise funds for a new Catholic girls' school were in full swing. I spent most of the evening witnessing these from the balcony of a local part-Samoan trader's house in the company of his vivacious daughter Paula. At a late hour her father took us off to the ship in his boat and I invited them for a nightcap in my cabin.

When he was ready to leave for the shore Paula's father suggested that she might spend the night with me onboard. Paula was not averse to the idea, which was certainly tempting. However, I indicated the enormity of such an offence according to Q.R. and A.I. and Paula reluctantly departed with her father.

Some two or three hours later the radio operator awakened me to announce that my name had appeared on the list of half-yearly promotions to captain. Pondering this good news I fell asleep only to be woken again, this time by an embarrassed and apologetic wireless operator – it was Commander R. D. Ritchie who had been nominated. Deflated, I fell asleep once more, only to be shaken a third time – yes, there *was* also a G. S. Ritchie on the list!

Dawn was near and I got up to brew a celebratory coffee. This was the first time that nominations were announced in advance of the actual promotions, leaving a six month period of probation. It struck me forcibly that had Paula been with me during the frequent nocturnal visits of the radio operator, my probation period might have lasted but six hours.

Niue Island, with a population of about 4,000 Polynesians, lies far from regular shipping routes about 250 miles east of Tonga. It was administered by a

Resident Commissioner representing the New Zealand Island Territories Department.

I first visited Niue in 1955 in *Lachlan* to land a party to survey the anchorage in Alofi Bay on the west side of the island. My men got on so well with the Niue islanders that we were invited to call in whenever we passed on our voyages to and from Samoa.

The islanders went so far as to send to me in New Zealand by the visiting steamship a Niue outrigger canoe. The non-existence of beaches and the high limestone cliffs, together with frequent stormy weather, makes it necessary to hollow out the logs forming the canoes until they are eggshell thin and thus so light that a single man may carry them up the escarpment to safety. Our canoe lay on our beach at Eastbourne, off which we learnt the skills of paddling an outrigger as one would learn to ride a bicycle.

The Niue islanders are enthusiastic dancers and during our visits our own band and those of the island would play alternately in the copra shed for dancing. On one such happy occasion I was overjoyed at winning, together with my Raratongan partner, a hard fought hula competition judged on both style and endurance. During untold misspent hours in Samoa and Niue I acquired Polynesian dancing skills sufficient to enable me, with the backing of the Hydrographic Office and the participation of Wrens and female clerical staff in Navy Office, to mount the floor shows at the annual Naval Balls in Wellington.

In November 1956 Commander Frank Hunt arrived from the U.K. to relieve me. My family and I sailed out of Wellington in the *Dominion Monarch*, escorted to the open sea by *Takapu* and *Tarapunga*, on our way to South Africa and the U.K.

Chapter XVIII

I Join the Feather-Bed Crew

Whilst in New Zealand I had had little opportunity to take leave with my family, except for a brief annual summer holiday with my old friends the Williams on Te Aute Station. The New Zealand Naval Board allowed me to store up my leave, which I used for a visit to South Africa to meet my in-laws on our way home to the United Kingdom.

We were in Cape Town for Christmas and New Year 1957, and whilst there I contacted Captain John Mallory, the South African Hydrographer. He suggested that I might wish to see demonstrated a new electronic measuring device, the Tellurometer, which had been invented by Mr. T. L. Wadley of the Commission for Scientific and Industrial Research and was now being manufactured in South Africa.

This opportunity was of considerable interest to me for, before leaving New Zealand, I had been discussing with the Lands and Survey Department how best they could provide surveying marks for ship sounding along the precipitous and inaccessible West Coast of the South Island. A traverse using a theodolite to maintain direction and a geodimeter to measure the distances was suggested. A geodimeter was, however, at that time both expensive and cumbersome; it measured distance by sending a light beam to a distant reflector and converting the time of double passage of the beam to and from the reflector into distance electronically.

As the geodimeter depended on the speed of light, so the Tellurometer employed radio waves. The equipment was composed of 'master' and 'remote' units, both the same size as a theodolite and capable of measuring much longer ranges than the geodimeter.

The two units of the Tellurometer compared the phase of high frequency radio transmissions in a similar way to that employed in Two Range Decca, but with a very much higher resolution, and hence accuracy. The equipment makes a basic measurement of time which is converted into distance by an assumed velocity of radio waves, which depends on the ambient temperature, atmospheric pressure and the amount of water vapour in the atmosphere, so these must be measured at each unit at the time of observation.

John Smith, technical sales director of Phillips Denbish, the manufacturer, set up the 'master' at a triangulation station at King's Battery on the slopes of Devil's Peak and we measured a distance of 16.6428 kilometers to a station on Tygerberg across the Cape Flats. I was extremely impressed with the ease of operation and the accuracy.

Back in London in early 1957 I found that I was to be the Assistant Hydrographer (2) to the newly appointed Hydrographer, Admiral Collins. I occupied an office alongside his in the Admiralty Building; my job was largely administrative, whilst I served as Kechil's right hand man during not infrequent encounters with other Whitehall warriors. I learnt then that every Hydrographer has to fight for his continuing existence in the corridors of power.

Edward Belcher, an active surveying officer for over thirty-five years in the mid-nineteenth century, rose to the rank of admiral without ever serving in the Hydrographic Office. He regarded the Hydrographer's assistants with disdain, referring to them as 'The feather-bed crew about Charing Cross'.

I saw my first duty as persuading Admiral Collins to purchase some Tellurometers, for I realised from my experience in Cape Town that their use would revolutionise the preliminary field work required to provide visible and fixed marks ashore for ship sounding at sea. No longer would it be necessary to extend triangulation from a single baseline; distances between stations could now be easily measured and a composite trilateration/triangulation could rapidly meet the surveyors' requirements. Two sets of Tellurometers were obtained before the year was out and Captain Irving was busy using them from H.M.S. *Vidal* in the West Indies in 1958. Among other ranges obtained were three long inter-island oversea paths from high points in Grenada, Tobago and Trinidad, the longest of which was about eighty-five nautical miles when the line of sight, required for Tellurometer measurements, was just skimming the surface of the sea at the mid-point.

On the domestic side we bought a family house at Wiveliscombe in Somerset, only ten miles from the Chart Printing Factory at Taunton. During the week I lived at my club, the Reform in Pall Mall, where for over fifty years I have remained the only member from the armed services, so that talking shop has not been one of my excesses there. At weekends I travelled by train to Taunton and, in those days, on by train to Wiveliscombe.

When my father retired to the family house in Collieston in Aberdeenshire he found the concrete pier, built in 1894 to protect the little harbour, in a ruinous state resulting from wartime neglect. He formed a local Amenities Committee to raise funds for its restoration and launched the first village Gala Day for that purpose in 1958.

Being responsible for the programmes of the surveying ships, I was able to arrange for a brief visit of H.M.S. *Scott*, under the command of Geoff Simeon, my old No. 1 from *Challenger* days, to Collieston on Gala Day. Boats took visitors out to the ship at anchor, the crew landed a diving display team and a skiffle group, and many came ashore to take part in the festivities. The day ended with free beer and a rollicking dance in the old Free Church Hall, culminating with the kissing and crowning of Miss Collieston by the ship's captain.

On 1st May 1958 I was invited to the Royal Society to hear the presentation by R. Stoneley F.R.S. of the lengthy paper which had finally resulted from the seismic measurements made by Tom Gaskell, Maurice Hill and John Swallow during *Challenger*'s world voyaging in 1950-1953.

The thickness of the sediment carpet of calcarious and silicious skeletons of countless millions of planktonic animals and plants had been found to differ greatly from one part of the ocean floor to another. In the Atlantic the thickness varied from 3,500 feet to practically nothing, whereas in the Pacific a carpet of about 1,500 feet was general.

Beneath the sediment, layers of rock continue downwards until the earth's true crust is reached about 36,000 feet below the surface of the sea. The meeting of these two provides a well-defined discontinuity which under the continents is not reached until nearly 100,000 feet has been penetrated. Such measurements seem to demonstrate that the earth's structure beneath the deep sea areas has always differed considerably from that under the great land masses.

Concluding the paper, the three former *Challenger* scientists recognised that their experiments had not been as comprehensive as they would have wished for, but they did provide a worldwide link between the work of others which had been more localised, and with many other seismic measurements which had been made at sea in the five years since *Challenger* was paid off for the last time.

The years 1957 to 1960 could be described as the 'Work Study Years' in the Royal Navy. Who was the instigator I never knew, but one was made aware of its importance at every turn to the extent that it became almost disloyal to question its efficiency.

A Work Study School was set up at Portsmouth where Commander Templeton-Cothill converted all who were sent as pupils, including myself. We thought that our most fertile field for the introduction of work study would be the printing works at Taunton, oblivious to the fact that at that time we had seven different printing trade unions under the umbrella of the Printing and Kindred Trades Federation, two of which, the Society of Lithographic Artists, Designers and Engravers (SLADE) and the National Association of Printers Operatives and Assistants (NATSOPA), had refused nationally to take any part in the monitoring and timing of technical activities which form the basis for further study. The substitution of 'method study' for 'work study' made little difference to the unions' attitude. Lieutenant Commander Weeks and Chief Petty Officer Hills struggled manfully to promote method study at Taunton, but I do not recall that a single process in the works was changed at that time as a result of their recommendations, although personally they were popular with the workers and Weeks is still remembered, when the cup he presented is skittled for annually by the various Sections within the Hydrographic Department – skittles, as opposed to ten pin bowling, being a popular West Country pub game.

When the team turned their attention to cartographic processes more progress was made. The advent of stable transparent plastic material gave them the opportunity to assess its value as a replacement for linen-backed paper on which to draw fair charts. The many thousands of soundings could now be traced on to the plastic directly from the collector tracing without resort to the laborious and meticulous use of sheets of transfer paper. The innovation was not initially welcomed at sea, for it seemed to undermine the traditional draughtsman's skills. However, the surveyors gradually realised that to draw neat and readable depth figures and to delineate coastal features clearly in this new medium required special skills. Ashore, the civil hydrographic officers welcomed the new transparent sheets as being more readily reproducible than the long established fair sheets.

During the two winters I worked in Whitehall I attended evening classes at St. Martin's Lane Art College where I painted comely nudes sprawled on paint-stained mattresses, or tried to draw shabby old men reclining in tattered armchairs. Not surprisingly my painting proved more successful than my drawing.

One Friday afternoon, when Admiral Collins had to leave early, and I was at a meeting, I left my country clothes in my office ready for a quick change and a dash to Paddington Station. I had also left a painting of a nude, of which I was rather proud, on my chart table. As I turned into the last corridor on the way back to my office I saw a merry little group of clerical staff gazing downwards. There was my canvas propped against the wall, and my cloth cap lying before it with a few pennies in it; a scrawled notice read, 'Four children and a wife to support.' Kechil had been up to his old tricks.

During 1957 I had the pleasure of attending the launching of three new Inshore Survey Vessels at different yards around the country. These craft, *Echo*, *Egeria* and *Enterprise*, of 150 tons displacement and 100 feet long, replaced ageing wartime motor launches and operated successfully for nearly thirty years as the Inshore Survey Squadron. Even today two of these vessels are still at sea as training vessels for the Marine Society.

The Annual Report of the Hydrographer of the Navy, which was said to be placed on the library table in the House of Commons, was of four brief pages and did little more than list the square miles of sounding completed by each of H.M. Surveying Ships during the past year. Known to us at sea as the 'acreage report', it was believed that the Hydrographer consulted each commanding officer's output when considering promotions!

I had long considered it a miserable document which would impress neither Members of Parliament nor taxpayers. Admiral Collins agreed with me, and in the 1957 presentation we made some modest improvements which included an illustration on the front cover of a Notice to Mariners block correction to the chart of Pemba Island resulting from a survey by H.M.S. *Owen*; we inserted a centre page world map showing the survey ships' activities, and a map of the work completed around the United Kingdom; and greater details were given of activities ashore and afloat, the Report running to eighteen pages. It was not impressive, but it was a start, and by 1960 the Report had become a well-illustrated and readable booklet with the first of the varying covers which reflect each year some interesting facet of the ever changing hydrographic scene.

After two years of feather-bedding I was ready to return to sea. I took command and commissioned H.M.S. *Dalrymple* at Plymouth on 9th July 1959.

Chapter XIX

Back to the Persian Gulf

Dalrymple was fitted with Two Range Decca, my first experience of this hydrographic fixing system. Our initial task, before leaving the U.K., was to carry out long distance trials to assess the extremes of range obtainable and whether accuracy was maintained at the greatest distances.

The two slave station crews proceeded to Cromer by road, where they established the stations and erected the masts near to each other. The ship arrived off Cromer on 22nd July 1959 and 'locked on' to the system. The convenient 'bump' formed by East Anglia would enable the ship to steam northwards off the East Coast as far as Peterhead whilst maintaining a clear seapath to the slave stations.

The object was for the ship to close the coast off various places on the way north where survey teams, having located triangulation stations, could fix the ship's position by theodolite intersections of the foremast whilst at the same time the Decca ranges from Cromer were recorded. As we steamed north visibility decreased, but we had anticipated this difficulty and were able to fix the ship by two simultaneous ranges from ship to shore stations using Tellurometers.

On completion of the trials the ship entered the Harbour of Refuge at Peterhead and secured to the single Admiralty mooring buoy maintained in that empty bay in those days before the offshore oil industry virtually took the anchorage over.

It was Bank Holiday weekend and there were a number of jollifications. Our soccer team, which was subsequently to win the Persian Gulf Trophy, made their debut against the prisoners in Peterhead Gaol where they were soundly beaten by these extremely fit men, despite vocal support for *Dalrymple* from all the prisoners along the touchline.

Mindful of the success of H.M.S. *Scott*'s visit only a year earlier, the Collieston Amenities Committee arranged motor coaches to transport sixty-five of *Dalrymple*'s people to the Village Hall for another rollicking dance. The Miss Collieston of 1958 had gone on to become Miss Scotland, so that the highlight of the evening was the crowning of a replacement.

Before sailing for the Persian Gulf we embarked Dr. Tom Allan of the Department of Geodesy and Geophysics, Cambridge, together with his assistant and his nuclear spin magnetometer. This instrument, which had been developed at Cambridge, when towed astern recorded the changing value of the earth's magnetic field and hence the magnetism of the rocks on or beneath the sea-bed. Thus a new tool became available to support seismic shooting in determining the nature of the ocean floor.

Arriving in the Red Sea we began to run transverse lines of magnetic recording and echo-sounding from the Arabian Coast on one side to the Egyptian and Sudanese coasts on the other. In hot and sticky weather we achieved sixteen traverses and recorded some extremely large magnetic anomalies as we passed over the central part of this great gash on the earth's surface. On arrival in Bahrein another scientist returned to Cambridge well satisfied with his work onboard a naval surveying ship.

The British Naval Base at Jufair was much extended since I was there in *Owen* ten years earlier and this, with a new fuelling wharf at Sitrah on Bahrein Island, combined to improve considerably the logistics for surveying in the Gulf.

A number of changes in the oil scene had taken place in the south-west part of the Gulf. Superior and International Marine, which had been awarded the concession off Qatar in 1948, had found little oil and relinquished their rights in 1952. The Ruler of Qatar had subsequently offered first option on the rights to the Shell Company and they had accepted, much to the annoyance of Anglo-Iranian who had in consequence had to move farther east into the waters of the State of Abu Dhabi.

In 1959 Shell had their headquarters in Doha and British Petroleum their field headquarters on the island of Das, and both were drilling far from land in areas requiring hydrographic attention. Our old friends the Qatar Petroleum Company were still exporting oil from Umm Said.

My Hydrographic Instructions were twofold. With the ship I was to extend from the recent work of H.M. surveying ships eastward into the area between

Jazirat Halul and Das. With the two surveying boats *Stork* and *Penguin* on detachment, I was to organise a survey of the coast and offshore islands eastwards from the southern end of the Qatar peninsula into the waters of Abu Dhabi. It was hoped that this work would reveal an inshore passage for British frigates operating in defence of the Trucial States.

By now I realised that I had an excellent team of surveyors onboard, led by the first lieutenant, Mike Baker, son of my hydrographic hero Buck, from whom he had inherited an outspoken, forthright attitude to life. The navigator was Lieutenant Commander Chester Read, a former submariner, but now an experienced surveyor with a captivating sense of humour. The surveying recorders were led by C.P.O. Cassam, a man of stature in both senses of the word, capable of taking his place in the field with the four junior surveying officers. I was eager to get to work with these men.

To cover the ship's sounding area Two Range Decca slave stations were to be erected on Jazirat Zarqa and at Umm Said. There were to be difficulties in establishing both stations.

At Zarqa a good site was found on the north-west side of the island, but the landing of the five tons of equipment and stores was a laborious business, every item having to be manhandled by the sailors from the surf boats across the shallow coral reef.

By 22nd October Green station was established and we left the crew of four men on this barren island, uninhabited except for friendly mice and unfriendly fleas, and a nightly influx of about a million Socotra cormorants. Except for a brief period over Christmas, when the men were airlifted by B.P. to Das, the crew remained, with only occasional replenishment, until 1st March the following year.

At Umm Said it was considered advisable to site Red slave within the Petroleum Company compound for security reasons. The only site available which was not subject to flooding was a large dome-shaped sand dune, and even with the use of a Company barge and their Land Rovers to ferry equipment to the summit, it was three days before the 100-foot mast and the two portable rondavel-type huts capped the crest of the dune.

The conductivity over sea water is constant, whilst that on land varies according to the nature of the surface. However close one was able to establish the slave stations to the coastline, an unknown discrepancy was introduced into the decometer readings onboard ship. This error was also likely to vary in different directions from the transmitting mast at the slave. It was therefore necessary to 'calibrate' each slave to assess the necessary correction to be

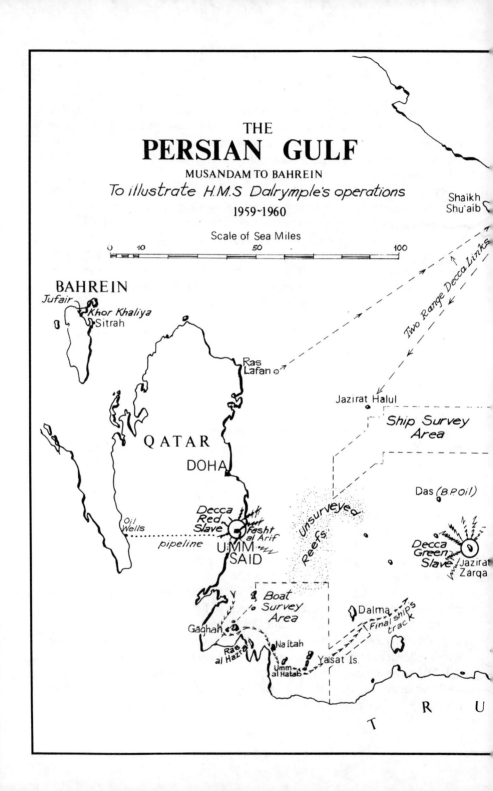

THE
PERSIAN GULF
MUSANDAM TO BAHREIN
To illustrate H.M.S Dalrymple's operations
1959~1960

Shaikh
Shu`aib

Scale of Sea Miles

0   10   50   100

Two Range Decca Links

BAHREIN
Jufair
Khor Khaliya
Sitrah

Ras
Lafan

Jazirat Halul

**Ship Survey
Area**

QATAR

DOHA

Das *(B.P.Oil)*

Oil
Wells

Decca
Red
Slave

pipeline

Fasht
al Arif

UMM
SAID

Unsurveyed
Reefs

Decca
Green
Slave Jazirat
Zarqa

**Boat
Survey
Area**

Dalma

Final ship's
track

Gaghah

Ras
al Hazra

Na'tah

Yalsat Is.

Umm
al Hatab

T   R   U

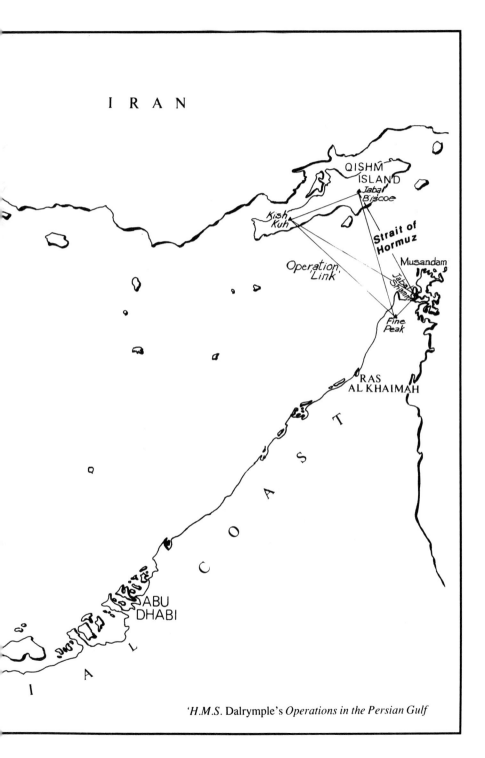

I R A N

QISHM ISLAND

Jabal Biscoe

Kish Kuh

Strait of Hormuz

Musandam

Operation Link

Jabal Shamm

Fine Peak

RAS AL KHAIMAH

C O A S T

ABU DHABI

'*H.M.S.* Dalrymple's *Operations in the Persian Gulf*

applied to the 'lane', or range circles, scribed on the sheet on which the ship's sounding progress would be plotted. Calibration was achieved by slowly steaming the ship around the arc over which the slave was to be used at a distance of about ten miles, during which Tellurometer distances were taken from ship to slave at every ten degrees change of bearing.

Once the calibrations were complete and the plotting sheet was ready for bridge use, ship sounding could begin. This should then have been plain sailing, but there were no means of identifying which lane the ship was locked into unless one was able to get a good fix by other means at the time of locking on. Once 'locked on' changing atmospheric and meteorological conditions, such as the onset of heavy showers frequent during shamal weather, or the unstable conditions at sunset or sunrise, could cause one or more lanes to be slipped. Sometimes this was made apparent by a sideways shift between one fix and another when the ship had remained on a steady course, or by excessive flickering of the needles in the decometers.

Surveyors who had used Two Range Decca had told me that it made ship sounding 'so boring' when compared with sextant and station pointer fixing. I found it to be more frustrating than boring; one had to be constantly on the alert for a lane slip; even if noticed one could not tell how many lanes had been lost and it was often necessary to steam many miles to one of the reference beacons we had laid in order to lock on again. Nevertheless, accurately positioned sounding far out of sight of land would not have been possible without Two Range Decca; its increasing use by sea surveyors marked a major technological advance.

Whenever the ship was sounding in the Halul-Das area it was necessary to maintain a record of the rise and fall of the tide, so that suitable reductions could be applied to our soundings to reduce them to chart datum. Fortunately, a solitary Indian meteorologist was maintained by the oil companies on Halul Island and so we established our resident tidewatcher there to keep him company. We alerted him by radio whenever we required tide readings to be taken.

Once the slave stations had been established the sounding boats were available for inshore work. At the end of October I steamed southwards through the area surveyed by *Owen* in the previous season to Gäghah Island, on which a party was established with *Penguin*, their object being to extend from *Owen*'s triangulation through the islands to the east. Another party with the Land Rover was established at Ras al Hazra on the mainland of Abu Dhabi for a similar purpose. We were able to land the vehicle in an inflatable raft supplied at Plymouth for such use. It was a prototype designed for the Royal Yacht *Britannia* when landing the regal car when an alongside berth was not available.

When he had completed the work on the mainland, Geoff Hope, the enthusiastic surveyor in charge, was to join up with the party on Gäghah, taking the Land Rover with him by raft. Some days later I received his signal – 'Regret to report floor of raft tore open when transferring Land Rover to Gäghah. Land Rover now lies in 6 fathoms. The vehicle is buoyed.'

Only the last sentence was good news. We relinquished ship sounding and I took *Dalrymple* slowly in through a passage sounded out by *Penguin* to anchor as near as I could to the sunken vehicle.

A frogman diver reported that the Land Rover was sitting erect on its four wheels, as if ready to drive away down a gentle slope; a giant red snapper had taken up residence under the canvas canopy.

We were able to secure beacon flotation drums by wires to the four corners of the main frame and by towing ahead with *Penguin* the Land Rover, witnessed by the frogman, trundled forward down the slope and became waterborne about forty feet below the surface as the snapper swam out. Back alongside the ship it was a simple, if lengthy, task to hoist the vehicle back onboard with the main derrick. The engine and the electrics were stripped by our engineers, and, with the help of spares obtained from the Naval Base at Bahrein, the Land Rover was, surprisingly, soon roadworthy again.

I advised the Admiralty that some further research and development of the raft appeared to be required before committing the royal Rolls to the deep.

Whilst salvage operations were in progress the triangulation which had been completed by the detached parties was balanced and plotted onboard. I was able to establish a two boat camp party on Gäghah to begin the sounding of the channels through the islands to the eastwards before leaving the area.

Until 1959 the two triangulation networks on either side of the Persian Gulf had never been connected, so that ships' navigators, when changing their fixes from one set of coastal features to the other, might experience an apparent shift in position of up to three miles. The need to remedy this state of affairs had recently become even more urgent as the Persian Gulf Lighting Service was about to establish a Decca Navigation chain with stations on either side of the Gulf. I had been instructed to attempt a closure between the two networks across the Strait of Hormuz, the narrow entrance to the Gulf.

About the time that I was in *Owen* in the Persian Gulf (1948-1949) the Indian Government, which had maintained the necessary lighthouses and lightships for Persian Gulf navigation, turned this increasingly burdensome task over to the British Government which had a major interest in the growing oil industry. The British formed the Persian Gulf Lights Board with representatives from the appropriate shipping and oil companies; resulting from their deliberations the Persian Gulf Lighting Service was born. By 1954 a base had been constructed at Bahrein and a light-tender, built on the Clyde, was operational. Named *Relume*, the ship was manned by British officers with an Iranian crew. The master was Commander Charles Russell, a retired naval navigation specialist to whom I had remained indebted since 1947 when, as Training Officer in Chatham Barracks, he had found me an office and classroom within his domain for the infant Hydrographic Training Unit.

In the late 1950s the Lighting Service, strengthened by light dues paid by an increasing number of oil tankers sailing Gulf waters, was busy maintaining well over 100 lights and buoys. Just before our arrival in *Dalrymple* the Lighting Service had decided to install two Decca Navigation chains.

The south side of the Strait of Hormuz is composed of high, bare sun-parched mountains frequented by allegedly fiercely independent tribesmen who carried their own version of an alpenstock, both as a weapon and as a climbing aid: the north side of the Strait is bounded by Qishm Island with mountains of a lesser height.

On Sunday 15th November Chester Read, Geoff Hope and Cassam landed with a small party of recorders to be based in a camp near Ras al Khaimah. Here they were met by Mr. Derham of Qatar Petroleum Company, who had established a dump of fuel for the use of a helicopter, provided for a week by the Consortium Oil Company.

'Operation Link' had been broken down into two phases; the first consisting of a Tellurometer and theodolite traverse from the most northerly station in the Trucial Coast triangulation (TC22), situated on a watch tower two miles south of Ras al Khaimah, in order to close an existing gap between it and Fine Peak (4,130 feet) and Jabal Shamm (2,709 feet), two stations in H.M.S. *Ormonde's* triangulation of 1930-1931, at the north end of the Musandam Peninsula over thirty miles away.

Owing to a series of razor-backed ridges affecting the Tellurometer readings close below the line of sight Fine Peak to TC22, a ship station, with the vessel moored head and stern, had to be used to complete the traverse.

The second phase of the operation entailed observing the angles and the lengths of the sides of the quadrilateral contained by the stations on Fine Peak and Jabal Shamm and Kish Kuh and Jabal Biscoe, two stations in the Anglo-Iranian Oil Company triangulation of 1949-1951 on Qishm Island.

Despite manning these four stations for two whole days, hazy conditions across the Strait of Hormuz prevented either theodolite or Tellurometer observations before the helicopter had to return to oil company duties.

To describe the difficulties encountered by the surveyors on the mountains I cannot do better than quote from Chester Read's account of events:-

'On the first arrival of the helicopter in the afternoon we attempted a helicopter recce of Fine Peak, but found it cloud covered. The pilot, seeking to engender confidence in himself and machine, and so as not to waste the entire mission, took us out over the open sea to demonstrate 'auto-rotation', the procedure in the event of the single engine failing. To this day, I remember my acute unease as he switched off the engine and we plummetted like a stone towards the waters of Hormuz from 5,000 feet. And this was despite having the benefit of briefing via the intercom of the pilot's intentions. My surveying recorder, Gilligan, in the rear of the cockpit had no such knowledge and, failing to interpret my distraught gestures of reassurance, he thought his last moments had come. Only after we landed back at Ras al Khaimah (having dispersed goats and camels in all directions on the approach) did it emerge that he had never flown before in any type of aircraft.

On the first full day, we 'landed' near the peak (the correct description is, I think, a 'wheel touch') and this with me standing on the external step of the machine and directing the pilot 'back a bit' or 'right a foot' over the headset intercom. When I finally stepped off onto terra firma, it was to find I had forgotten to take off the headset and I was near suspended by its cord.

The day and its first observations passed uneventfully and successfully, and the take off seemed satisfactory in mid-afternoon until the ashen-faced pilot confided that we had 'fallen off' Fine Peak rather than lifted off. Apparently the increase of humidity during the day, together with our altitude, caused much decreased lift from the rotor. Because of this danger, the pilot determined on a two stage approach to and from the peak in future.

Accordingly, next day, the machine put down an a patchily cultivated plateau about a thousand feet below the summit, and I off loaded with half the gear, whilst the pilot went on to put down Gilligan on the Peak with the remainder. I suddenly felt very lonely and vulnerable as the helicopter dwindled into the height and distance, and in light of all we had been briefed upon concerning the mountain men and their axes. My concern was to say the least, sharpened by whoops and yells from figures converging in leaps and bounds from nearby mountain sides. I unholstered the clumsy Naval issue revolver from my waist, but I don't think that it ever occurred to me that I might actually have to shoot anyone with it. And this was especially so as they got closer, and I realised that the twenty or so of them were all women. Gathered round me, they jabbered and shrieked incomprehensibly and excitedly, and tested between forefinger and thumb the quality of my brief tropical clothing – and eyed my dangled revolver with covetous recognition. How, I wondered, would this pinching progress? Would I be ill mannered in Arabic terms if I did not pinch them back? And what would be my captain's reaction if I confessed to 'giving' my revolver to a pack of women? (Not to mention a Tellurometer etc.)

Fortunately, such horrid conjecture was curtailed by the clatter of the returning helicopter, echoing and re-echoing across the ravines and steep mountain sides. The ladies scattered excitedly to a safer distance as it approached and touched down. When the pilot throttled back the rotor to idling, a few of the bolder ones came back to assist me in loading the gear.

For the benefit of the ex-R.A.F. pilot, I extended to them a leisurely and even affectionate farewell, in what I hoped was nonchalant R.N. fashion reflecting such an everyday encounter.

The ladies for their part, were ill rewarded for their interest. As the throttles went forward and the down draught increased for take off, they were scattered with their flimsy garments – not always in correct attachment – across the scorched plateau like a large scale and highly coloured kaleidoscope, glimpsed through a dust storm and gesticulating angrily.

Arrived at Fine Peak and re-united with Gilligan and the gear, I looked across the arcs to the south over blue, brown and purple ridges of mountain and ravine, and to the north the almost sheer drop of over 4,000 feet to the sea below. No one, I concluded, could approach up this cliff, and I would have ample warning and view of other directions. Accordingly I removed the unwieldy webbing and revolver and laid it upon a convenient rock out of the way of the surveying operation. Shortly afterwards, eyes glued to electronic distant prospects in the visor of the Tellurometer, I was startled to hear, and then turn to see, Gilligan greeting a pair of hands and a bearded face which had appeared over the impossible cliff edge. As the rest of this agile mountaineer followed, it came as little surprise to note that he was carrying a long-handled and exceedingly sharp looking axe – the raison d'être for the revolver so uselessly distant. Would he perhaps be followed by chums? And all out for vengeance for the awful dishonour to their ladies on the plateau below?

Happily, not so. The sole tribesman was incoherently affable, noisily interested, albeit very disappointed at the 'picture' on the Tellurometer. The upside down figures in the theodolite were more amusing to him, but his real bonus came when, on being offered a Rowntree's wine gum, he took the whole box as a naturally offered present and disappeared back down the cliff from whence he had come. Perhaps to this day, he and his ladies talk of this visitation and crave wine gums in the mountain fastness of Musandam.'

Admiration for *Ormonde*'s surveyors who had scaled Fine Peak with their theodolite back in 1930 was widely expressed.

Almost exactly a year later *Dalrymple* was back at Ras al Khaimah with Mr. Derham again providing a fuel dump, this time for two helicopters. Aided by an Iranian naval liaison officer and clear visibility, Operation Link II was successful, and the triangulation networks on both sides of the Gulf were finally harmonised.

As we were receiving such generous hospitality from the oil people at Umm Said and Das Island, I thought that we should do something to reciprocate, and suggested to the ship's company that a concert party should be raised.

Fifteen volunteers for the show and five for a skiffle group were soon forthcoming. I acted as entrepreneur and E.R.A. Watt was the producer. Time was short, but talent was not lacking; songs were written, sketches were devised and costumes created for our rehearsals onboard. I had with me my grass skirts and Polynesian records and found that my hula appeared to be as popular in the Gulf as it had been at the Naval Ball in Wellington.

Our first performance was at the cinema in the naval base at Jufair. Unfortunately, our anchor man, a stoker who claimed long experience in naval 'concert party work', took one large whisky too many before the performance and when introducing in humorous style the third turn of the evening 'dried up', despite loudly whispered advice from the two prompters, who finally had to drag him from the stage, passing this struggle off as part of the show. For the rest of the evening we had to improvise his comic continuity role while he quietly wept offstage. 'That's show business,' we said as we accepted his resignation.

A week later the show was at Umm Said in a fine open air theatre with a running buffet and bar for the performers behind the stage; a fortnight after that we were with B.P. on Das where an open air theatre had been constructed specially for the occasion.

Before leaving Plymouth I had persuaded an able seaman to embark his expensive set of drums which I believed could be an asset; and so indeed they now were. The first lieutenant was not enamoured with the concert party and its requests for the rigging of a stage and screens on the quarterdeck for rehearsals; nor did he look favourably upon the drummer who, even if he caught the last boat off after the show, often failed to bring his precious drums for which a boat had to be sent inshore at dawn before the ship sailed.

The concert party reached its apogee during a brief visit by the ship to Karachi for a Christmas break. On the evening of Boxing Day we were able to stage two separate shows simultaneously at the prestigious Gymkhana Club and the popular Boat Club; both offered generous hospitality to the players and our supporters from the ship.

No. 1 did not conceal his pleasure when the drums had been retrieved for the last time, the costumes disposed of and the troubadours disbanded.

By mid-December the detached party on Gäghah had achieved the target I had set them, to sound out the channels and delineate the coastline as far as the narrow strait of Na Itah. They were withdrawn with the intention of establishing another camp to the eastward in the New Year 1960. We had selected the small island of Umm al Hatab for this camp and to reach it I took the ship into the uncharted area between Dalma and the Yasat islands.

My aim here was to pass south of the Yasat group and then to make my way north-westwards to Hatab. Shortly after we were committed to this plan, thick fog descended and we had to rely on the echo-sounder and the radar to make our way onwards. The ship passed over one hair-raising patch of four fathoms rising abruptly from a general depth of seventeen fathoms. We reached Hatab as the fog cleared.

Although the small island rose to only about fifteen feet above high water, the terrain seemed suitable for a camp. A two boat detached party under the navigator, Chester Read, using four tents, was established. The two surveying boats, having lifted ashore a copious quantity of stores and fuel, were lying at their newly laid moorings on the south-east side of the island by nightfall and the ship returned to the sounding area south of Halul early next morning.

About this time Mr. Godfrey, general manager of Shell at Doha, invited me to take a flight in one of his helicopters over the reefs where our boats were working, and through which it was eventually hoped to navigate the ship; such aerial reconnaissances over reef-strewn areas are invaluable.

Towards the end of January the fierceness of shamal weather was demonstrated. Somewhat to my dismay a Danforth[1] type anchor had been substituted for an Admiralty pattern anchor as *Dalrymple*'s port bower before we left Plymouth. Whilst lying to this anchor on the survey ground one night during a shamal, the ship began to drag before coming up 'all standing'. More cable was veered and the ship lay relatively comfortably until dawn when, on weighing, one fluke of the Danforth was found to be broken off entirely and the other badly cracked.

A couple of weeks later when the ship lay alongside in Doha to allow the officers and men to accept hospitality from Shell, Captain Dunn of the Marine Department of the company lent me a thirty-hundredweight Admiralty pattern anchor to replace my virtually useless Danforth. As any seaman would, I had felt extremely naked with only one serviceable bower anchor.

Perhaps this is the place to record the generous co-operation which many oil companies in the Persian Gulf, including Qatar Petroleum, Shell and B.P., extended to Royal Navy surveying ships charting the waters of the Gulf during the twenty-five years following World War II.

With the partial failure of Operation Link I, I was faced early in 1960 with a requirement to provide co-ordinates for a site proposed for a Decca Navigator station to be erected for the Persian Gulf Lighting Service on the island of Shaikh Shu'aib off the Iranian coast. These co-ordinates would have to be in harmony with the Trucial Coast co-ordinates which were to be used to locate stations at Doha, Das and Abu Dhabi.

---

[1] The Danforth anchor which was said to give greater holding power for a given weight was introduced in the Royal Navy in 1949. It resembled a lightly built stockless anchor, both in appearance and method of operating, but had a small stock which passed through its crown which prevented the anchor from rolling when its flukes dug into the bottom.

I was informed that a large wooden beacon had been established by Decca employees to mark the site on Shaikh Shu'aib; so, locking on to the Two Range Decca close east of Ras Lafan the ship steamed northwards across the Gulf. On arrival off the island no beacon was to be seen; only a large single tree and a tower in the nearby village, the inhabitants of which may have coveted Decca's timber, were conspicuous. These were fixed by intersecting gyro compass bearings as the ship steamed back and forth half a mile offshore carefully recording Two Range Decca readings.

Back southwards we then steamed to the vicinity of Halul, where we were able to find that, happily, there had been no lane slip during the round trip to the Iranian shore. Reasonable co-ordinates for the tree and the tower, compatible with those in use for the other Decca stations, were thus made available.

By the end of January the camp party on Hatab had completed the complex triangulation as far as the Yasat islands, and in two days of a furious shamal Chester Read and Cassam, windbound in their shuddering tents, managed to complete the computations necessary to balance the triangulation.

All was now ready to make the plotting sheet onboard when the ship arrived off Hatab for a fleeting visit to revictual the camp. As the ship passed the Yasat islands on the way back to her survey ground, a tidewatching party of two was established there to supply daily tide records by radio to the sounding teams on Hatab, and to delineate the coastlines of the islands.

I had been warned by letter from the Hydrographer that a work study team would arrive onboard during the season to look into the cleaning and maintenance of the hull section of Dampier class surveying ships, in particular *Dalrymple*. Why we had been singled out was not apparent; perhaps because I had been involved with the imposition of work study while assisting Admiral Collins he had decided to put me on the receiving end for a change.

We had relegated this threat to the back of our minds as we pressed on with the survey. In the New Year came a signal from the Admiralty – *Dalrymple* was to receive an electrical officer, Lieutenant Commander Boadle, together with C.P.O. Hills, fresh from his struggles at Taunton, and a chief mechanician, as a work study team.

They were very soothing on arrival, informing everyone that their early weeks would be spent in observing; recommendations would come later. The boatswain took the offensive, voicing the view that the traditional manner of detailing off the hands at 'Both Watches' at 0730 daily was the way to send men to their employment, doubling them away to the task allotted to them at the strident commands of the chief bosun's mate (the Buffer). The boatswain was therefore surprised after a week or two when the work study team confronted him with a record of where every one of his men had actually spent his working hours.

One particular seaman, whose sandals were in an advanced state of disrepair, had spent most of his working hours sitting on the heads reading comics. C.P.O. Hills checked his presence there every half hour, identifying him by his sandals which he could see through the gap beneath the heads' door. Other less conspicuous loafers were identified and the boatswain reluctantly agreed to the recommendation. Every seaman reporting for work would receive a job card prepared by the Buffer, using a complex and impressive progress board installed in his 'office', previously his 'come in handy' store. The job card set out in detail the task which was to be achieved, the time it should take, and the tools and materials which the rating would have to draw and sign for before commencing work.

I cannot recall whether efficiency was improved; I can only remember that men working on deck, in all but the calmest weather, either lost their job card overboard or returned it, signed and completed, in such a sodden or mangled state that it was unworthy of taking its place on the prized progress board.

I do not recall either how the chief mechanician of the team got on, but I expect he found the daily allocation of work to each of the stokers by the chief stoker from the cosiness of his office, a system evolved since the early days of steam, more akin to modern methods than 'Both Watches of the Hands'.

In order to return hospitality to our good friends at Umm Said, the ship's company decided to give a children's party, and the officers a cocktail party, onboard. The date turned out to be well chosen, the 19th February 1960.

Just as the guests were arriving for the cocktail party the signalman showed me an Admiralty general message – Her Majesty had given birth to a son. I ordered the firing of a twenty-one gun salute with champagne openings which got the party off to a fizzing start. Next day as we steamed out along the approach channel we fired the salute with our ancient saluting guns, followed by 'Splice the Main Brace'. We did our best to launch a future Royal Naval officer, Prince Andrew.

As there were a number of surveying tasks to be undertaken on the way home to Plymouth, where the ship was due by mid-May, we had to start gathering in the widely scattered camp parties.

Green slave on Zarqa presented the most formidable embarkation problem and the ship arrived there on 1st March which had dawned clear and calm.

I adopted a method similar to that employed at Malden Island. Two mooring buoys were laid in deep water clear of the reef edge from which grass lines were run to holdfasts high on the beach. First, the whole of the equipment forming the slave station and the associated huts had to be manhandled across the coral flats to the surf boats on the reef; when loaded, each boat was hauled by the crew hand over hand along the grass line until the mooring buoys were reached, whence the motor cutter towed them to the ship. A team of thirty men from all departments embarked by this means five tons in five hours and the ship was underway by nightfall in a rising north-westerly shamal.

Next we proceeded to Hatab to embark the camp party from the lee side of the island. As soon as Chester Read came aboard he was despatched downwind in the motor cutter to recover the tidewatcher, who had been camped on the Yasat islands for over a month.

Whilst the ship was still embarking the camp party gear, Chester sent a signal to report that the motor cutter was making water in very heavy weather in the head sea on its way back to the ship, whilst Able Seaman Wallis, a surveying recorder who had been the tidewatcher, was suffering acute stomach pains. Read had turned back to await the ship in the shelter of the Yasat islands.

Surgeon Lieutenant Williams was despatched in *Stork* with drugs for Wallis and seasick pills for himself. I gave orders to raise steam for full speed and an hour later the ship was on her way.

Off the southern tip of Yasat there was sufficient lee to hoist the boats, and as Doc had already made known the seriousness of his patient's condition the ship was soon speeding for Doha, where it was planned to send Wallis into one of the most modern hospitals in the world.

Soon after 1900 that evening the doctor decided that his patient was deteriorating so rapidly that he must operate at once – the first operation that the young man had performed on his own. I informed a surprised paymaster sub-lieutenant that the doctor had chosen him as his anaesthetist, a task he would perform by dropping chloroform onto a mask over the patient's face.

The sick-berth attendant had already prepared the operating table and the four main actors in this drama were locked in the sick bay by 2000.

The ship battered on through the windy night, cutting corners round the reefs so recently surveyed. Slowly the smell of chloroform pervaded the ship, even to the open bridge where the navigator and I were peering into the blustery darkness. To my nostrils the smell became so overpowering that twice I descended to the sick bay flat for news, but all was locked and silent. The awful truth dawned on me: so much chloroform had been used that the whole team had passed out, while the patient was dying a slow death. I must do something before it was too late.

For the third time I went to the sick bay flat. As I reached the foot of the last ladder I saw Able Seaman Walkner in the passageway, his body bent and eye glued to a tiny hole left inadvertently in the sickbay bulkhead by the dockyard. 'Stop breathing your foul germs into the operating theatre,' I cried. 'Get to hell out of here!' As soon as Walkner was out of sight I clapped my own eye to the hole. My relief was immense. There, like a scene on television, the operating theatre lay before my gaze, illuminated by hospital floodlights. The three men in white caps, masks and smocks beavered about their business; Doc was threading a needle, there was a glimpse of the open wound, all was going according to plan – only the patient was asleep.

An hour later Williams was on the bridge. 'Here it is, Sir.' He had the burst appendix in a small bottle which he waved triumphantly.

I descended for the fourth time that night to join the operating team for a cup of tea and a can of beer, as we sat round the slowly waking patient. From time to time he half rose from the waist to pour abuse upon his tormentors who quietly pushed him down again.

Nearly thirty years later I met Wallis at a hydrographic conference in Amsterdam. He was then the Government hydrographic surveyor for the State of Qatar. He informed me that the luxurious hospital in Doha where we sent him to convalesce had now been replaced by an even finer one.

Having completed the recovery of Red slave at Umm Said, we sailed southward to the edge of *Owen*'s 1958/1959 survey, and next day began a final passage through the inshore route which our surveyors had opened up from Gäghah, through the narrow Na Itah strait, past Hatab to the southern end of the Yasat islands, then north-eastwards along a three-mile-wide channel which the ship had surveyed to Dalma Island and deep water charted by *Owen* in 1952 – a total distance of sixty-five miles.

There had been criticism in recent years that sea surveyors finding uncharted reefs in Gulf waters were giving them names of no local significance. On this final voyage I was able to take with me an experienced dhow naukhada, or skipper, to help me assign the proper names; he spent much time with me on the bridge, one of our Somalis interpreting, although the exigencies of Ramadan curtailed many of our discussions. My final conviction was that the so-called 'correct names' were difficult to come by, for different names are used for the same features depending on what part of the coast the dhow master comes from, whilst many of the smallest reefs, although known to the Arabs and widely avoided, remain nameless.

My hours with the naukhada brought to my mind how few Bedu I had encountered compared with ten years ago. These wild, generous people whom we used to meet in the desert in 1949 had, with their love of money, been tempted into the oil camps. Here they had exchanged their rifles, with which they were highly skilled, for shovels and spanners, and their headcloths and Arab shirts for hard hats and overalls, whilst their unshod feet were forced into rubber working boots. They had become unskilled labourers and the desert was empty as never before. Only at Ras al Khaimah and in the Musandum peninsula, where oil had not yet been found, did we find the Bedu still widely dispersed.

As the ship neared the Strait of Hormuz at the start of our passage home, I received a signal informing me that I was to come ashore on arrival in U.K. to take up the post of Assistant Hydrographer (1) at Cricklewood, handing over command of *Dalrymple* to Mike Baker.

So that was to be the last time I would conduct a survey in the Persian Gulf which, with its vast areas of unsurveyed water, its countless uncharted reefs and unmapped islands, presented an imposing challenge to the commander of a survey ship. We had often had twenty-five men in the field in four or five detached parties, each in daily radio contact with the ship, each contributing to the overall progress of the survey and each officer or man in charge relying every day upon his own initiative and ability.

To plan, organise and orchestrate such widely spread operations had been my privilege and one which I was most reluctant to relinquish.

Chapter XX

Deskbound

I became Assistant Hydrographer (1) a few weeks before Rear Admiral Irving took over from Collins as Hydrographer on 7th July 1960. I found myself back in the Cricklewood building where I took my seat at the desk in the room, overlooking the coal yard, which Admiral Wyatt had vacated ten years earlier.

My appointment was to be an exceptionally long one of three years duration; I felt some affinity with Captain Cook when he was appointed to the captaincy of the Royal Greenwich Hospital on his return from his second voyage to the Pacific. To his old master, John Walker of Whitby, he wrote, *'My fate drives me from one extreme to another a few Months ago the whole Southern hemisphere was hardly big enough for me and now I am going to be confined within the limits of Greenwich Hospital.'*

My wife found for me a bedsitter on the ground floor of an old terrace house near Kilburn Underground station; a corner of the room had been converted to a small kitchen with gas cooker; French windows opened onto a derelict garden. At week-ends I travelled by car to Wiveliscombe, a journey of five hours in those days, which commenced each Friday evening with a major traffic jam on the North Circular Road.

My job was concerned with the preparation of Hydrographic Instructions for the ships and the close study of the fair charts resulting therefrom; I was responsible for supervising the work of the naval sections – Notices to Mariners, Tides, Sailing Directions and Oceanography; whilst all the time I had to work closely with Mr. Atherton, the Chief Civil Hydrographic Officer. He was a large, somewhat ponderous man of long cartographic experience, slow to make decisions, but I valued his counsel. He was in charge of seven geographical sections, each under the direction of a principal civil hydrographic officer. Every survey or plan received in the office, from H.M. ships or other sources, was first sent to the appropriate section for close examination. A weekly climax was reached when the heads of the geographical sections brought the newly received work to my office, together with their recommendations for the use of the material – N to M, a new edition or a new chart. We were gathered, together with Mr. Atherton, to meet the Hydrographer who arrived from Whitehall to 'Take the Work'. He listened to each recommendation and when a decision was made he entered it in the 'Work Book', a tradition of long standing.

Life in the office began quietly, but once Egg Irving got into his stride things became more lively; interesting visitors began to arrive, more exciting projects were to be planned. By 1962 a seaborne gravimeter had finally been devised, augmenting the echo-sounder, seismic equipment and the magnetometer in the weaponry available for investigating the nature of the ocean floor. The survey ships *Owen* and *Dalrymple* were provided with these instruments for their participation in the International Indian Ocean Expedition for which, once again, scientists from the Department of Geodesy and Geophysics at Cambridge were embarked. Some of *Owen*'s work tended to confirm the theory, long held by geologists, that the eastward tilted continent of Africa extended beneath the waters of the Indian Ocean. The '*Owen* Fracture Zone' began to appear as a major feature on charts and geological maps.

The advent of deep-diving submarines and the increasing difficulty of finding them from anti-submarine vessels began to highlight the importance of oceanography in the defence field, particularly with regard to the changing patterns of temperature layer depths in the sea and the reflectivity of the ocean floor.

A temporary escape from Cricklewood was provided not infrequently by meetings of the Cartographic Committee of NATO, on which served military chart and map makers from each of the Allied nations. Mr. Atherton or I attended the meetings where we discussed at length the establishment of complex specifications for all manner of thematic graphics which would be required on the outbreak of war. I travelled widely to attend these gatherings in Oslo, Copenhagen, The Hague, Paris, Hamburg, Genoa and Florence; as our hosts in each location took us sightseeing during non-working periods, these visits were tantamount for me to the Grand Tour of earlier days.

For both CENTO and NATO meetings I went each year to Istanbul and on by DC3 over the bumpy mountains to Ankara. This capital was not renowned for nightlife but the committee members, including a large United States delegation, usually attended a dinner dance at the leading hotel. One night the band struck up Chubby Checker's 'Let's Twist Again'. Top of the Pops in Europe, Chubby's fame had not yet reached Asia Minor; no one took the floor until I persuaded a U.S. Embassy wife to join me. By the end of the evening everyone was twisting and the orchestra were wilting.

Returning from Ankara I used to spend a day with Admiral Akoglu, the Turkish Hydrographer, in his office at Çubuklu on the eastern side of the Bosphorus, which we crossed by boat at midday for a few rakis and a superb seafood lunch in the company of this charming man of long hydrographic experience.

Admiral Irving was extremely active, and finally successful, in persuading the Admiralty Board that new survey ships required to be custom built for an increased oceanographic role, and to merchant ship specifications, rather than naval, to reduce the size of complements required to operate them. Once Egg had got these principles established, plans for a new class of Hecla ocean survey ships began to move ahead.

During the whole of my time at Cricklewood Lord Carrington was First Lord of the Admiralty, and a very good friend to the Hydrographic Department he proved to be. By 1962 he was already deeply engaged in the formulation of the Polaris programme, and so it came about that I was informed one day by the Director of Publicity (Royal Navy) that I was to receive Chapman Pincher of the *Daily Express* for an interview on the charting requirements for Polaris submarines. I was alarmed at the prospect as the Polaris project was subject to considerable secrecy at that time; I gave the matter much thought.

When Chapman Pincher arrived in my office I had with me the current holder of the post of S.O.B., Desmond Scott, extremely well read in oceanographic matters. Mr. Pincher readily agreed that Scott might monitor our conversation and that if I let slip any matter of high security he would point this out and Chapman would delete it from his notes. The interview passed off easily with Desmond spotting no breaches of security, whilst Chapman Pincher was well satisfied. Next morning the *Daily Express* carried a feature article headed by a sinister black and white representation of a Polaris submarine breaking surface. Although no secrets were revealed, a casual glance at the piece gave the impression that I had made some important revelations.

Lord Carrington, pleased with what he read, got his secretary to telephone the First Sea Lord for information about me. It appears that, without studying the article in detail, the First Sea Lord assumed that I had been responsible for a breach of security and ordered the Hydrographer to institute an enquiry which,

Egg informed me by telephone, would take place next day; I went home to my apartment for a sleepless night.

At 0930 next day Egg was on the line. 'Steve,' he said, 'you won't believe this. I was at a reception in Whitehall last night when Lord Carrington came up to me and enquired "Who's this fellow Ritchie? He and Chapman Pincher did a good job for the Navy in this morning's *Daily Express.*"'

Not long after this Lord Carrington came to Cricklewood; Admiral Irving had convinced him that it was high time that a compilation office should be built alongside the Printing Works at Creechbarrow, Taunton, where the Admiralty had held the necessary land since 1938. Egg was abroad when Lord Carrington made a quick inspection of the Cricklewood facilities. 'I'll land by helicopter at Creechbarrow at 1030 to-morrow. Meet me there,' said he, and I set out by road for Taunton. The following day the First Lord took a look at the Printing Works and then I showed him the extent of the available land. 'Such a division of effort between Taunton and London is ridiculous,' he said, and within a few days he gave the order for the planning of a new building at Creechbarrow to begin.

As the publishers of my book *Challenger* had suggested to me that another manuscript would be welcome, I decided soon after taking up residence in Kilburn that I would eschew London life and employ my evenings in writing a history of the Surveying Service in the nineteenth century. The bedsitter was quiet and conditions ideal for writing, except when the landlady, who occupied an adjacent room to mine, received her commercial travelling gentleman. The first two or three evenings would pass off peacefully, their amorous exchanges the murmuring of doves; there would follow on subsequent nights a rising torrent of dissent and shouted abuse, culminating with the banging of doors and a sudden stillness as the lover stamped out into the night for another two or three weeks on the road. In three years of these fluctuating conditions I was able to complete *The Admiralty Chart.*

Whilst at Cricklewood I was able to broaden my dancing experience into the field of ballet. I was induced to take the leading role of charlady in a show for the Christmas Party in a nearby dancehall. The ballet, *Office Cleaners*, was choreographed and produced by Eric Parrot, a civil hydrographic officer of tubby aspect and an enthusiastic balletomane. He rehearsed us relentlessly in the double basement in our lunch breaks, taking us through the steps he had devised with the adroitness and the sensitivity of Frederick Ashton himself.

One day when at my desk I received a phone call from Rosa, a former leading seaman in the Fijian Navy who had sailed with me in *Lachlan*. For some reason the Colonial Office had recently disbanded the Fijian Navy, dispensing with the services of many of the men to whom we had given sea experience in *Lachlan*. The British Army, aware of the fighting potential of such men, sent out a recruiting team. Rosa and eight other former sailors were now stationed in Aldershot undergoing training as parachute troops. They felt lonely and wished to have some contact with those in England who knew their country.

I invited them to visit our home in Wiveliscombe where we had already entertained from time to time Mairama Suvaki, a female Fijian probation officer training in Taunton, and a Fijian prison officer on a course in Bristol.

Under Mairama's directions my wife used to make for our guests ikan vakalolo, a dish of fried fish on spinach with coconut milk, popular in our family to this day.

Since we came to Wiveliscombe the annual Catholic fête had been staged in our grounds at Sharpe House to raise funds for the building of a new church. Father Formosa, our Maltese priest, and one of the truest Christians I have known, had an unbounded enthusiasm which was highly infectious.

One weekend when some of the Fijians were at our house, the prison officer suggested that the soldiers should stage a kava ceremony at the forthcoming fête. They readily agreed, proposing further that pigs should be cooked in an earth oven. Father was delighted and from then on we were committed.

The seven Fijian soldiers, and three island girls, whom the Army had also recruited as radio operators, were to travel by minibus from Aldershot on the day of the fête. My good friend Ivor Burston, a retired petty officer who lived across the road, and I were to dig a pit, line it with smooth river stones, and then light within a fire of hardwood logs before 9.00 a.m., which would burn out about 1.00 p.m., the time of arrival of the party from Aldershot. Two 100-lb dressed pigs were obtained from a local farm.

It was essential, said the Fijians, that the pigs be wrapped in banana leaves prior to being placed on the white hot stones and covered with wet sacks and a mound of earth. Aware that many an H.M. Ship had, over the years, brought home botanical specimens for Kew Gardens, and knowing that there were a number of banana trees in the hot houses, I wrote to the Director seeking a few leaves for our purpose. His reply was curt – 'Kew Gardens are maintained for the provision of specimens for scientific research and not for cooking pigs.' The Director of the Botanical Gardens in Cambridge was more accommodating, and all was ready for wrapping and burying the pigs when the Fijians arrived.

During the afternoon the local schoolmaster and I sat as honoured guests at the kava ceremony, which was performed with all the reverence and dignity one might expect on the lawns of Government House in Suva. The tanoa (kava bowl) and yanggona (powdered kava ingredient) had been sent from Fiji by Stan Brown, former Commanding Officer of the Fijian Navy.

At 6.00 p.m. came the opening of the pit. As the earth was shovelled away and the wet sacks were removed everyone's doubts, which had been freely expressed during the afternoon, were dispelled as the savoury aroma of superbly cooked pork pervaded the evening air.

I was entranced to watch the Rotuman girl, Betty Foster, dancing in our West Country orchard as I had seen her sisters dancing on her island when we were ashore from *Challenger*. It was intriguing, also, to realise that some of the Fijians who were now carving and distributing the roast pork to the townsfolk of Wiveliscombe were those same men who had dealt with the turtles onboard *Lachlan* off Palmerston Island half the world away.

The requirement for oceanographic data grew greatly in importance during 1963 and early in the year I began to prepare plans for a major oceanographic survey of the North Atlantic to be code named 'Navado'; the ship to initiate this project was to be *Vidal* which I was to commission in September.

The main thrust of Navado was to be the taking of oceanographic observations along parallels of latitude 3° apart from the European to the American shores. The considerable expense involved meant that the maximum scientific value must be obtained from each crossing of the Atlantic and it was an intriguing task to draw in appropriate scientists with their instrumentation from the three nations which were to be primarily involved. From Britain projects were put forward by the Hydrographer, the Admiralty Underwater Weapons Establishment, the Admiralty Research Laboratory and the Department of Geodesy and Geophysics, Cambridge; from the United States the Office of Naval Research, the U.S. Oceanographer and the Lamont Geological Observatory; and from Holland the Dutch Hydrographer and the Vening Meinesz Laboratory for Geophysics and Geochemistry. Not all these institutions were to take part throughout Navado, but representatives were to come and go as best suited the programme.

Whilst we were engaged in planning Navado in 1963, Lord Carrington set his seal on the need to expand our oceanographic as well as hydrographic knowledge of the oceans. In an address to the Royal Geographical Society on 10th June 1963 he said:

'In order to promote naval knowledge of marine exploration we have some thousand men and eleven ships under the command of the Hydrographer of the Navy, and the job that he is doing is of the utmost importance – not only to the Navy but to all of us. The need for oceanography has always been appreciated . . . but perhaps today its importance is greater than ever. One has only to remember that we are building four 'Polaris' submarines to realise how important the knowledge of the seabed can be. It is quite possible in the future that more and more warships will be submersible and, indeed, it is on the cards that a large part of the freight trade will go under the water rather than stay on the surface. How important, then, is this science of oceanography: and no doubt as time goes on we shall more and more find ways and means of extracting minerals from under the sea and making more use of the two-thirds of the earth's surface that is covered with water.'

About this time the Hydrographer received a letter from the Portuguese historian Armando Cortesão requesting a set of used Admiralty charts of the entire coast of Africa as base material for working up his *History of Portuguese Cartography*. I had met Cortesão when he was in exile in England in the late 1940s and was aware of his massive 'Tabularum Geographicarum Monumenta Cartographica' which he had published after his return to Coimbra, Portugal, in 1955 in which was reproduced every Portuguese portulan still existing in the world to-day. I had no difficulty in persuading Egg that such a famed cartographic historian should be provided with a set of new charts, and that I should present them to him at Coimbra University whilst *Vidal* was berthed at Oporto on our way south to the first Navado line in the autumn. Thus did I prepare a 'bonne bouche' for the early days of *Vidal*'s commission, which I was anticipating with mounting excitement.

Chapter XXI

Vidal I

I commissioned H.M.S. *Vidal* in Chatham in early September 1963. Much dockyard work had been devoted to installing a gravimeter, seismic equipment, oceanographic instrumentation, a new precision depth echo-sounder and numerous other special items required for Navado, which was to involve scientists and ships from three different nations during the next few years.

First we had to spend ten days at the Sea Training Base at Portland where an old Dartmouth term mate, Admiral Patrick Bayley, and his staff put the ship and her company through every conceivable emergency – fire onboard, steering gear breakdowns, towing a stricken vessel and landing parties at all times of day and night. When we sailed for Hamburg we felt ready for anything.

The ship arrived off the Elbe Light Vessel at midnight and embarked a pilot. My confidence in the navigator, Lieutenant Commander Richard Campbell, was complete and, aware that the whole of the following day would be spent in official calls and discussions in the German Hydrographic Office, I left him to take the ship up the river to Hamburg where seven hours later we were due to embark Admiral Irving from the harbourmaster's launch.

At 0800 I was pleased to fall in with Richard Campbell's plan to have curry served on the bridge, as the ship was spun rapidly by tugs in a river infested with speeding ferries, tugboats and barges. The pilot joined us in this unusual breakfast. We berthed smoothly alongside the inner side of the great Uberseebacke landing stage beneath the towering new Deutsches Hydrographisches Institut.

The next three days and nights were spent receiving and returning official calls, at cocktail parties, dinners and day-long discussions between Dr.

Zwiebler, the German Hydrographer, and Admiral Irving and their staffs, some of whom had arrived with us in *Vidal*. I was not excused participation in these discussions but brandy served by Dr. Zwiebler's secretary at tea and coffee breaks kept me awake.

We had brought with us Captain S. J. Hennessey and Mr. V. G. E. Hildreth who had been involved in Hamburg in 1945/1946 helping to re-establish the war-torn hydrographic office. Their efforts had not been forgotten and were constantly referred to by Dr. Zwiebler and his associates in the speeches that were made on every social occasion.

Admiral Irving struck his flag onboard and flew back to U.K. on the afternoon of the third day of our visit and all that was left to be coped with was a 'quiet night' in Hamburg, inevitably terminating in the early hours. As we sailed at 1000 on the morrow handkerchiefs, towels and even tablecloths waving from many of the austere windows of the Hydrographisches Institut were a token of the comradeship which had been formed between our two hydrographic offices and which endures today.

Hamburg has been in the business of entertaining seafarers for a thousand years or more, and the Reeperbahn provides adequately for sailors' tastes. Watchful police scoop up those who have over-indulged and bring them back to their ship without complications.

After a brief visit to Portland to embark a number of last minute scientific items and eight scientists of various nationalities, the ship sailed for Port Leixoes, the harbour for Oporto close north of the entrance to the Douro River. When planning to take a set of Admiralty charts to Professor Armando Cortesão of Coimbra University, I had conveniently discovered that it would be necessary to take a 'gravity departure' from a station of known value in south-west Europe before setting out with our gravimeter across the Atlantic. Fortunately, there were two such stations in the vicinity of Oporto and the scientists were able to make the necessary connection with a portable gravimeter.

The Hydrographic Department had stowed Armando's charts in an impressive cabinet; a visit to Coimbra to present them was soon arranged by the British Consul General, Mr. B. C. MacDermot. My wife had joined me and we were living with the MacDermots in the Consulate.

In *Vidal* I was pleased to have for the first time my own helicopter, albeit an ancient Dragonfly, so aptly named, with a speed of little more than fifty knots. She was piloted by Mike Styles, a jolly red-bearded extrovert, with whom I was to have many exciting flights. So keen was I to get airborne that I decided to fly the seventy-five miles to Coimbra, whilst the consular party, together with my wife, travelled by road; the cabinet of charts was carried south in the ship's Land Rover. Mike informed me that there were no navigational problems as he was following the railway which linked Oporto with Coimbra; we circled low over the University and landed at a nearby airstrip.

There was an impressive little ceremony for the presentation of the charts. Armando was clearly delighted with the gift, whilst I was able to draw a parallel with the gift by Captain Vidal in 1823 of a set of his Cape Verde charts to the Captain of the Port of Lisbon. The party then adjourned to the Palace Hotel deep in the woods of Bussaco for lunch, after which we assembled at a viewpoint overlooking the battlefield where Wellington had soundly beaten the French with considerable assistance from the Portuguese Army.

Of the many social events at Oporto I recall in particular a luncheon for officers and scientists in the Factory House, formerly used as a clearing house for British trade, but in 1963 a club with membership restricted to British port wine shippers. The recent vintage on the Douro had been a good one and our hosts were in rare good humour. Needless to say, the table wines and the post-prandial port were superb, and we readily accepted advice that we should embark some cases of selected port for we were told that, served ice cold, it drank well after lunch or dinner even on the equator. Subsequent experience proved the theory.

On sailing from Oporto we began to make trial oceanographic stations in preparation for the commencement of Line Alpha, at 3°N the first trans-Atlantic traverse of Navado. On each traverse we could expect to run down the continental slope, cross a wide ooze-covered abyssal plain at depths between 2,000 and 2,500 fathoms, then to pass over the rocky Mid-Atlantic Ridge, before crossing a second abyssal plain and climbing up the opposing continental slope. The precision depth recorder was to be run continually to reveal the morphology of the ocean floor, whilst at selected positions oceanographic stations would be made. At each of these a seismic refraction line would be run, using the helicopter or a boat to lay charges at various ranges from the drifting ship beneath which hung the receivers; meanwhile, by coring and deep sea photography we were to investigate the ocean floor. The special corers supplied consisted of long plastic tubes so fitted that a trip wire, lightly weighted, would hit the sea floor ahead of the corer releasing weights at the top of the tube to drive it into the sediment; cores of fifteen to twenty feet were in fact retrieved and stored, still in their plastic tubes, for analysis onshore. The underwater camera was similarly fitted with a trip wire which on touching the sea-bed opened the lens and exposed a strong flashlight; the tripping of the wire sent a pinging signal to the earphones of the winch operator so that he could lift the camera a few fathoms above the sea-bed and lower it again for the next photo. A range of such photos could then be taken as the ship drifted slowly on the surface current.

Each traverse was to take about fourteen days during which half a dozen oceanographic stations, each taking about six hours to complete, would be occupied. It was an exciting programme for the surveyors and scientists, but for many of the ship's company there was to be little to occupy their leisure hours. Thus we had, like our nineteenth-century predecessors wintering in the Arctic, to devise forms of recreation such as concert parties and deck games.

On completion of line Alpha the ship arrived in Trinidad to land a survey party of two officers and twelve men with two surveying boats to make a survey of the western approaches to Port of Spain during the ship's absence on lines Baker and Charlie.

Starting close south of Barbados the second Navado traverse in 13°N terminated off the coast of Gambia and a three-day visit was made to Bathurst just one year before Britain's last African colony was to achieve independence. Among the social events during our stay was the Red Cross Ball, held on a hard tennis court at Government House where the African Black Star Jazz Band played Hi-life music. The Gambian women are large and dignified, appearing even more stately when wearing their towering headgear fashioned from printed cotton as boldly patterned as their capacious dresses. In Hi-life dancing the men appear almost diminutive as they caper and shuffle to the rhythmic music astern of their majestically advancing partners.

My feet got hotter and hotter as the night wore on; there was no 'sitting one out' when invited to dance by these formidable women. At about 0400 when I retired to bed in Government House I found the soles of my feet to be red raw, exposed as they had been to the gravel of the tennis court once the soles of my shoes had worn away.

We had embarked for the return passage to Gambia five men of the Trinidad Coastguard to give them some wider sea experience. They much enjoyed this brief visit to the land of their forefathers but, as citizens of a recently independent country, they confided in me that they thought the Gambians were 'not quite ready for it'.

Before leaving Bathurst my old friend and shipmate of *Challenger* days, Dr. Tom Gaskell, joined the ship on behalf of the Department of Geodesy and Geophysics, Cambridge, to oversee the seismic work. He was in time to lead the scientists (The 'Noggies') in their act in our first mid-Atlantic concert. Before the concert the organisers were frequently approached by one of the ship's cooks anxious to demonstrate his skills in fire swallowing, but they had been unimpressed with his act. Nevertheless, on the night of the concert the excited cook appeared backstage in the helicopter hangar brandishing a flaming torch from which he took frequent gulps; my blood ran cold with thoughts of the disaster which could overtake us all. As actor-manager I ordered stage hands and performers to remove him bodily and douse his flambeau.

Line Charlie terminated south of Guadeloupe, whence we sailed to Trinidad to recover our survey party, their work complete. By New Year the ship was in Barbados where I was invited to stay for a few nights in Government House. Lady Stow was a most understanding person; when I told her that I would be spending New Year's Eve with friends who had come over from Trinidad, and would be very late home, she gave me the key to the turret up which a stairway led to my bedroom. About 0400 I was at the locked gates about 200 yards from Government House in a violent rain storm that was making so much noise on the tin roof of the sentry box that my cries remained unheard by the sheltering soldier. I began to throw stones over the high wall with the object of striking the iron roof and flushing the sentry; at the third attempt my stone hit the roof and a startled black face under a white helmet emerged gazing skyward in alarm. He heeded my call from the gates and I was admitted. I have entered the grounds of many Government Houses around the world, but never was I so pleased to do so as on this unconventional occasion, soaked as I was to the skin in a thin tropical suit.

Line Delta in 19° North began on 3rd January 1964 and, on completion a fortnight later, we set course for Santa Cruz in the Canary Islands for a pleasant four days' visit before sailing for Chatham. Anxious to achieve his statutory monthly flying hours, Mike Styles flew the helicopter off to the airfield where my steward and I readily agreed to a sight-seeing flight over the holiday beaches at La Playa. Long before we reached our objective the pilot realised that the following wind was increasing rapidly; with some difficulty he turned the aircraft back into the wind and we set out for home with three mountain ridges to surmount. We were flying slowly against the increasing wind when I saw far below a peasant driving his donkey, heavily loaded with bananas, in the same direction and, incredibly, he was overtaking us. I mentioned this over the intercom to Mike who, for once in his life, was not amused. 'We must terminate the flight as soon as possible,' said he. Anxiously I gazed down on a waving sea of banana palms interspersed with small concrete reservoirs; I wondered where Mike would decide to touch down but we staggered on past the farmer who was by now unloading his beast at the stable. An hour later we landed thankfully on the very edge of the airfield.

On 4th February I was at the Admiralty for what the Navy calls a 'wash-up' meeting on the first four Navado traverses. A number of involved scientists from the U.K. and the U.S.A. attended and expressed themselves well pleased with our results, the chairman recalling that it was just twelve months since the first Navado planning meeting, at which I had been present. I returned happily to Chatham to prepare the ship for the next stage.

The introduction of nuclear-powered submarines with their almost limitless submerged range brought a requirement for precise charts of many oceanic areas; in particular, attention was being directed to the western approaches to the Straits of Gibraltar out to a distance of 200 miles or so. Phase II of Navado, which I was now ordered to undertake, was a sounding and oceanographic survey of this extensive area.

The positional control was to be provided by Decca Lambda, which had been developed from the Two Range system to include constant lane identification, thus eliminating the problems we had experienced in *Dalrymple* five years earlier whenever we 'lost lock'.

For the northern part of the Navado II area one slave station would be required on Spanish soil near the Portuguese border and the other close south of Cadiz. Admiral Balén Garcia, the Spanish Hydrographer, had readily fallen in with Admiral Irving's plans to establish these stations and he persuaded the Spanish Government to co-operate.

Suitable sites for the slave stations had first to be found so I despatched Richard Campbell and Mike Styles to Madrid for a reconnaissance while I got the ship to sea and to Portland in readiness for the passage to Gibraltar.

One day in March I travelled from Portland with the ship's rugby team and supporters to my home town of those days, Wiveliscombe. Our team were overrun on the field, but we were doing much better during the evening's entertainment in the 'White Hart' when there was a dramatic entry. The tall, black-bearded figure in deerstalker hat and flowing tweed cape was Richard Campbell who, having ascertained my whereabouts on his arrival back from Spain, had driven hot foot in his ancient open Lagonda across southern England to report the successful completion of his mission to Andalucia.

A signal went to Deptford, where the Decca convoy was assembling under the leadership of Mr. Pearce, the boatswain, to proceed with 'Operation

Overload', so aptly named by the first lieutenant. The operation was to entail a 1,400 mile road journey through France and Spain to a rendezvous near Seville. Each of the two slave stations consisted of a long wheel-base Landrover towing a twenty-two foot caravan, and a Bedford van, in which were installed the electronics, towing a trailer containing two diesel generators. From the moment when one of the Bedford's trailers broke loose and narrowly missed a group of irate French workmen in Boulogne, until the sites were eventually reached, many a blacksmith along the way earned a few francs or pesetas for bodging up the towing arrangements for the next stage of the journey.

First I had to sail to the Clyde for, again, to utilise *Vidal*'s full potential whilst the ship was engaged on ocean surveys I had been ordered to carry out a number of hydrographic instructions on the west coast of Scotland. Two officers, twelve men and two survey boats were detailed for this purpose, Lieutenant Edge having steamed a motor fishing vessel from Rosyth to act as a floating base for the party.

Leaving the ship on arrival at Gibraltar, I set out by road with Campbell for Cadiz which we reached in the afternoon of Friday 10th April to be welcomed on Saturday morning by Mr Bruce Scott who had been British Vice Consul in Cadiz for many years. He and his Spanish assistant Millie were to be endlessly helpful to us in the months ahead, for there were always many minor problems to overcome.

That evening news came from the British Consul General in Seville that the Decca convoy had reached that city. A rendezvous between ourselves, the boatswain and Mr. Pete Toy, the senior of the three Decca engineers who had come out independently by road, had been arranged for the following morning at the Consul General's residence. Soon after dawn, on a crisp Sunday morning, we left Cadiz and, with only a brief stop at a venta for bocadillos for us and three anisettes for our Spanish driver 'to kill the insects in his stomach', we arrived at the Consul's residence on time where four dusty travellers sipped fino in an immaculate drawing room.

We then proceeded to the convoy's camp in an olive grove west of the city and having made plans for the morrow we joined the men of 'Overload' in celebrating their arrival with finos, tapas, plates of paella and a corrida in the city's bullring.

Next day the two slave stations parted company, Green slave to a site just south of the tunny fishing village of Sancti Petri, and Red slave to Redondella near the border with Portugal.

Campbell and I went to Jerez de la Frontera for the signing of the contracts for the lease of land for the sites. To obtain an interpreter for these legal proceedings we visited Mrs. Swithinbank, Vice Consul in Jerez. As her consulate was situated inside Williams and Humbert's bodega, and our interpreter was a sherry taster, it was some time before our business was complete and we were on the road again.

Whilst Campbell went to supervise matters at Sancti Petri, I spent the following day in the Spanish Hydrographic office in Cadiz discussing the future surveying arrangements with Admiral Garcia and obtaining the data which would be required to fix the two Decca sites within the Spanish triangulation network.

On Wednesday I was back in Gibraltar and the ship sailed so that men could be landed by boat or helicopter to assist the site crews in digging in the earth mats and raising the 100-foot masts. When all was complete at Green slave I took off by helicopter for the ship lying half a mile distant. When only about six feet airborne there was a bang and we were back on the ground. 'Good thing that didn't happen over the sea, Sir,' said Mike phlegmatically. It was a serious engine defect and, as there was no means of lifting the spare engine from the motor cutter alongside at Sancti Petri, we landed the men of the flight with the engine at Cadiz to go by road to Sancti Petri with the unenviable task of changing engines in a sandy windy wasteland.

Next day we were off Red slave and, with no helicopter and faced with a shallow shelving beach and heavy surf in front of the site, it was necessary for us to feel our way in the motor cutter up a shallow river three miles to the east. The boatswain met us with the Land Rover as did Sergeant Angelo of the Guardia Civile, who took our passports and accompanied us to the site. In the evening when all at Red slave was complete we reclaimed our passports from Corporal Jesus and returned downriver and out to the ship.

The next two days were spent calibrating the Decca transmissions from both slave stations using the tellurometer. The difference between the two ranges, the so called 'locking constant', was 0.6 of a lane over the whole area, which was a simple discrepancy to correct.

During Navado II there was a requirement for a full oceanographic station every fourth day. I decided that the first station would be a fixed, rather than a drifting, station with the ship lying to a floating beacon for twenty-five hours. The beacon was anchored with taut wire in 1,350 fathoms in a position about 100 miles from each slave station; thus we were able to observe the night effect on the transmissions. Unlike the Persian Gulf, there appeared to be very little night effect here so that we were able to plan for sounding to continue throughout the twenty-four hours. Sounding commenced at 0340 on Saturday 25th April, three and a half weeks since 'Overload' had left Deptford – it was a satisfying moment even at that hour of the night.

I closed Sancti Petri on Monday evening to embark the helicopter with its new engine. The presence of the ship's flight personnel, augmenting the slave crew, had enabled an international football match to be played on Sunday on the village ground, the result being an honourable draw. A fine cup was presented by the villagers and throughout that summer it changed hands on many occasions, the villagers and the 'slaves' challenging each other in events as diverse as swimming and dominoes.

To thank all the Spaniards who had helped us to get Navado II under way, from the Captain General of the Maritime Province, a senior admiral, to junior members of the hydrographic office, I embarked Admiral Irving at Gibraltar on 28th April, and sounding through the night entered Cadiz wearing his flag after firing a National Salute.

There followed a three-day visit packed with ceremonial calls, social events and an inspection of the Spanish Hydrographic Office. The similarity of the printing works with our own was explained when Admiral Garcia told us that in 1942, in the midst of the War, he had spent three months in Taunton at the invitation of the British Hydrographer before returning to Cadiz to build his own printing works.

To investigate the deep current which flows outward from the Straits of Gibraltar, the measurement of bottom currents was to be made with Dr. Jack Carruther's 'Pisa'. I had embarked him for the voyage from Portland to Gibraltar so that he could demonstrate the operation of this peculiar instrument. Each Pisa consisted of a baby's plastic feeding bottle, half filled with coloured jelly in which floated a tiny magnetic compass. The whole apparatus was lowered in a sealed tube containing hot water which kept the jelly liquid. A lump of sugar, so placed that it prevented the spring-loaded lid of the tube from opening until it had dissolved on reaching the sea-bed, allowed cold bottom water to enter the tube and set the jelly at a slant dictated by the angle at which the tube was held by the current. Back on deck the slope of the jelly surface compared with calibration tables revealed the speed of the bottom current, whilst the set of the compass gave its direction. Despite the hilarity with which the sailors boiled water on the forecastle and set the lump of sugar like a bait in a mouse trap, the system worked. At one station a bottom current speed of 0.43

knots was measured, supporting evidence being provided by the bottom photographs which showed extensive sandwaves on the seafloor.

We were ship sounding well to the westward of the area on the afternoon of 10th June when I received a signal informing me that the depôt ship H.M.S. *Adamant*, approaching Gibraltar from the west, had launched a sailing whaler at 0730 leaving her to sail the eighty-odd miles to Gibraltar as an exercise in seamanship. Increasing south-westerly winds were now causing anxiety about the safety of the boat, under the command of Midshipman Jenkins. Next morning I received a weather report from Green slave that the wind there was blowing force eight from the south-west, which led me to believe that the whaler could have failed to weather Cape Trafalgar and might be well to leeward in the vicinity of Sancti Petri. We alerted Green slave and in the early afternoon they sighted the whaler running before the wind under a storm sail, apparently in search of shelter. The bar at Sancti Petri in such southerly winds would have looked most uninviting, and despite our men waving him in Jenkins put about in an effort to tack to seaward. At this moment Radio Operator Hartley leapt into the waves and managed to swim to the whaler a few cables offshore. Hartley had been to sea with the tunny fishermen and knew the bar to be navigable despite its appearance. Jenkins and his men hauled the radio operator onboard, astonished at the flow of British sailors' language as he took charge and piloted them into the little harbour.

The whaler's crew were exhausted after thirty-six hours in a wild sea and were taken care of at Green slave where the Guardia Civile ordered them to remain. On receiving my signalled report that his men were safe, *Adamant*'s commander sent a minibus from Gibraltar to Sancti Petri to collect the crew, who might not have been freed by the Guardia Civile but for the excellent relations which had been built up by our men at Green slave.

Some days later we hoisted the whaler onboard off Sancti Petri and on our next visit to Gibraltar exchanged it with the commander of *Adamant* for £25 for our Guide Dogs for the Blind Fund. There was some amazement in naval circles in Gibraltar that *Vidal*, 150 miles out in the Atlantic, had conducted such an efficient rescue operation.

As the sounding of the northern area of Navado II was nearing completion it became necessary to leapfrog Red slave from Redondella across the Straits of Gibraltar to a site in Morocco to provide adequate fixing cover for the southern area. On 1st July the ship berthed in Casablanca for discussions with civil and military authorities and Mr. Johnston, the British Consul General.

I had made many official calls during *Vidal*'s varied commission but those in Casablanca were uniquely exhilarating, for the Military Governor provided me with transport. As we sped through the city ignoring traffic lights, police on point duty and the finer points of etiquette at roundabouts, the driver appeared to be involved in a desperate chase to keep in touch with our screaming outriders on their impressive motor cycles. On arrival at the 'call' I sank thankfully onto a divan and sipped mint tea with my host in a room draped with luxurious carpets which dimmed the nearby street cacophony to a gentle hum.

My next task was to travel south with Mr. Johnston and a reconnaissance party consisting of Robin Dathan, the first lieutenant, Mike Styles and Pete Toy to meet the Chefs de Cercle of the districts of Azemoor and El Jadida. We left in two cars, the Consul driving one and his driver, Mohamed, the other. Time was short, but French influence dictated that we stop for a large lunch with wines at a restaurant along the way to Azemoor some fifty miles to the south-westward.

A political desperado had recently slain three policemen in Casablanca and was now on the run, necessitating the establishment of spiked barriers restricting the width of the road at police control posts, one of which was established but a few yards from our destination, the residence of the Chef de Cercle of Azemoor where a guard of ancient, burnous-clad soldiery awaited us at the 'present'. Our arrival was marred by Mohamed failing to observe the police barrier, which proved its effectiveness by puncturing two of his tyres. He departed for repairs leaving us with a transport problem.

We entered a cool, well-carpeted room and settled ourselves on divans to await the results of the mystic activities of a tarbooshed teamaker with his gigantic silver urn. Three rounds of mint tea were served as conversation flagged, my French having its first outing since Tahiti eight years previously; then followed a round of sticky cakes as daylight began to ebb away. At last maps were found and attention was turned to the task in hand and we began to make towards the door, but even as we did so the manservant was on hand with squash and mineral water and even larger cakes. Conversation began again to drift away from Decca sites as the Consul General and the Chef de Cercle were discussing how the difference between the Arabic dialect of an Egyptian and a Moroccan could be equated with that between a Parisian and a French Canadian – an interesting comparison but the sun was fast sinking towards the inevitable blackout.

Finally we got on the road, huddled into a single vehicle. We spent the two remaining twilight hours in looking at sites which were either ideal but utterly remote or close to civilisation but quite hopeless. At last when it was too dark to continue it seemed likely that a suitable site lay further south and 2030 found us in conference with the Chef de Cercle of El Jadida on a barren piece of ground beneath the towering height of a slowly flashing lighthouse.

How could tomorrow's activities be progressed? Mohamed was somewhere in the souks of El Jadida in search of inner tubes, the patches having blown after the first repairs. There were several possible courses of action – some could stay the night at El Jadida, some could return to Casablanca, some could come south early on the morrow, some late, for there were still a host of potential official callers expecting VIP treatment onboard. It was like some parlour game, everyone could think of a different ploy but each came up against some formidable snag. Despite his Moslem faith it was the Chef de Cercle who came up with the only possible answer – we should adjourn to an hotel bar in the town for a cold beer. And there, as we relished the ice cold drinks, things began to clarify. No. 1 was able to telephone the ship to organise a relief party for the morrow, Mohamed arrived having found new inner tubes, and by midnight we were back onboard.

Next day, after an early start, the relief team in the Landrover met both Chefs de Cercle at a rendezvous in the forest of El Jad and were guided to an ideal site. I spent the forenoon onboard explaining our work to the Heads of the Lighthouse Authority and the Institute of Fisheries, the Civil and Military Governors and, finally, the Chefs de Cercle of Azemoor and El Jadida who had travelled north to lunch onboard with me. I became a hesitant French gramophone record as I repeated, without the aid of alcohol as my guests were Moslems, the necessity for surveying the ocean and why we required the erection of masts and the establishment of camp parties in remote coastal locations.

In late afternoon I was back at the lighthouse to find that Robin Dathan with tellurometer and theodolite to fix the Decca site from the lighthouse was unable to gain admission. This difficulty was finally ironed out but not without repeated throat-cutting gestures by the keeper as he reluctantly showed the way to No. 1 and his survey recorder up the 230-foot circular stairway. We wondered whether the gestures indicated what he was going to do to our first lieutenant, or what his superiors would do to him when they heard that he had admitted infidels. We were happy to see Robin Dathan back onboard by midnight, his throat parched but intact.

The new site was ideal in every way. It lay on a lonely and lovely beach two miles from the main road along a good track through the forest, and about six miles from the town of El Jadida with a cinema and two hotel bars – in fact everything a Red slave could desire.

After a couple of days refitting in the dockyard at Gibraltar the Red slave convoy crossed the straits by ferry and reached the site at El Jadida without difficulty. The ship anchored off El Jadida to land assistance for the establishment of the site, the helicopter found the landing satisfactory and after calibrating the newly established station we were in business again, sounding twenty-four hours a day in the southern area of Navado II.

In mid-August relief crews for Red and Green slaves arrived by air in Gibraltar and *Vidal* sailed for Portsmouth, where I turned over the survey data for Navado II to Commander Paton in H.M.S. *Owen*, who was to take over the completion of the survey from me.

Vidal sailed on to Chatham to prepare for another venture.

Chapter XXII

Vidal II

On arrival in U.K. I had received the exciting news that we were to take Admiral Irving, together with some of his civilian staff, to Leningrad to visit the Soviet Hydrographic Office and to confer with the Hydrographer, Admiral Rassokho.

Together with the navigating officer and the supply officer I visited the Directorate of Naval Intelligence in Whitehall for a briefing. Admiral Irving had stipulated that this was to be a visit of friendship and collaboration and was in no way to become an intelligence gathering exercise. It was eleven years since an H.M. Ship had visited the Soviet Union, the vessel being the aircraft carrier *Bulwark*, so the Directorate had little up-to-date information to give me, but I was cautioned about the dangers of vodka and the dire necessity for sobriety when my men went ashore in Leningrad. Fortunately, just before leaving the Directorate we were ushered in to a small office where a Russian dissident welcomed us; I confided in him my forebodings but he quickly reassured me. If my officers were only going to accept two vodkas at a reception the Royal Navy would become a laughing stock in Soviet naval circles; we should be expected at any social gathering to drink eight vodkas to respond to varying toasts, and finish off with two Georgian brandies. As long as we got into training and consumed plenty of caviar during the receptions, all would be well. As for my men onshore, no navy in the world had more experience in dealing with drunken sailors; they would simply be brought back onboard by the Soviet naval patrols.

Whilst in Whitehall we met the three sub-lieutenants (Sp) who were to come with us as interpreters; they were young graduates, one of whom had studied in Leningrad University. Each had special interests, navigation, protocol, etc.

They proved to be so efficient that one hardly noticed their presence when conversing with a Russian.

Returning to Chatham we called at Saccone & Speed's to order the immediate delivery of a dozen cases of vodka so that training might begin. Among other preparations for the visit was to extract, for once, some really up-to-date films from the Naval Film Corporation; these included the Beatles' *Hard Day's Night*, yet to be generally released.

Only one worry remained. Reading *Bulwark*'s letters of proceedings of their visit to Leningrad I learnt that, despite having a ship's company of over a thousand men to choose from, she was beaten on the soccer field by eleven goals to nil by a team from the Leningrad Naval Base. What could we do with a crew of only 150? Admiral Irving had the answer; in the Hydrographic Office at Cricklewood there was a draughtsman named Gerry Cakebread, who had been the goalkeeper for Brentford, a leading London club, for eight years. He would be one of Egg's technical staff for the visit.

On the forenoon of 7th September 1964 Admiral Irving embarked and, wearing his flag for the third time during the commission, *Vidal* sailed from Chatham. We passed through the Kiel Canal and reached a rendezvous in the Gulf of Finland on the morning of 9th September, where a Soviet minesweeper came alongside to deliver onboard the British Assistant Naval Attaché, three Soviet naval liaison officers and an elderly civilian pilot. We set off at a brisk speed astern of the minesweeper but it was already dark when we passed the naval base at Kronstadt; despite the darkness *Vidal* fired a national salute which evoked a spectacular reply from an anti-aircraft battery, augmented by rumbling thunder and brilliant sheet lightning.

The three liaison officers had already become troublesome on the bridge, interfering with the business of navigation which was being quietly conducted with the aid of our confident pilot. I sent for the new first lieutenant, Geoff Hope, and told him to try and distract the liaison officers elsewhere. 'I'll show them the *Hard Day's Night* in the wardroom,' said he. So, unmolested, we sailed steadily up the Neva River through Smidt's Bridge to secure to head and stern buoys abreast of the Admiralty Building at 0300. The liaison officers only reappeared as the engines were rung off.

When we awoke in the morning the thunder and rain of the night had passed away, giving us our first view of the beautiful city that lay around us, the gilded dome of St. Isaac's Cathedral and the spires of the Admiralty glittering in the morning sunshine.

I accompanied Admiral Irving for his call on Admiral Baikov, Flag Officer Leningrad, to whom I took an immediate liking; a vast man with a long row of orders and medals stretched diagonally across his chest, his first suggestion to Admiral Irving was that I should be promoted to Rear Admiral from the moment of *Vidal*'s entry into Soviet territorial waters. Egg looked discomfited as he explained that such an instant promotion was not possible. 'What, haven't you got a procedure in the Royal Navy for promotions in the field?' said Baikov disdainfully. I had to wait a further two years for my promotion.

The Hydrographer, Admiral Rassokho, was a smaller man than Baikov, yet stocky and sturdy in appearance; whilst Baikov was a teller of stories, largely directed against the Jews, Rassokho enjoyed reminiscing about salmon fishing in Siberia or sturgeon fishing in the Caspian. Discussions between Admiral Irving and his staff and the Soviet Hydrographer were cordial, lengthy and useful, leading to the first extensive exchange of charts between our two countries. My impression of the Hydrographic Office at that time was of an enthusiastic team, a large proportion of whom were young women, trying to cope in premises which were in no way ideal, and in a printing shop in the Admiralty which was both ancient and dingy. The Hydrographer, a comparatively young man, with many years ahead of him in the post, was determined to change all that in his drive for a worldwide series of modern Russian charts. I was intrigued to find a young cartographer making a copy of a chart of the port of Napier which I had published in New Zealand ten years earlier.

There was a statutory laying of wreaths by Admiral Irving and myself, supported by our Guard of Honour, on the memorial in the mass graveyard at Piskarovskaya where over a million citizens who died in the siege of Leningrad lie buried – a sobering experience.

There were receptions both ashore and onboard, visits to the Hermitage and the Kirov Ballet, and one afternoon, following an alcoholic midday reception given by Rassokho onboard the ancient cruiser *Kirov*, we adjourned to the Naval Sports Stadium for the football match. *Vidal*'s team were defeated honourably by two goals to nil; Gerry Cakebread played a superb game, saving a succession of sizzling shots from the Soviet Navy's competent forwards. As we sat on the stand in uniform, a motley crowd of civilian spectators below us, I was shouting vigorously in support of *Vidal* when a peasant-like figure turned round and, from beneath his broad-peaked cap, spat out some words of abuse towards me. 'What does he say?' I enquired of the interpreter beside me. 'He says "Put on your short trousers and get on the field yourself!"'

We sailed at midnight after witnessing a glittering performance at the Kirov, our same three Soviet naval liaison officers embarked. 'What shall we do with them this time?' I asked No. 1. 'I'll show them the *Hard Day's Night* – with the three reels in a different order,' said he. The film had served us well, being viewed continuously by our many ship's visitors who found the Beatles a far greater attraction than a tour of the ship.

We had enjoyed many receptions where our vodka training had stood us in good stead. Eight vodkas and two Georgian brandies was the norm, just as our Whitehall Russian had forecast. Stolitsnya was, however, far superior to the English vodka on which we had trained and in those days caviar was still available in abundance. Also, as forecast, the only sailor who missed the last boat at midnight was returned to us in a stupor at 0200 by the Soviet naval patrol as a matter of routine.

At an evening reception after the football match, Egg, elated by the result, referred in his speech to his 'secret weapon', and Cakebread's covert activities in goal were soon revealed. When Admiral Rassokho visited the Pool of London the following year in his new surveying vessel *Nickolai Zubov,* his ship's company declined a soccer match against a Chatham naval side, fearing perhaps that they would be up against the whole of Brentford's professional team.

Admiral Irving flew back to the U.K. after a most fruitful series of meetings with the Soviet Hydrographer. In these days of perestroika it is difficult to visualise the breakthrough that Egg had made in 1964. Meanwhile *Vidal*'s officers and men had enjoyed the most cordial relations with their Soviet counterparts.

I decided to enter the locks at Chatham, where Admiral Hogg, Flag Officer Medway, awaited us with the Royal Marine Band, with the ship's company on deck in No. 2s wearing fur hats, as everyone onboard had bought one in Leningrad. When I met Admiral Hogg on the quay after berthing I apologised for our unusual dress. 'It was great,' said he, 'but I was annoyed with the bandmaster. When I told him to play the Volga Boatmen he said he hadn't got the score.'

During the first half of 1965 *Vidal* was to be employed on a programme in the North Atlantic which would entail the re-running of the first four Navado lines and surveys in Jamaica and British Guiana.

Scientists who had been processing our previous data had now come up with a number of technical improvements to the corer, the deep-sea camera and the towed magnetometer, whilst we onboard had devised hoisting arrangements for recovering the motor cutter in seas up to fifteen feet in height, thus increasing the frequency of seismic refraction experiments along Navado lines.

Professor Ewing of the Lamont Geological Observatory in Colombia University, New York, had developed an airgun profiler and would send it to sea in *Vidal* with a team to operate it. The equipment comprised a high pressure airgun towed beneath the surface astern from which was emitted at ten-second intervals sound pulses directed towards the ocean floor. Such pulses were capable of penetrating some thousands of feet of sediment to obtain a returning signal from the surface of the rock layer beneath. The time of double passage of the sound pulses was recorded onboard on magnetic tape, thus providing a continuous profile of the thickness of the ocean floor sediment layer.

We had carried scientists from the Admiralty Underwater Warfare Establishment during 1964, engaged as they were in developing an inertial navigation system for long range submarine navigation; they now returned onboard with their prototype before we sailed to re-run Line Bravo early in the New Year. Meanwhile the Dutch naval survey ship *Snellius* had joined Navado and was engaged on the next four lines to the north of us.

All went well on Bravo and we arrived in Kingston on 3rd February. We had three tasks to perform in Jamaica – a resurvey of Kingston Harbour and Port Royal, a survey of Port Kaiser (a newly opened bauxite loading terminal on the south-west coast) and a detailed survey of the approaches and site for a new deep-water berth for cruise liners in Montego Bay.

First of all reconnaissance parties had to be despatched to recover trigonometrical stations and, in the case of Montego Bay, to arrange accommodation for a detached party. Mr. Cleveland Lewis, Minister of Communications and Works, an energetic and amusing politician, arranged transport for the work and for me an official car. After a few days Mr. Lewis 'phoned me to say that the driver, Fitzroy Stanley (happily commemorating two fine nineteenth-century surveyors), was complaining that I was only using his services for daywork and that he was missing his overtime pay. I promised to rectify this matter and at once I began to live life to the full as I toured the beautiful island with new-found Jamaican friends. Fitzroy, who always addressed me as 'Admiral', insisted on raising the Union Jack on the bonnet of the Mercedes whenever I embarked, whether in uniform for an official call or in a calypso shirt when returning from a ska session in downtown Kingston in the early hours. I was fearful that news of the ever-fluttering Union flag would reach the ears of Sir Alexander Morley, the High Commissioner, who would surely have resented a rival on the island.

The survey of Kingston Harbour showed some changes, whilst that of Port Royal was extremely interesting as we were able to use a newly trained survey diving team under the direction of Sub-Lieutenant Gobey. This had been made possible by the introduction of a new underwater communications system employing a telephone cable inside the lifeline from the officer-in-charge in the boat to the diver investigating the many coral outcrops to be found in the vicinity of Port Royal.

The ship and her boats had a boisterous time off Port Kaiser, but the approaches to the exposed bauxite berth were well covered by the boats, and the ship completed the work by running a selected leading line into the wharf. After establishing a detached party of two officers and twelve men in the old airport terminal building at Montego Bay, we hurried off to Trinidad. During our previous visits to the Caribbean I had been impressed by the frequent references to Trinidad Carnival, and had been dismayed to hear that H.M. Ships were never allowed to attend this bacchanal, particularly because many Trinidadians adopted the uniform of a U.S. sailor when carousing about Port of Spain at carnival time.

I had been at pains to get the ear of the British High Commissioner, Sir Norman Costar, and the various Trinidadian authorities with whom we had worked, to invite *Vidal*'s attendance at the 1965 Carnival. Once they had given their blessing I had written to the British Senior Naval Officer, West Indies, requesting that during the Carnival my men should be permitted to go ashore in 'plain clothes'; the request was granted, a unique privilege in those days.

And so on the evening of Friday 26th February *Vidal* came alongside in No. 1 Berth, the best in the harbour, right on Independence Square, where we awaited with eagerness, amidst the increasing pandemonium, the advent of the carnival.

Carnival develops each year in a traditional fashion. During the previous week steel orchestras practise in their 'yards' about the city, Calypsonians try out their new numbers in their 'tents', and the half dozen Road Marches, which the carnival 'bands' will use to encourage them on their long marches through the city on Monday and Shrove Tuesday, blare from bars and stores and pulse endlessly from the radio; each composer, be he Lord Kitchener, the Mighty Sparrow, or some newcomer, hoping that his March will catch the public's imagination and win the coveted 'Road March of the Year', that used by the greatest number of bands when crossing the 300-yard stage on the Savannah on Shrove Tuesday.

Calypsonians, steel orchestras, brass bands, carnival kings and queens all have their own nights of glory on the stage on different evenings immediately preceding carnival, whilst on Sunday there is a midday exodus to houses in the surrounding countryside for fêtes (parties) where the throbbing music still follows.

At 0500 on Monday morning, with the moon high in the night sky, a gun is fired and 'jouvêt' (jour ouvert) begins. Then those thousands of revellers who have gathered around their favourite steel orchestras on the perimeter of Port of Spain begin their jumping procession into the ever-increasing crush which culminates in Independence Square. After dispersal at about 1000 the members of the many different bands assemble at their respective 'camps', the more modestly costumed to parade through the streets in a rehearsal for the morrow under the direction of their leaders. On Shrove Tuesday the kings, queens and all manner of leading personages in their glittering costumes join the less flamboyantly dressed members of the band for the great day-long march through the city, which includes statutory passages across the Savannah stage and through Independence Square.

There are about eight big bands of 6,000 members, and many smaller bands, all dressed as part of a different theme – Gulliver's Travels, Polynesia, Mariners, Our Kind of People – countless ideas on which the designers and Indian seamstresses have been working for weeks. Each band is divided into two sections, one moving ahead and the other astern of their steel orchestra, processing with its drums on low wheeled trolleys, blasting out the selected Road March.

It is not marching as the European knows it, but a kind of shuffle and jump which is hard to describe but comes naturally when the irresistible music begins. The marching ends by about 7.00 p.m. but the day is not over, nor are the rum bottles empty, for at 9.00 p.m. begins 'last lap' when, wherever you are, be it on the Tranquillity Tennis courts, at the Country Club or in the streets, the jump up dancing continues without ceasing until the midnight gun announcing Ash Wednesday is heard. The carnival is over and even those in the most fabulous and expensive costumes may sink down to slumber wherever they find themselves, for it is a long walk home when the music stops.

As *Vidal*'s captain I could not enter fully into the revelry which every one of my men ashore was enjoying. I viewed the proceedings from a VIP seat above the Savannah stage, but I longed to join that happy, roistering throng of masqueraders and wondered if I ever would.

I had reserved for Ash Wednesday a Hydrographic Instruction requiring the ship to anchor a few miles west of Port of Spain to observe the rate and direction of the tidal streams; only four men were required for this task whilst the rest of us took life very slowly as every good Trinidadian was doing.

From Trinidad *Vidal* sailed to re-run lines Alpha and Charlie, calling briefly on the completion of line Alpha to collect mails and fresh provisions in the Cape Verde Islands. As in all Portuguese ports visited during the commission I found the harbour and administrative authorities at Porto Grande both friendly and helpful. A month after leaving Trinidad we were in Montego Bay to embark the detached party who, under Lieutenant John Myers (now Hydrographer of the Navy), had completed the surveys of Montego Bay and the small port of Lucea a few miles to the west.

Myers' survey for the new wharf on the western side of the bay enabled me to bring the ship safely to a running moor in a suitable position to act as Guard Ship for the finish of the Miami-Montego Bay yacht race. Fitzroy awaited me on the quayside to provide me with the necessary mobility to enjoy four days of active social life, which included Mike Styles' wedding to Auriol Bowles in St. James Church, the constant attendance onboard of members of the Montego Bay, Royal Jamaican and Biscayne Bay Yacht Clubs, timing and recording the arrival of the yachts, and the plethora of receptions, cocktail parties and dinners which such activities generate. The weather was good and when social obligations permitted one could laze on the famed Doctor's Cave beach sipping the customary rum punch. Early in the visit I had met a charming woman, Mary Petschek, on holiday from New York, who has remained a friend to this day.

When this happy period was over we sailed for British Guiana for the next and final major survey of the commission. The inhabitants consisted largely of two ethnic groups, Indians and Africans; for some years Cheddi Jagan and Forbes Burnham had been leading their respective peoples towards independence, which was now being actively encouraged by the Governor, Sir Richard Luyt, a highly competent and respected South African. Our job was to chart the colony's continental shelf and the sea boundaries with Venezuela on the west and Suriname in the east, which entailed discussions with the Chief Justice 'Sonny' Ramphal, later to become Secretary General to the Commonwealth.

The work was to be controlled again by Decca Lambda; Pete Toy and his Decca engineers were back with us for the landing and erection of the slave stations. Green slave was established at Suddie to the west of the Demerara River, the crew having excellent accommodation in the local courthouse, with welcome access to the village store where our men managed to repair the long defunct juke box. Haversham to the east, where Red slave was sited, was in a remote area, the crew having to live in the two Uniport huts provided for the instrumentation. By day the camp was surrounded by curious, staring Indian cane cutters armed with their cutlasses, whilst by night hordes of mosquitoes moved in from the adjacent marsh. I was glad to be able to arrange a daily visit by a patrol from a detachment of the King's Own Borderers stationed nearby. Even fresh water had to be supplied daily by the Army.

In the Barbice River, which forms the border with Suriname, I received close co-operation from Lieutenant Commander van Grondelle, the captain of the Netherlands survey ship *Luymes*.

The work at sea was difficult: frequent rain squalls and generally damp weather led to frequent loss of lock on Lambda; by night the atmospheric conditions prevented any useful sounding being completed while the ship lay at anchor rolling heavily in the constant and considerable swell, which also prevented the use of boats. Fortunately the local hydrographic launch *Herbert N. Critchlow*, named after a former Guyanese trade union leader, was available for Lieutenant Edge to embark with two survey recorders for the inshore sounding work. An elderly crew under Captain Ben were extremely capable and when Ben came onboard to see me, in his uniform cap and sweatshirt, I found him a most likeable and amusing character.

During one weekend *Luymes* and *Vidal* berthed together in Georgetown when van Grondelle and I stayed at Government House enjoying the Luyts' hospitality. The wharf was partially in ruins as a result of previous years' riots and arson, and much of Georgetown showed signs of neglect. Nevertheless, I found the people amiable and well disposed now that independence was in sight. I recall 'jumping up' one night in an overcrowded first floor of a great wooden building in the town. Byron Lee's popular Jamaican band of twelve musicians who were blasting out the rhythm did not miss a beat as the police moved in, arrested a dancer in mid-floor, handcuffed him and led him through the tight mass of pulsating humanity.

The chief and petty officers had an unfortunate run ashore. Meeting one night the director of a distillery which had supplied the Royal Navy with rum for many years, they were able to arrange a visit for a coach party to this desirable establishment. I happened to be on the deck outside my cabin when the party returned in the evening. There were no smiles, no laughter as the sad little party came over the gangway. I sent for the coxswain in the morning – 'What happened?' I asked. 'It was dreadful, sir. During the whole tour of the distillery the odour was dead right, but when we reached the end of the visit, instead of the expected tot of pusser's, we were invited to gaze into a cask of solid gunge. That's how it is exported to U.K.' The coxswain was normally a man of great good humour, but he never saw the funny side of that day's outing.

This difficult survey was at last completed and *Vidal* sailed for Trinidad. When about 100 miles south-east of Tobago I lowered both surf boats with volunteer crews to sail for Man of War Bay. The wind was easterly at force six with a moderate sea, but I had confidence in Lieutenant Edge and Sub-Lieutenant Gobey, in charge of the boats, as seamen, and left them reaching comfortably at a speed of about seven knots.

After a weekend in Port of Spain, *Vidal* sailed in company with the new Trinidad Coastguard patrol vessel *Courland Bay*, commanded by Lieutenant Goldstraw, a former boatswain in *Vidal* before he emigrated to Trinidad.

We sailed into Man of War Bay to see our surf boats on the beach where the crews had been enthusiastically welcomed by the villagers and the local policeman; their reception could not have been more cordial had the surf boats crossed the Atlantic as the villagers at first supposed.

Our two surf boats, two dories and two dinghies enabled Geoff Hope to organise a superb regatta in the calm waters of the bay. The highlight was perhaps the Centipede Races; I had always enjoyed this sport, which entails manning a whaler or surfboat with twenty-four men each armed with a paddle as supplied in those days with Carley rescue rafts. My *Lachlan*'s crew had taken the Centipede Cup at the Auckland Regatta, I had challenged and beaten the Senior Naval Officer Persian Gulf, and now I was happy to steer my crew to victory in the finals over that of the Buffer. The art is for the steersman, by the banging of a stick on an oil drum, to ensure that every paddle enters the water simultaneously as each great thrust forward is made. It is traditional for the losing crew to board the victors at the finishing line in an effort to cast them into the sea.

Visiting Barbados to embark a number of scientists for line Delta on 5th July, with our long paying off pendant hoisted for the first time, we set off across the Atlantic. We had ten scientists onboard for this last cruise of the commission, including Dave Folger, 'the cosmic dustman' from Lamont, who rigged an apparatus on the flying bridge for the collection of terrigenous and cosmic dust. During Navado we had carried a total of forty-two scientists, many for two or three voyages; it had been our privilege to offer assistance in every way possible, whilst I greatly enjoyed daily discussions with the scientists enabling me to organise matters onboard so that each project got its fair share of the valuable sea time available. I flatter myself that I was successful in this, for I had many warm letters of thanks from our 'philosophers' and as further evidence I have before me an impressive framed certificate presented to me by Dr. Baas Colette of Utrecht University, a hard man to please, my Dutch colleagues have told me. The certificate commends me for carrying out the 'First continuous seismic profiling onboard a British ship together with the Lamont Geological Observatory and the Vening Meinesz Laboratory.'

The Beatles had received their M.B.E.s in June and whether or not they deserved them was a matter of fierce debate onboard as continuous as their music, which flowed daily from the ship's broadcast system. I had obtained a copy of the relevant '*Times*' in Barbados and in my 'Weekly Bulletin' I see that I carried out an investigation, with the aid of a magnifying glass, of the two small print columns to compare other awards in the same list. Did the Beatles who had been entertaining much of the world for three years deserve their medals more or less than – 'The non-medical supervisor of midwives, Merioneth', their fellow scouse 'Trade Union Vice-Chairman, Merseyside District Advisory', or even the 'Senior Warning Officer Truro Group Air Raid Warning Organisation' who must have been having a hard time in the mid-sixties? Remembering how our Russian liaison officers had been lured away from the bridge by the Beatles whilst I was navigating the Neva on a pitch black night, I had no doubt that the Beatles had richly deserved their awards.

On our way home to Chatham to pay off, we had been somewhat alarmed to receive a signal ordering us directly to the Clyde to take part in a Fleet Assembly in the presence of Her Majesty the Queen. Pausing briefly at Plymouth for a wash and brush up we anchored in our assigned position on Sunday August 5th and Admiral Irving came onboard to address a gathering of surveying officers from the eight survey ships present at the Assembly.

I had been appointed A.D.C. to Her Majesty who was attending the Review as Lord High Admiral. A.D.C. to the Queen is an appointment granted to some fortunate senior captains during their final months in the rank. Many such A.D.C.s never have the chance to meet Her Majesty, but I was summoned to my duties in H.M.S. *Lion* onboard which the Queen was attending a dinner. It was my pleasant task to conduct her among the various groupings of officers whom she met before and after the meal. She was shortly to visit the West Indies and discussed with me my impressions at some length. She told me that she had warned her Ministers that the Federation was unlikely to come about, her impression being that individual countries were increasingly interested in controlling their own national affairs.

On sailing from the Clyde, with our long paying off pendant streaming from the masthead, I took command of the eight surveying ships, formed into three divisions, as we steamed down the Clyde – a fitting conclusion to my last days of command.

Vidal entered the North Locks at Chatham to pay off on Saturday 14th August 1965 and I rang off main engines for the last time. Alone in my cabin I felt deeply wistful after eight years in command of four of Her Majesty's Surveying Ships. Although I now knew that I was to be appointed Hydrographer of the Navy in the New Year, I also knew that never again would I have a ship's company and a ship of my own to care for, to work with and to be proud of.

If you command a good ship, and given the magnificent manpower material in the Royal Navy it is only your fault if it is otherwise, then whatever the emergency, whatever the task you face, you know that every member of your company will support you to the utmost of his ability. Where else, I wondered, did such loyalty exist.

How fortunate I was to have been granted so many opportunities to enjoy this tremendous experience.

Chapter XXIII

The Hydrographer of the Navy

In January 1966 I became the nineteenth Hydrographer of the Navy since Alexander Dalrymple took office in 1795. It is an honourable post which I could expect to hold for five years. I had an excellent turn-over from my predecessor and old friend Rear Admiral Sir Edmund Irving; three new ocean surveying ships of the *Hecla* class which he had planned were about to come into service; plans were on the drawing board for four new coastal surveying ships; building was about to commence on new chart compilation offices alongside the printing works which had been constructed at Taunton in Somerset in 1940; and the former Director of the Naval Weather Service was soon to join Hydrographer as head of a new Division of Oceanographic and Meteorological Services, reflecting the growing requirements of both submariners and their hunters for day-to-day forecasts concerning the state of the ocean environment in which they both operated.

I was soon to be relocated. I moved, reluctantly at first, across Whitehall from the Admiralty to the Old War Office Building, to be installed in an impressive circular office formerly occupied by a senior general.

Ageing single-colour printing presses at Taunton presented the opportunity to install new three-colour Crabtree Sovereign machines, enabling me to launch an internal chart modernisation study which would change the traditional grey format of the Admiralty Chart to a coloured version which would be easier to read under the varying conditions experienced on the bridge at sea; at the same time, hill shading and dotted fathom lines would be replaced by continuous contours, anticipating the introduction of automated scribed cartography.

First we had to get the colour machines into operation. The first two arrived in 1967 at a time when we still had seven different trade unions in the printing works at Taunton, and when there were not yet national house agreements on pay rates for operating multi-coloured precise printing machines. The sparkling new red Sovereigns lay under wraps while we endeavoured to reach an agreement with the Fathers of the Chapel concerned during protracted discussions, sometimes lasting long into the night. The Rt. Hon. Roy Mason was the Minister of Defence (Equipment) to whom I was responsible in this matter, and in order to achieve an acceptable rate of pay for the machine minders I probably over emphasised to Mason the complexity of the Sovereigns and the skills required to operate them. Eventually the Minister decided to make a personal visit to resolve the matter. When I met him as he descended from his helicopter at Taunton, I was able to inform him that at long last the machines had begun operation on the previous day; he seemed almost disappointed that his negotiating skills were not now required, he himself having the experience of being a union official in the coal industry.

Mason approached the minder operating a Sovereign with the enthusiasm of a boy with a new toy –

'The Admiral tells me that these machines are difficult to operate successfully,' said Mason.

'Oh, no, Sir,' came the reply. 'It's like driving a Rolls Royce and one can adjust the registration while the machine is in movement with ease.'

The Minister gave me an amused and quizzical look and we moved on to talk to Bill Ogden, the machine minders' Father of the Chapel, who was operating a Milander flat-bed machine in the Proving Room. The two men got into conversation concerning the length of apprenticeship in the printing trade.

'If we raise the school leaving age to sixteen surely you are not still going to insist on the five-year apprenticeship?' queried Mason.

To my alarm Ogden took hold of the Minister's lapel to emphasise his reply 'You wouldn't operate this ruddy machine to the standards required here after only three years' apprenticeship.'

I need not have worried; the two men settled down to a forthright and amicable discussion on a variety of trade union matters.

During 1967, when we were finalising the format of the new four-colour chart, the Labour Government decided to encourage the general adoption of the metric system: although no Bill was passed a Metrication Board was established. Bearing in mind that it was nearly fifty years since the International Hydrographic Organisation had passed a Resolution to the effect that all depths and heights should appear on charts in metres, it seemed to me that the introduction of coloured charts, which would look startlingly different from the traditional Admiralty Chart, presented the unique opportunity to go metric.

The Navy generally were not enthusiastic, nor were Trinity House pilots or yachtsmen, but merchantmen offered me encouragement. As a yachtsman A. P. Herbert advocated in letters to *The Times* the formation of 'The Friends of the Fathom' to oppose me, but sadly he died before we were able to organise a public debate.

Although it was likely to take until the end of the century to convert, area by area, the Admiralty's world coverage of charts to the metric system, I decided, with the backing of about two-thirds of my staff, to go ahead with metric heights and depths on the 'new look' charts. However, there were some sleepless nights to come, for soon after we were committed there was a change in Government with a number of back-bench Conservatives vowed to oppose all forms of national metrication. Happily for me, the new Government was soon so beset with difficulties imposed on them by the coal miners and others that the anti-metrication lobby never had a chance to table their opposition.

I believe that had we not adopted metrication in the mid-1960s the Admiralty Chart would not have continued to occupy its revered position worldwide; and its new metric look had a major influence on the style and appearance of an acceptable International Chart being developed in the 1970s by the International Hydrographic Organisation.

The Training Unit for surveying recorders which I had opened at Chatham in 1948 had been enlarged in 1966 to provide training for surveying officers, with a three month initial course and two further advanced courses at suitable stages in their career. The Hydrographic School was now established in H.M.S. *Drake*, the naval barracks at Devonport, with Commander Richard Campbell in charge. He met me at Plymouth station in his ancient Lagonda, my flag fluttering from a flagstaff on the bonnet; the sentries on the Barrack gates goggled at this apparition, while presenting arms as we sped through to the sound of the 'Still' on the bugle. After calling on the Commodore in company with Captain Geoffrey Hall, the Assistant Hydrographer, we proceeded to the School for its inspection. Since those days some hundreds of surveyors, from many different countries, have learned their trade at the R.N. Hydrographic School.

H.M.S. *Protector* had for a number of years been providing a British presence in the Antarctic and the Falkland Islands, but by 1966 she was too elderly to continue and there were no plans to replace her. She had transported hydrographic surveying parties south every southern summer and I was dismayed to think that this programme would end. However, I was able to elicit the support of Rear Admiral John Adams, Assistant Chief of Naval Staff, who agreed that a replacement vessel should be provided. Accordingly I sent Lieutenant Commander Wynne-Edwards, an enthusiastic member of my staff, to Denmark to investigate the ice-protected merchant vessel *Anita Dan* which was advertised for sale. The owners, Messrs J. Lauritzen of Copenhagen, allowed Wynne-Edwards to take a trial voyage down channel, and finding her satisfactory we were able to persuade the Admiralty to buy her. She was taken to Harland & Wolff's yard in Belfast where, after suitable conversion, she was appropriately re-named *Endurance* by the Hon. Alexandra Shackleton, daughter of Lord Shackleton, Leader of the House of Lords, who had given us great support for the project. In October 1968, painted red overall and flying the White Ensign, the new ice patrol ship was off to the Antarctic. As Sponsor of the procurement of the vessel I had hoped to make her a surveying officer's command but in this I was disappointed. However, she was well equipped for surveying and carried a suitable launch for detached parties.

The widely publicised decision by the Government in early 1982 that *Endurance* was to be paid off in order to save £1 million annually undoubtedly encouraged General Galtieri to make his fatal move. Happily, the Falklands War led to *Endurance*'s reprieve and she continued her good work in the Southern Ocean until 1991.

The four new coastal survey vessels of the *Bulldog* class were completed in the yard of Brooke Marine Limited at Lowestoft during 1968. Lady Bush, wife of my direct superior, Admiral Sir John Bush, Vice Chief of Naval Staff, launched *Bulldog*, and my wife launched *Beagle*, a great name in hydrographic history. *Fox* and *Fawn* made up the quartet of these 1,000 ton vessels capable of worldwide operation in coastal waters.

For only twenty-five years after its creation was the Hydrographic Department a complete entity. About 1820 the engraving of the copper plates was put out to contract for the remainder of the century and from then on until 1968, because of wars, geographical location and administrative convenience the Department has, in different ways, remained split. The move of the compilation office to the new building alongside the printing works at Taunton was thus highly significant. The transfer, which included many tons of original charts dating back to Captain Cook's time and earlier, I placed under the overall direction of Captain Tony Cooper, who was currently on loan from the Royal Australian Navy as Assistant Hydrographer at Cricklewood.

Once the entire Department was concentrated at Taunton I had to divide my time between my new office there and my office in Whitehall. Egg Irving had impressed on me that to abandon Whitehall and the mid-week staff meetings of the Vice Chief of Naval Staff would seriously weaken my ability to defend my corner as a Whitehall warrior. I became a regular traveller on the Western Region between Paddington and Taunton.

Our 1968 Christmas party was to be held on a Friday night in the Civil Service Club in Taunton and had for its theme the 'Wild West'. As I had a meeting in London in the afternoon, it was arranged that I should change on the evening train and be taken direct to the party. Soberly clad in my city suit I found myself in the carriage opposite a maudlin drunk who insisted on engaging me in conversation. Passing Westbury I went with my suitcase to the toilet to change into my sheriff's outfit, completely stupefying my drunken friend as I returned to my seat with my stetson tipped forward on my head. As the train pulled into Taunton station I was astonished to hear the announcement 'This is the 5.30 from Paddington arriving at platform three. Onboard is the tootin', shooting Hydrographer.' As I leant from the carriage window there was a howl of Indians and the sound of gunfire. I was manhandled onto a station trolley and borne away by a posse of cowboys; as the train pulled out I saw the drunk peering incredulously through the window at the wild stampede on the platform.

The Department had used limited external computer assistance since 1964 for such processes as converting raw data from hyperbolic fixing systems into latitude and longitude, or for computing the free air anomalies from gravity data being collected by Navado ships. In 1967 we set up an internal feasibility study group to decide upon the type of computer best suited to meet the requirements of the whole Department from the processing of data to the sale of charts.

Meanwhile, we had no form of automated draughting equipment at a time when automated cartography was being widely introduced. The National Environmental Research Council (N.E.R.C.) had developed a complete system which they were keen for us to adopt, but we decided that the only sound way ahead was for us to develop our own process on a step by step basis carrying our staff along with us on the long road of experience. Accordingly, once we were established at Taunton we formed a working party to select the type of automated draughting equipment most appropriate to our needs. After extensive research we settled for the Kingmatic system being manufactured by a former weapons company in Norway. The control panel and the draughting machine were installed at Taunton in November 1968, and after some teething troubles we began scribing chart borders and hyperbolic lattices on red coated stabilene film on the Kingmatic flat bed plotting table, thus providing the necessary medium for transferring the image to a chart printing plate.

The next step was to enable graphics such as coastlines, depth contours and, later, 'point' data such as the positions of lighthouses and depth sounding figures, to be digitised into co-ordinates for input into the Kingmatic control panel. We had been experimenting with a D-Mac Line Follower since 1966 and this equipment, later modified to include voice acceptance, met these requirements. The input was achieved by following the line it was desired to digitise with a reading pencil, or by placing a reading head over various points on the drawing. A mechanism beneath the tracing table followed the pencil or the positioning head and passed signals to the output device, an electronic console giving a visual display and providing punched tape acceptable to the Kingmatic draughting system, a second one of which was soon on order from Norway.

What was happening at sea? The massive collection of data when running Navado lines had brought home to me even before I left *Vidal* that the time had come to supersede the laborious recording by hand in deck books by an automated system. We experimented onboard with a comparatively crude form of punched tape logging of data from the gravimeter, together with an input of position and thus the varying speeds of the ship, as this knowledge is essential when computing the free air gravity anomalies experienced over the oceans.

By early 1968 we had developed with the electronic firm of Elliott Brothers a shipborne logging system to record bathymetry and other parameters together with regular ship fixing co-ordinates which were automatically plotted in real time. The first system was installed in *Hecla* that year and the other two ocean survey vessels, *Hecate* and *Hydra*, were fitted in 1969. The eventual aim was to record the whole of the ship-obtained data on punched tape which could then be used to scribe a chart on the Kingmatic system in the office.

During the years 1969 to 1971 the officers onboard these three ships struggled to overcome the many problems encountered in developing the Automated Data Logging system (A.D.L.). Perhaps the major problem was that in those days the surveying officer on the bridge had no previous experience of computers. While striving to master automation it was also vital that the surveyor should maintain his critical oversight of the accuracy of the positioning and the undulating profile of the sea-bed graphically displayed by the echo-sounder.

Interfaces had to be introduced for a number of new electronic ship fixing systems, including satellite navigation receivers. The first real time plotting system was seriously flawed as the fixes appeared only on a drum-type plotter which deprived the surveyor of an overall view of progress. This difficulty was resolved by the fitting onboard of Kingmatic flatbed plotting tables which, although designed for use on land, were found to operate quite satisfactorily onboard these lively ocean survey vessels.

Although the echo-sounders throughout the survey squadron had all been converted to the metric system, the task of digitising the graphic records was possibly the hardest problem to solve for it was vital that every random shallow peak sounding should be recorded.

Despite these persistent difficulties we never gave up hope of developing a satisfactory system of automated hydrography, keenly aware that at least six other leading hydrographic services around the world were engaged in similar struggles. Now, some twenty years on, and after completely remodelling the system three or four times, I understand that the goal which we envisaged has been satisfactorily reached in Britain's latest survey ship H.M.S. *Roebuck*.

Admiral Sir John Bush, Vice Chief of Naval Staff, had a reputation for fierceness and certainly his weekly staff meetings were stimulating; he pulled my leg unmercifully from my first day when, having been wined and dined in my old ship *Vidal* on the previous evening, I had appeared in his office wearing a pair of grey trousers that did not exactly match my jacket. In 1967 Bush became Commander-in-Chief of the Western Fleet with his headquarters at Northwood; he was quick to inform me that I was still under his command and responsible to him for the conduct and direction of the surveying squadron.

In July 1969 Admiral Bush assembled his Fleet in Torbay for a visit by Her Majesty The Queen and the Duke of Edinburgh, accompanied by the Prince of Wales and Princess Anne. Sir John's flag was worn by the aircraft carrier *Eagle*; I, with my flag in *Hecate*, commanded a mixed flotilla composed of the coastal surveying ships *Fox* and *Fawn* and four R.N.R. minesweepers.

One of the highlights of the four days was to be a dinner for the Royal Family and on our first night in the anchorage the four admirals afloat were ordered onboard *Eagle* to dine, together with *Eagle*'s captain John Treacher and his supply officer, at Sir John's table. The menu to be served to the Royal Family was being tried out, with a post mortem after each course; even the beautiful dinner plates especially manufactured for the occasion were used. Sitting opposite the Commander-in-Chief, John Treacher idly turned his plate over whilst awaiting the service of the main course – 'The Nagasaki Stoneware

Factory – that's odd,' he murmured thoughtfully. Admiral Bush was at last caught out himself as he swiftly turned his plate over to read, 'Minton – Founded 1793 – Bone China – Made in England.' I tried to mollify him by informing him that at the Clyde Assembly of 1965 the special plates, also made by Minton for the dessert, were far smaller than his magnificent dinner plates.

The big day came when Her Majesty was to present a new Colour to the Western Fleet at an impressive parade in *Eagle*'s hangar. An easterly gale was holding the ship across the tide raising waves six feet high along the starboard side. Four admirals were to board the *Eagle* in succession followed by Her Majesty, each in their respective barges. I was the first to arrive in a survey launch immaculately disguised as a barge and was directed towards the starboard gangway, traditionally the one for officers' use. Three times I attempted unsuccessfully to clamber in my full dress uniform from the heaving boat to the platform at the foot of the gangway; on the final occasion I fell forward and would have plunged down between the platform and the barge, which was pounding against it, and probably to certain death had not my Flag Lieutenant for the day, Lieutenant Bashforth, seized hold of my ancient swordbelt and pulled me to safety. Seeing this near disaster, the officers on deck waved us to the port side where I ascended a stable gangway on the lee side of the great ship; as I reached the deck to the shrilling of boatswains' pipes *Eagle*'s commander, whose name happily escapes me, said to me, 'You have proved, Sir, that the starboard gangway is today un-Queenworthy.' Could Sir Walter Raleigh have done more?

The highlight of the Assembly for us surveyors came on a calm afternoon when, with *Fox* and *Fawn* berthed alongside *Hecate*, we welcomed Princess Anne for a visit to the three ships. She showed not only great interest in matters hydrographic, but also in our domestic arrangements. I was quietly amused when an admiral, who accompanied Her Royal Highness, was trying in vain to intervene in a lively conversation between the Princess and *Fox*'s chef on the culinary skills required in making a figgy duff, in order to inform her that she was already late for the tea party onboard H.M.S. *Blake* for the Chief Petty Officers of the Fleet where she was to join the Queen.

I was no 'Yellow Admiral' as Hydrographer, for Admiral Bush, a good friend to the Surveying Service throughout my term of office, encouraged me to get to sea in the twelve surveying ships afloat around the world in those days. I had heard much from the officers at sea of the liveliness of the *Hecla* Class ships, particularly when heading into heavy seas, but the true facts were not brought home to me until I embarked by helicopter in *Hecla* off Northern

Ireland for a passage with Captain Geoffrey Hall to Iceland. Sitting with him after dinner on the first night in his cabin in the fore part of the ship I found the heavy pounding into a north-west gale most disturbing and, to the well-disguised amusement of Captain Hall, I had to excuse myself for a visit to the heads. Not since I was a Dartmouth cadet onboard the training sloop *Forres* had I felt so queasy; as a once and for all cure for seasickness, our term officer took advantage of rough seas to send us to the oil store deep in the bowels of the engine room for a practical lecture on the viscosity of oils by an elderly petty officer suffering from acute halitosis.

In 1969 I visited a number of organisations in the Pacific with whom we did business, and arranged to be in New Zealand in time to accept an invitation to take part in the Bi-Centenary Celebrations of Captain Cook's first landing in Poverty Bay on 9th October 1769. Naval vessels from five nations assembled in the small harbour of Gisborne or anchored in the bay under the general directions of Captain Neil Anderson (my former navigator in H.M.N.Z.S. *Lachlan*) who was Naval Officer in charge of the celebrations. H.M.S. *London* wore the flag of Rear Admiral Terence Lewin, later Lord Lewin and a notable Cook scholar. The ship looked large indeed as she turned deftly in the small basin and berthed on the wharf aided by a diminutive tug and hampered by a passing squall.

My first pleasant task on 8th October was to open an exhibition of the charting of New Zealand in the Art Gallery. Commander Bill Smith, the first New Zealander to occupy the post of Hydrographer, had the happy idea of publishing a new chart of New Zealand (N. Z. II) on the anniversary day; by mutual agreement between us this chart replaced Admiralty Chart 1212 which had developed over nearly 200 years from the one originally compiled from Captain Cook's running surveys. N.Z.II was a beautiful chart in four colours with heights and depths in metres; *Endeavour*'s original tracks were overprinted and Cook's original chart was shown in an inset.

Thursday 9th October was the great day with ideal weather, a light westerly breeze tempering the heat of the sun. The day's programme began at 9.00 a.m. with a naval service at the Cook Memorial close alongside the ships berthed at the wharf. This tribute was marked by a plaque affixed to the existing memorial which I was given the honour of unveiling on behalf of the five navies assembled at Gisborne. There followed a long day of military ceremonies and civilian displays, all in the presence of Sir Arthur Porritt, the Governor General, and his Lady. One hundred massive floats trundled through the streets portraying every aspect of New Zealand life, both Maori and Pakeha, as well as great Maori war canoes, Captain Cook's longboat and the *Endeavour* with Young Nick pointing from the crow's nest.

The weather changed dramatically overnight and by Friday morning a strong southerly was blowing with relentless heavy rain. It was the day on which the Ngati Porou Maoris were to have their own ceremony at Anaura Bay some miles to the north where Cook's encounter with the natives on the 21st October had been extremely friendly and without the bloodshed that had occurred in Poverty Bay.

My association with the Ngati Poneke of Wellington when I had served in New Zealand had led to my nomination as Chief Guest of the Ngati Porou. Anxiety for the ships riding to hurricane hawsers at the wharf kept Neil Anderson in Gisborne while his vivacious wife, Barbara, accompanied me northward along the winding country roads to Anaura Bay, there to be confronted with a Maori challenge on the sodden marae. This has to be overcome before the welcoming songs and action dances can begin and involves a Maori male armed with a taiaha, a combination of spear and club, advancing towards the visitor in an attitude of defiance accompanied by hideous grimaces to test the visitor's friendliness of purpose and personal bravery. Three times the menacing advance is made; a dart laid at the feet of the unflinching guest enables him, when it has been recovered by his aide, to advance until the third dart is picked up and he is accepted.

My aide was Commodore Vallant of the New Zealand Navy. We were both in full uniform with swords and medals, mud-bespattered to our knees as we faced our challenger on the soggy turf; before laying the second dart, the Maori in his defiant exertions slipped and fell on his back in the mire to the enormous amusement of his assembled tribe. This so enraged him that on his third advance his grimaces were so ghastly and the handling of his taiaha so violent that I feared for our lives. We were, however, accepted, and after unveiling a tablet on a rock above the beach with a few suitable words, I was conducted to the comparative shelter of a billowing marquee for the welcome and a feast of pork and kumeras cooked in an earthen pit, or hangi.

A number of diplomats and their wives had come on from the national celebrations in Gisborne to witness events at Anaura Bay; they were ill prepared for the atrocious weather, some of them losing their stiletto-heeled shoes in the morass even before reaching the tent. The Maori organisers remained completely unruffled and provided a most palatable feast. On my right at the table sat the elegantly dressed wife of the United States Ambassador, on my left a merry Maori matron, whilst we were served by a boy wearing his father's tin-hat and camouflaged cape, brought home from the Western Desert, to protect him from the pouring rain on his errands to and from the exposed hangi.

H.M.S. *Argonaut*, having sailed from Gisborne, anchored in Anaura Bay on her way north to Fiji and her captain, Commander Garnett, and some of his men landed on the beach by helicopter. They joined us in the afternoon in the Ngati Porou meeting house, where the commander and I were seated on the stage on either side of an elderly Maori who gave a discourse on the natural supplies which Captain Cook might have gathered here for his men. Before him was a basket containing various dried leaves and grasses, misshapen fruits and gnarled roots; holding up a sample of each in turn he described their medicinal properties – this one prevented scurvy, that one cooled the blood and another was a strong aphrodisiac (although by all accounts Cook's people were not in need of the latter). Finally the old man presented me with the basket; I thought quickly and with generous words passed the gift to Commander Garnett, for was he not bound on a long sea voyage; he and his men would doubtless be in need of medication and stimulation before Fiji was reached. He could not refuse, and my last sight of the commander was as he clambered into his helicopter clutching the bounteous basket.

When in 1965 I was taking *Vidal* up Channel for the last time, thick fog enveloped Dover Strait. To avoid a hazardous and sleepless night I decided to take her along the French side of the Channel as far as Sandettie before heading north for the Thames Estuary. With only a sprinkling of shipping showing ahead of me on the radar, I could see to the north a mass of vessels between Beachy Head and South Foreland moving in both directions into a series of head-on encounters in the fog.

As long ago as 1959 Commandant Oudet of the French Hydrographic Service had pointed out in an article in a French maritime journal that, for safety's sake, traffic in the bottleneck of Dover Strait should be diverted into separate one-way lanes; the following year he and Commandant Poll, a Belgian maritime superintendent, set out their proposals at a meeting of Britain's Institute of Navigation. This resulted in the formation of an Institute working party, quickly expanded to include members of the French and German Institutes representing shipping, lighting, pilotage and hydrographic services to study the idea. From that time onwards the British Institute of Navigation pursued this matter under the dogged and persistent guidance of its Director, Michael Richey. Rear Admiral Irving chaired the first meeting of the working group, which was followed by a second meeting in 1962 chaired by the French

Hydrographer, Ingénieur Général Gougenheim, when it was decided to send a questionnaire to all shipmasters thought to be using Dover Strait. This poll was organised by the International Chamber of Shipping and of the 3,755 forms returned only 107 were against routeing.

Of the many schemes drawn up, the one by Captain Lynes, a cross-channel ferry master, was accepted, which used the natural features in Dover Strait to separate the streams of traffic. It was considered by the Maritime Safety Committee of the Intergovernmental Maritime Consultative Organisation (IMCO), a U.N. agency recently established in London, when Michael Richey opened the discussion in January 1963. The proposal was accepted but the Committee recommended various improvements to navigational aids in the Channel before the scheme could be introduced, so it was not until 1967 that IMCO informed its Member States that the plan should be followed.

It was vital to inform shipping generally and this I did in a Notice to Mariners in 1967 which gave details of the main routes and those set aside for coastal traffic. It was made clear that the scheme was not mandatory, but happy in my mind that the system had the backing of IMCO we overprinted the routes on relevant charts.

Many ships ignored the recommendations and in 1970 several serious collisions occurred in the Dover Straits involving vessels navigating in the wrong lane. In the consequent media and political clamour it came to light that Trinity House and the Honourable Company of Master Mariners had never really accepted the scheme and were recommending a revision of the system in the Straits of Dover by reversing the direction of both traffic flows. This greatly alarmed me for I had been encouraging shipmasters through our various publications over the past three years to adhere to the voluntary separation routes. I would never be able now to persuade seamen to throw away their overprinted charts, to abandon the well-publicised scheme and adopt another. Furthermore, it seemed to me that to forsake the traditional rule which directs shipping to use the starboard side of a channel would have a malignant influence on the many other separation routing proposals already being considered for other critical areas. I had recently been elected President of the Institute of Navigation and was invited to chair a meeting on 3rd February 1972 of appropriate representatives from U.K. and the Continent to consider what should be done next as regards separation routing. It was vaguely believed that about 700 ships passed through the Channel daily but there was no idea of the pattern of shipping involved and it was resolved at the meeting that what now was required was a professional survey of daily traffic in Dover Strait, and fortunately the National Physical Laboratory agreed to arrange for their newly established Division of Maritime Science to make such a survey.

In May 1972 when the data had been acquired and analysed a Symposium of Marine Traffic Engineering, sponsored by the Institute of Navigation and the Institute of Naval Architects, was held at the National Physical Laboratory. Representatives of the British Government took part in this important symposium which was a turning point towards mandatory routeing as a number of Governments began to represent their views directly to IMCO. By the year's end the Trinity House proposals had lapsed, the starboard hand concept was maintained and the Dover Strait scheme became the first of many mandatory traffic separation routes in critical areas around the world. The International Hydrographic Organisation now began to formulate with IMCO a series of internationally agreed symbols for delineating separation routeing schemes on charts; a stipulation was also drawn up whereby a government proposing a new routeing plan must ensure that modern hydrographic surveys are available in support of the scheme.

Throughout my time as Hydrographer, Very Large Crude Carriers (VLCC) continued to be built in ever increasing size and draught ignoring, it seemed to us, charted depths of as little as 21.9 metres in the Dover Strait and southern North Sea. These shallow areas formed a difficult hurdle for a heavily laden tanker to clear at the end of an 11,000 mile voyage from the Persian Gulf via the Cape to North-West Europe. In close co-operation with the Netherlands Hydrographer, our two services worked to survey and re-survey these critical and unstable areas.

We never really found out what under-keel clearance VLCC masters were willing to accept in meeting their tight schedules. Tankers with draughts of nineteen metres were sailing through Dover Strait; with their broad beams a roll of only 2° could increase the draught by half a metre, whilst the squat of such great vessels when underway in shallow water was another figure difficult to obtain. Studies of sandwave patterns on the sea-bed, attempts to predict the lowering of sea level in negative surges in times of high barometric pressure and the use of sea-bed tide gauges offshore to provide additional data for the production of co-tidal charts were among the many refinements we tried in order to give the mariner the most accurate depth information possible. Above all, the side-scan sonar was increasingly brought into service; this is an instrument which extends the surveyor's view to the bottom topography which lies between one line of echo-sounding and the next. The equipment consists of a towed 'fish' from which pulses are emitted on either beam directed downwards across the sea-floor; the returning echoes are recorded on a graphic display onboard from which shallow areas may be pinpointed for later examination by echo-sounding.

Laden tankers bound from the Persian Gulf on the 11,000 mile voyage to Japan meet a similar 21.9 metre hurdle when passing through the Malacca Strait. In the last months of my time as Hydrographer, Commander Roger Morris (later Hydrographer), in command of H.M.S. *Hydra*, was surveying a route ten miles wide through the 180-mile length of the Malacca Strait. Control was provided by Hi-Fix with the master station onboard and the slaves along the coastline on the Malaysian side of the Strait. Hi-Fix was Decca's improvement on Lambda for hydrographic work, of slightly shorter range, the slave stations were much more transportable and the system could be used in a two range or hyperbolic mode. As *Hydra*'s work progressed the slaves were leap-frogged down the coast in roughly forty-mile steps, being airlifted by the ship's Wasp helicopter.

I flew out to visit *Hydra* and also the Hydrographic Offices of Indonesia, Singapore and Malaysia, for they were collaborating with Japan in making a survey of Phillip Strait which leads from the southern end of the Malacca Strait. This joint effort was to relieve the U.K. of its formerly accepted responsibilty for routine surveys of the shallower parts of both the Malacca and Singapore Straits.

In January 1971, less than a month before my retirement, the Treasury approved the building of an additional and improved *Hecla* class survey ship for which I had long been striving. Tenders were about to be invited with a completion date for the vessel in July 1973. I was happy that my proposal for the name of the vessel had been accepted – *Herald* – an honoured hydrographic name in both the nineteenth and twentieth centuries and my own first survey ship thirty-five years earlier.

On the morning of 5th February 1971, my last day in office, Vice Admiral Griffin, Controller of the Navy, came to Taunton to open our first general office computer, which had eventually been installed as the result of our feasibilty study. The Admiral asked me to explain some peculiar signals exchanged between myself and the Trinidad and Tobago Coastguard which he had seen in the Admiralty signal log – but that is another story.

In the afternoon my wife and I were met by the assembled staff who presented me with a number of nineteenth-century volumes relating to hydrographic voyages, in each of which was inserted an illuminated bookplate printed from an engraving by Frank Clay, one of our last copper engravers. The bookplate records that the volume was presented to me by 'The Surveying Officers and Recorders of Her Majesty's Fleet and the Staff of the Hydrographic Department' – 'as a tribute of esteem and grateful acknowledgement of his unremitting kindness and attention to their welfare and likewise in token of the very high sense they entertain of his eminent abilities.'

These words were first engraved on a magnificent punchbowl which his officers presented to Captain W.F. Owen on completion of his great African surveys in 1826. I was indeed honoured to share such a tribute with one of my heroes and I was near to tears while saying farewell.

I had come to realise over the years that our whole company, civil and naval, laboured as one to sustain the impeccable standards demanded by the Admiralty Chart.

Chapter XXIV

Natural Break

From:- Commanding Officer Trinidad & Tobago Coastguard
To:- Admiralty for Hydrographer
No excuse now. You are in Edmund Hart's Band send measurements.

From:- Hydrographer
To:- C.O. Trinidad & Tobago Coastguard
Reference your signal. Forty-three, forty-three, forty-three the original cylindrical admiral. Will arrive one week before Carnival.

Commander Mervyn Williams, currently in command of the Coastguard, had sailed with me in *Vidal* and was aware of my wish to take the Road during Carnival. Seeing my retirement announced he realised that I could be in Port of Spain by Shrove Tuesday.

When one leaves the Service one gets a month's terminal leave on full pay and, if one wishes, another month for a rehabilitation course. Business management and similar courses were offered to me, but as I was not going into commerce I opted for bricklaying and house decoration as my preparation for civilian life. In order to be in Trinidad for Carnival it was necessary to take my terminal leave first, to be followed by the rehabilitation course.

I was unaware of Edmund Hart's carnival theme until I was met by my good friend Betty Bourne, a High Court Judge in Trinidad, at Piarco Airport. 'Edmund Hart is doing Butterflies and Moths,' she said, 'you are to be a Speckled Moth.' Arriving at Trinidad direct from an English winter it was necessary to walk the roads to harden up, and laze on the beaches to get a suntan before jumping up for two days through the torrid streets of Port of Spain.

218

There were also visits to be made to an Indian household for fittings of my costume which was taking shape, not forgetting a pocket for the rum flask. A black and white speckled bodice and leotards formed the basis of the dress, a magnificent pair of diaphanous wings sprouted from my back, whilst from my headpiece arose a pair of waving antennae.

I felt a little self conscious on arrival at the 'camp' on the Monday morning for the rehearsal march, but the festive atmosphere soon embraced me as we revellers took the Road to the compelling music of our steel orchestra. This first day was strenuous. Shrove Tuesday, after a night of gaiety, was utterly exhausting. As the 6,000 masqueraders in our Band advanced along our route, the various species of butterflies and moths became wildly intermingled as old friends met and welcomed each other; yet as we approached the great stage on the Savannah, vigorously directed by our more exotically dressed leaders, the scattered members of each group came together to form the multi-coloured pattern just as our designers had planned months earlier. To allow the preceding Band to clear the 300-yard long Savannah stage, the oncoming Band is halted by traffic lights at the base of the ramp. While waiting at the red lights our leaders urged us into a frenzy of jumping activity until, as the lights changed to green, we surged up onto the stage to the sound of our steel orchestra hammering out Lord Kitchener's Road March 'Play Mas.' Maintaining our 'Spirit of Carnival', so much prized by the judges, right across the long stage we finally staggered down into the dust of the Savannah, there to be plied with warm kola, lemonade or green coconut milk by stall holders well aware of our needs after such activity in the heat of the day.

All too soon the steel drums' insistent message got us going again through the crowd-lined streets towards Independence Square and on into the suburbs. I was a somewhat tubby moth and at one point an equally tubby Trinidadian stepped from the bystanders and, tapping my speckled stomach, shouted, 'I see you'se making the baby moths for next year's Carnival.'

I have returned for Carnival on a number of occasions, staying with my dear friend Bobbie Muir who keeps open house in her old colonial-style residence in St. Clair during this festive period. Twice more I have marched with a Band, once as a Blackfoot Indian and again as a Brain Person from Outer Space. The excitement never palls, the new Road March music is always compelling and the sheer sense of happiness infectious. Ash Wednesday is for recovery after which, for six weeks or more, one remains acutely aware of the therapeutic properties of Carnival – life is vibrant and immune from stress. True to the Trinidad Constitution there are no racial problems on the Road, no 'steamers' race through the masqueraders, nor do hooligans interfere, for every Trinidadian is committed to Carnival to the exclusion of all else.

Back in England, I exchanged the role of butterfly for that of bricklayer as I arrived in Portsmouth for my rehabilitation course and donned my overalls. The class was composed of myself, a lieutenant, a C.P.O., two P.O.s, a stoker, an able seaman and a steward. Our civilian instructors were helpful but strict: if one's wall was not perfect it was knocked down to be built again; if adjoining wallpaper patterns were only slightly misaligned the whole had to be stripped. One day when I was on a high scaffolding in the school attempting that most difficult of tasks, pasting up ceiling paper, a voice called up from below, 'You are making a pretty poor job of that, Ritchie.' Gazing up at me was Admiral Sir Horace Law, Flag Officer Portsmouth Area, making his inspection tour of the Barracks. As I was so soon to pass out of naval jurisdiction I took a chance. 'Come up here and try it yourself, Sir,' said I. The Admiral was amused but did not join me.

During the final week of the course we travelled daily to Waterlooville where, with two of us allocated to each room, we redecorated South Africa House, a naval orphanage. We aroused considerable curiosity when, in our smart white overalls, we visited the local pub for our midday pints. We let it be known to an inquisitive barmaid that we were a team of professionals from London engaged in delicate renovations at a noble country house. Each day as we clustered round the bar we were amused to see the ripple of interest as the barmaid's information was passed knowingly from one local drinker to another.

When my forthcoming retirement was first announced Professor Henry Charnock of Southampton University invited me to join his Oceanographic Department as a Senior Research Fellow, whilst Sir George Deacon, Director of the National Institute of Oceanography, obtained for me a generous grant. So in March 1971 I took up my University post and began research into the historic developments of hydrography in Europe. I had three years before me with the option that, if I was elected the following year as a Director of the International Hydrographic Bureau, I would be released after eighteen months. My project soon proved to be gargantuan as I set about gathering from my hydrographic friends on the Continent any information they had concerning the origins of their establishments.

After the rigid routines of service life, I found those of the university to be refreshingly liberal. The Department of Oceanography was headed by two professors representing the physical and biological sides of the science. The long morning coffee break was indicative of how things were done; the entire staff, from the professors to the young woman who looked after the fish tanks, assembled in the central lobby on equal terms, and there discussed with one another the breakthroughs or problems they were encountering in their work, and learnt from such informal exchanges. From mid-morning onwards, when we had returned to our laboratories or rooms, work appeared to gather momentum and it was often long after the Staff Refectory had closed for the night that I laid down my pen and accompanied two or three Ph.D. students for sausages and chips in the Students' Union.

It was the wealth of knowledge within the university which could so easily be drawn upon that excited me. Whatever query arose in my studies, be it concerned with Portuguese history, Pythagoras' theories or the meaning of a German nautical term, there was somewhere a professor, lecturer or foreign student who would, apparently willingly, give me an hour or more of his or her time to impart particular knowledge. Then there was the library, only a few metres from my room, which was strong on nautical works, even subscribing to the International Hydrographic Review. It was a magic time for me as the eighteen months went by; I was happily spending all my days on what had formerly been for me but a pleasurable leisure pursuit. I failed to achieve my proposed hydrographic history, but I was able to compose a 5,000-word essay which assembles in compact form the main elements of the long story. It provided the Introduction to *The Sea Chart*, an historical survey based on the collections in the National Maritime Museum by Derek Howse and Michael Sanderson.

In the early 1950s the Royal Institution of Chartered Surveyors opened its doors to hydrographic surveyors and a trickle of Royal Navy hydrographers began to study for associate membership and fellowship within the Land Surveying Division. At that time the great majority of sea surveyors in the world were trained and employed by national agencies, many of them naval, and port authorities. With the advent of the offshore oil industry in the late fifties and sixties there was a 'hydrographic explosion' with the urgent need for sea surveyors to carry out accurately positioned seismic surveys, drilling site investigations, the siting of massive structures and the precise laying of pipelines along the sea-floor. At first former naval surveying officers and recorders met the demand, but soon it became necessary to train land surveyors in hydrographic skills; one of the first establishments to tackle this task was London North East Polytechnic where Alan Ingham, a former naval surveyor, was a teacher.

During 1971 and 1972 I used to visit the R.I.C.S. in London to take the chair at Hydrographic Sub-Committee meetings; on one such occasion Gerry White, Chief Surveyor in the Port of London, another former naval surveyor, came to see me at the Institution. He informed me that a number of hydrographic surveyors, led by Alan Ingham, had formed themselves into a steering committee to bring about the establishment of a Hydrographic Society to embrace the widest interests of all classes of sea surveyors. It was the steering committee's wish, he told me, that I should agree to be the first President of the new Society. Initially the R.I.C.S. was apprehensive that such an organisation would militate against hydrographic membership of the Institution. In time I was able to assure Council that the proposed society would not be involved with examinations and professional qualifications, being conceived as a fraternity of all classes of sea surveyors for the exchange of technical knowledge, through a journal, symposia, meetings, discussion and, in due course, conferences.

Once I had got this message across, I accepted the Presidency of the new Society with alacrity for I had been aware for some time of the growing requirement for such an association. Today, The Hydrographic Society has a worldwide membership of over 2,000 in seventy different countries and seven National Branches. I am proud to have been the first of twelve distinguished Presidents of five different nationalities.

Chapter XXV

I.H.B.

In 1848 a son was born to H.S.H. Prince Charles of Monaco and christened Albert. He was destined to become one of the world's great oceanographers and to have a major influence on international hydrography.

At an early age Prince Albert went to sea as a junior officer in the Spanish Navy. At the age of twenty-five he purchased in England a small sailing schooner which he named *Hirondelle* and sailed to Monaco. From then onwards he made many scientific cruises in the Mediterranean and the North Atlantic in *Hirondelle*, the first of four research yachts which he commanded himself during the next forty years.

Albert succeeded his father as Prince of Monaco in 1889, and after three years' involvement with affairs of state he resumed his oceanographic voyages in a new 600-ton steam yacht *Princesse Alice*, which was superseded by another new vessel *Princesse Alice II* in 1898, from which he continued deep sounding and dredging of specimens from the ocean floor in areas of the North Atlantic from the Azores to Spitzbergen. The Prince employed mixed crews of Breton and Azorean seamen with whom he closely identified himself; he was accompanied by scientists including Jules Richard, and John Buchanan who had sailed on the *Challenger* Expedition.

In 1911 he purchased his last yacht *Hirondelle II* in which he continued his research until shortly after the outbreak of war. The hundred or so illustrated volumes of his 'Resultats des Campagnes Scientifiques accompliés sur son Yacht' continued the tradition of the *Challenger* Reports and added massively to the knowledge of the oceans.

At the Seventh International Geographic Conference in Berlin in 1899 a commission was set up to study the terminology to be used for naming deep-sea features and to draw up plans for a bathymetric chart of the oceans. Prince Albert took the chair at a meeting of this commission in Wiesbaden in 1903, where he agreed to organise and finance the production of the 'Carte Générale Bathymetrique des Océans', a series composed of twenty-four sheets on a scale of 1/10 million on which seven draughtsmen began to work at once. Seven months later the Prince was able to present the litho-printed charts to the Eighth International Geographic Congress in Washington D.C. in January 1904.

This first edition of 'Gebco', as the series is still known to-day, contained 18,000 soundings selected from Admiralty charts, obtained from cable laying ships and taken by the Prince himself. There were many huge gaps of unsounded water, but it was the beginning of the charting of the oceans beyond the continental shelves.

During the first decade of the twentieth century the Prince devoted much of his time between voyages planning, and later supervising, the construction of the Musée Océanographique which clings to the towering cliffs of the Rocher on which are situated ancient Monaco Ville and the Palace. It was opened in 1910 and housed thousands of specimens collected by the Prince from whale skeletons to microplankton.

At the inauguration of the Musée the Prince launched the second edition of Gebco which, hampered at first by war and extended by the ever increasing inflow of bathythermic data, was not completed until 1930 under the direction of Dr. Jules Richard.

Ingénieur en Chef M. J. A. Renard of the French Service Hydrographique de la Marine, aware of a resolution passed at the International Congress of Navigation in St. Petersburg in 1908 that a meeting of seamen and surveyors would be beneficial to the standardisation of charts, attended as a representative of France the Congress of Navigation held in St. Petersburg in 1912. At this latter Congress he outlined the advantages that agreement on many aspects of chart production would bring to seamen; but the very many maritime matters being considered by the delegates convinced him that a special conference limited to oceanography would be the forum for real progress. Accordingly, when Renard assumed the post of Directeur du Service Hydrographique in January 1913 he began to work towards arranging a hydrographic conference. War intervened, but as soon as it was over Renard collaborated with Admiral Sir John Parry, the British Hydrographer, to arrange a meeting. This was called in London by the Lords Commissioners of the Admiralty and the first International Hydrographic Conference was attended by delegates from twenty-two countries in June 1919. Considerable progress was made during this conference in standardisation of symbols and chart specifications; perhaps most importantly it was decided to establish a permanent international bureau of hydrography. A steering committee consisting of Renard, Parry and Rear Admiral E. Simpson U.S.N. was elected to pursue this objective.

Any international agency formed subsequent to the establishment of the League of Nations was automatically incorporated into the League, and thus the International Hydrographic Bureau was to become its first technical agency and might well have found itself installed in Geneva. However, the steering committee, whilst meeting in Paris, were received by Prince Albert of Monaco; he believed that a landlocked base for an organisation involved with maritime affairs was unacceptable and invited the Bureau, once established, to take its seat within the Principality on the shores of the Mediterranean. Such an invitation from the world's greatest ocean hydrographer was readily accepted.

In May 1921 nineteen Member States elected, by postal ballot, the first Directing Committee of the Bureau – Admiral Parry, Captain Phaff (Netherlands) and Captain Muller (Norway). It was extremely sad that on the very day the ballot papers were despatched from Carlton House Terrace, London, Monsieur Renard, the chief architect of the Bureau, passed away suddenly, thus removing him from the list of candidates. The three elected Directors, with Admiral Sir John Parry as President, moved into a rented building in Monaco and engaged a young Italian girl, Mademoiselle Serra whom the admiral had met in London, as their Secretary in July 1921. The Bureau's generous host, Prince Albert, died just over a year later, but the Princely family and the Government of Monaco have continued to support the International Hydrographic Bureau to this day; in 1929 the Government raised a magnificent building on the port as headquarters for the Bureau.

The League of Nations crumbled away before the outbreak of World War II and was finally terminated in April 1946. During the war the Bureau itself declined, and at one point, during the German occupation of Monaco, the office virtually closed; with the return of peace the Member States began again to gather together and sixteen of them sent delegates to the Fifth International Hydrographic Conference in Monaco in April 1947, ten years after the Fourth Conference.

By the time of the Ninth Conference, when I attended as leader of the United Kingdom Delegation, the membership had risen to forty-one. Without the former authority of the League of Nations the statutory position of the Bureau had become unclear, and a new Convention had been prepared by legal experts for ratification at the Conference, creating an international organisation with the Bureau as its secretariat. I carried the written authority of the Rt. Hon. George Brown, the British Foreign Minister, enabling me to sign the Convention in the office of the Minister of State in ancient Monaco Ville.

To quote Article II of the Convention will elucidate the purpose of the organisation, whilst the election of a Directing Committee is explained in Article III:

ARTICLE II

The Organisation shall have a consultative and purely technical nature. It shall be the object of the Organisation to bring about:

(a) The co-ordination of the activities of national hydrographic offices;

(b) The greatest possible uniformity in nautical charts and documents;

(c) The adoption of reliable and efficient methods of carrying out and exploiting hydrographic surveys;

(d) The development of the sciences in the field of hydrography and the techniques employed in descriptive oceanography.

ARTICLE III

The Directing Committee shall be composed of three members of different nationality elected by the Conference, which shall further elect one of them to fill the office of President of the Committee. The term of office of the Directing Committee shall be five years.

At the Tenth Conference (1972) I was nominated by the United Kingdom as a candidate for election as a Director. On this occasion and again in 1977 I was elected as President of the Directing Committee; Rear Admiral Kapoor, previously the Indian Hydrographer, was also elected as a Director on these two occasions. We had with us for the first five-year term Rear Admiral Jim Tison, formerly of the Coast and Geodetic Survey, a real old-fashioned gentleman from Southern Carolina, whilst in our second term we were partnered by Captain Jim Ayres of the U.S. Navy.

Having advanced in the Navy on the recommendations of my seniors I found it a stimulating change to be elected to my final post by my peers.

Rear Admiral Hall, the British Hydrographer, led his delegation to the 1972 Conference and entertained Prince Rainier and Princess Grace to a reception onboard his two coastal survey ships, *Fox* and *Fawn*, which were in the Port of Monaco. These small vessels had but one steward between them, so seamen and stokers had been pressed into service. As a guest I was standing talking to the Prince when a mechanical engineer who had served with me in *Vidal* rushed up to welcome me. 'How good to see you, Sir. I'll look after you all right, I'll get you a double whisky for a start,' said he as he hurried off without even a nod in the Prince's direction. The Prince laughed when I apologised for taking precedence over him in this important matter.

Soon after taking up office in 1972 I had to say farewell to Elena Serra, who was retiring after fifty-one years as Secretary to the Bureau. She wrote a short account of her life in the monthly I. H. Bulletin.

> '*It always seems such a short time between Conferences. After the busy time of its preparation, and the bustle of the first day to receive all the delegates the thrilling time comes at the end when the voting takes place for the election of the new Directors. – That's when the staff have some apprehensions, for they will have to work under the new Directors for at least five years.*'

During those five years a multi-national team of Directors and staff have to settle down and work together to carry out the programme set out for them by the Conference and to cope with the new developments in the worldwide hydrographic field.

It is a bilingual organisation, French and English. My daily discussions with the Office Manager, Mr. Lahire, both trying to speak the other's language with an equal lack of skill, were a cause of widespread merriment and should have been recorded.

By the time of the Ninth Conference (1967) the essential chart format and symbols, although far from complete, had reached a stage where the Conference was able to establish a commission to draw up a scheme and specifications for small-scale charts covering most of the seas of the world, designated as the International, or INT, Chart Series. Then serving as the U.K. Hydrographer I was appointed as chairman of this commission.

The concept of the INT Charts at small scales was to reduce duplication of time-consuming small scale generalised chart compilation. Some Member States of the I.H.O. known as 'Producer Nations' each undertook to compile a number of sheets in the series and to make the reproduction material available to other Member States, to be known as 'Printer Nations', who wished to reprint the charts.

Our report was sent to all Member States three years later setting out proposals for two series of charts, one on a scale of 1/10 million to cover the wide oceans and the other on a scale of 1/3^1/$_2$ million to cover the offshore continental waters.

The project was highly successful and within ten years almost all the eighty-odd charts had been produced and reprinted by several countries. This provided international shipping with uniform modern chart coverage for all ocean and sea pasages.

The success of the small-scale INT Chart series led inevitably to consideration of extending the concept to include charts at medium and large scales. Accordingly, the Tenth Conference (1972) formed a commission to assess the problems by making a pilot study of the North Sea. This was given the name North Sea International Chart Commission (N.S.I.C.C.) and Mr. Derek Newson, the Chief Civil Hydrographic Officer in the U.K. Hydrographic Office, was nominated as chairman. The commission consisted of members from the hydrographic offices around the North Sea with some other Member States joining in. Mr. Newson was able to present his report at the Eleventh Conference (1977).

It had become obvious to the members of the N.S.I.C.C. early in their deliberations that the successful production of INT charts on larger scales would require a much greater level of chart symbol standardisation than the Bureau was currently achieving on an ad hoc basis.

While accepting the N.S.I.C.C. Report as an excellent pilot study for the more general adoption of the INT chart on medium and large scales, the Eleventh Conference resolved to continue a commission under Derek Newson's chairmanship titled the Chart Specification Committee (C.S.C.), its task to develop a full set of chart specifications for worldwide charting application.

By the Twelfth Conference (1982) the C.S.C. had achieved remarkable progress, with the result that the Bureau had been able to print and distribute to Member States a full range of Chart Specifications including symbols, abbreviations, terms, styles, etc., all of which were adopted by the Conference. The Commission was re-designated as the Charts Standardisation Commission, to which all future changes of specifications or proposals for new symbols would be referred for consideration before implementation by the Member States. Thus in 1982 for the first time in sixty-three years the complete range of chart symbols had been internationally agreed, and these will be slowly adopted worldwide as new national and INT Charts are developed.

On my first meeting with Prince Rainier after taking up my post as President of the Directing Committee, he told me that, although he himself was aware of the good work being done, no-one outside the Bureau seemed to appreciate this; he likened the Bureau to a sleeping princess whose hour of awakening was due. Some months later, as a part of this process, we arranged an 'Open Day' at the Bureau, preceded the previous evening by a reception attended by Prince Rainier and Princess Grace. It was clearly apparent that the Bureau was little known: even the police directed our guests to the Musée Océanographique, whilst I was not infrequently asked if I 'worked for Cousteau'. During the evening the Prince and Princess visited my office to see the van Keulen atlases which had recently been reprinted in the Netherlands. My 'Too Difficult' tray, now re-named 'Trop Difficile', amused the Prince who suggested to the Princess that such a tray might be useful at the Palace.

Some months later the Prince asked me, at the annual reception on the eve of the National Day, how we were doing at the Bureau. I replied that, as there had been a French postal strike for the last eight weeks, business was slack – 'Ah well,' said he with a smile, 'that will have given you time to empty the "Trop Difficile" tray.'

When the second edition of Gebco was published in 1930 the Government of Monaco had asked the I.H.B. to take over the task of keeping Gebco up to date; the Bureau later introduced an innovation whereby eighteen volunteering Member States became responsible for maintaining a record of incoming ocean soundings in their respective areas on plotting sheets at the larger scale of 1/1 million. Nevertheless, by 1972 only three sheets of the third edition and four sheets of the fourth edition of Gebco had been produced under the direction of a Gebco Committee. The plotting sheets had proved valuable, but the editing of the charts themselves had lacked true scientific input at a time when the study of deep-sea morphology was advancing rapidly.

Soon after arriving in Monaco I attended the Second Congress on the History of Oceanography, held in Edinburgh in September 1972 to commemorate the centenary of the *Challenger* Expedition. There I met Dr. Gunther Böhnecke, the first postwar German Hydrographer, whom I have mentioned earlier. He was a former chairman of the Gebco Committee and both an oceanographer and a hydrographer; as I was going on to the Scottish Marine Biology Laboratory at Oban for a meeting of the Scientific Committee for Oceanographic Research (SCOR) Working Group, where the future of Gebco was to be discussed, I sought Böhnecke's advice. This left me in no doubt that the way ahead for Gebco lay in a joint approach by the International Oceanographic Committee (I.O.C.) and the I.H.O.

Desmond Scott, the former S.O.B. who had helped me in my interview with Chapman Pincher, was now Secretary to I.O.C. and was at the Working Group meeting in Oban where the fifth edition of Gebco was born. Back in Monaco I asked my co-Director, Rear Admiral Kapoor, to work with Scott to set up a Joint I.O.C.-I.H.O. Guiding Committee for Gebco which, with their enthusiasm, and the brilliant leadership of Dr. Eric Simpson of South Africa as chairman of the committee, eventually involved every scientist of standing working in the field of ocean-bed morphology in putting together the fifth edition of Gebco. It was printed by the Canadian Hydrographic Office and published in its entirety in time for the Twelfth I.H. Conference ten years later.

Writing a joint preamble to a booklet published with the fifth edition of Gebco the newly appointed Secretary to I.O.C., Mario Ruivo, and I described the new edition as

> '*a highly sophisticated set of sheets on which the relief features of the world ocean floor are reliably and intelligently depicted with accuracy commensurate with the modern state of knowledge. Its publication as a complete edition in 1982 is most opportune in view of the implication of the new ocean regime resulting from the Third United Nations Conference on the Law of the Sea.*'

The fifth edition of Gebco measures, when the sheets are placed together, approximately four metres by three metres and serves as a wall map in many maritime establishments around the world, testifying to the success of ten years' work by a band of dedicated scientists and hydrographers working closely together, whilst preserving the memory of its founder – Prince Albert of Monaco.

After a year at the I.H.B. we were fortunate to obtain the services of Commodore Tony Cooper as the senior professional assistant in the Bureau. Retired from a third term as Australian Hydrographer, he put all his energies into the Bureau during the next ten years; it would be difficult to overstate his influence, particularly on the re-organisation of the five yearly Conferences. Précis writers were introduced, a complex yet logical system of dealing with conference documents was brought into being, and, using the printing machine which we established in the Bureau, he devised a means of reporting the work and resolutions of the Conference to Member States with a minimum of delay.

Tony and his wife Betty lived in a flat overlooking the Bureau and, more importantly, the most exciting part of the Grand Prix course. Their all-day parties on Grand Prix day will never be forgotten by those fortunate enough to have enjoyed them.

Only once did I inadvertently ruffle Tony's feathers. It was during the Conference of 1977 when as its Secretary he was working flat out; on the night when the chief delegates were invited to dinner onboard the Soviet Surveying Vessel *Bellinghausen*, Tony decided he could, for once, have an early night. The party onboard was hilarious, attentive waitresses dispensed a lengthy dinner, vodka flowed, speeches were made, toasts abounded, songs were sung and at about 2.00 a.m. Rear Admiral David Haslam, the British Hydrographer, and I stumbled ashore and made our way up the Avenue d'Ostende. On passing Rosie's famous Bar we heard merriment within and found that a coachload of young Australian girls were still having a party. It seemed to us in our befuddled state that it would only be right to inform Tony. We crushed together into Rosie's telephone box, 'Hey, Tony, come on up to Rosie's. There's a bunch of lovely Aussie sheilas in here.' His drowsy voice told us in no uncertain manner to 'get lost' and we felt offended. It was well after midday on the morrow before Tony deigned to converse with us, over 'horse's necks' in Rosie's at our expense.

Resulting from a resolution at the Tenth (1972) Conference, an I.H.O. Commission was set up to consider a worldwide system for promulgating radio navigational warnings to shipping. Working in co-operation with the International Maritime Consultative Organisation (IMCO, now IMO) the idea was developed to divide up the world into sixteen 'Navareas', each with one of its major hydrographic offices acting as 'Area Co-ordinator' responsible for collecting information from all the other hydrographic authorities within the area, analysing it, and broadcasting warnings to ocean-going shipping within its Navarea.

So close was the worldwide co-operation of the Member States of the I.H.O. that the sixteen Navareas were in operation by 1st April 1980, overcoming communication and language difficulties to provide an English language Worldwide Navigational Warning Service informing shipping of new-found dangers and important changes to charted information.

I have highlighted only two or three of the major advances made by the I.H.O. and its Bureau in support of greater safety at sea in the years 1972-1982. It would take a book itself to describe the work of those twenty dedicated people of different nationalities who labour away in Monaco. Their loyalty to the Bureau and to the Member States is truly remarkable.

During our ten years in Monaco my wife and I spent many weekends in the beautiful pine-clad mountains of the 'arrière pays'. There, one could walk from one mountain village to another along the ancient 'sentiers' formerly used as donkey tracks. We usually based ourselves on the town of Sospel on the River Bevera and I felt at home there; the Ricci family were much in evidence, whilst in the square was the Palais Ricci where Pope Pius VII stayed in 1809.

We would take with us two 'pan bagnats' (flat round loaves stuffed with tomatoes, hard-boiled eggs, olives, onion and anchovies, liberally dressed with olive oil) and a litre of Provencal wine. After three or four hours' walking these ingredients provided a heavenly feast while we rested on the herb-scented mountain side.

The month of September was hazardous in the mountains as the chasseurs opened the hunting season but the danger of being inadvertently shot had to be ignored if one was to take part in the 'chasse aux champignons'. Early in the morning one left Monte Carlo by car and as dawn broke over the hunting grounds others would already be turning the pine needles with their sticks in search of the lurking cèpes and chanterelles.

In April 1974, as there was an important cartographic conference in Madrid, I decided to visit the Portuguese and Spanish Hydrographers *en route*. My wife and I flew to Lisbon and, after visiting our friend Armando Cortesão at his old family home near Coimbra, we returned to Lisbon. I spent a day visiting the beautiful Hydrographic Office, an ancient monastery which had been converted for the purpose to replace the former office destroyed by fire. Over lunch I asked the Hydrographer how he had managed to obtain such fine premises. 'The Chief of Naval Staff is a very good friend of mine,' said he.

The following morning, Thursday 18th April, we set off in our self-drive hire car eastwards across the Alta Alentejo, spending the night in an isolated Government Pousada a few miles from the Spanish border. Except for the occasional bleating of sheep the hours of darkness passed in silence, and after breakfast we were early at the frontier post. The customs official, lounging in his chair beneath a colony of nesting swallows, waved us through and we were on our way south-eastwards through Spain to reach Cadiz six hours later. There we were greeted with amazement – there had been a revolution in Portugal and the borders had been sealed since midnight. It was fortunate for us that the peasants of the Alentejo had been so quick to sever telephone communications; we had spent one of the quietest nights of our lives in the midst of a revolution.

The Chief of Naval Staff and his friend the Hydrographer were among senior officers deposed by the Revolution.

At the 1977 Conference it was decided by an overwhelming majority of votes that the People's Republic of China was the rightful incumbent of the seat of China within the Organisation, and steps were taken to enrol the People's Republic as a Member State. Two years later I was invited to visit China for a week to explain the work of our Organisation and how the Bureau could help the Chinese hydrographers. Welcomed first by the Director of the Marine Safety Administration for a day of talks in Beijing, I was dined magnificently in the Peking Duck Restaurant in the evening. The following day my two guides and I travelled to Tianjin by train to inspect the Chinese Navy's mapping agency where the charts were produced.

Arriving in Tianjin soon after noon we sat down at once to a meal in a restaurant in the city with the elderly Director of the Agency, who had been running it since 1949; sitting on my left he insisted on refilling my glass with that unusual drink mowtai at frequent intervals for goodwill toasts. It is a strong harsh liquor and I had to complete my meal with my left hand over my glass whilst I manipulated my chopsticks with the other, greatly to the delight of a small crowd of children who leant in at the open window on this hot afternoon. Zombie-like from the effects of mowtai, I inspected the chart compilation division where male and female naval ratings did the work; then on to the printing shop operated by the industrial printers. Mowtai neither assists one to take in technical information nor to offer intelligent comment. It was a long afternoon.

Next day we flew to Shanghai for a trip down the Yangtze to see the side-cast dredgers with their hydrographic systems which have to work round the clock to keep the port of Shanghai open. My companions had promised me an 'exciting surprise' during our voyage. 'There it is,' they said, handing me the binoculars – I saw a smart Chinese frigate – 'No, further right', and there I saw first one, then two and finally three Royal Navy frigates sailing up the estuary on their way to a Shanghai visit. These were the first British naval vessels to enter the river since *Amethyst* sailed out thirty years earlier.

I was busy answering eager questions throughout the visit with only a brief forty-five minutes break at midday, while my companions took an instant nap wherever we might be. On my last afternoon it was decided that I should see the Great Wall, a two hour run in an official car from Beijing. We walked about half a mile along the steep wall high above the pinewoods; when we returned to the car our chauffeur opened the boot to show that he had been more usefully employed in the woods than we had been on the Wall. He had, in our absence, collected a magnificent basket of cèpe mushrooms of which any 'chasseur' in the Alpes Maritimes would have been proud.

I had always believed that as long as the Soviet Union with its vast fleets of naval and merchant ships remained aloof from the I.H.O. the organisation could not be considered truly international. On arrival in Monaco I began to correspond with Admiral Rassokho, still Soviet Hydrographer twelve years after I had taken Admiral Irving in *Vidal* to meet him in Leningrad.

Eventually the U.S.S.R. applied for membership in 1977 and the Member States were not slow to support the application. Three years later Admiral Rassokho invited me to visit him in Leningrad, where he welcomed me warmly. As Commanding Officer of *Vidal* in 1964 I had been presented with a fine statuette of Pushkin in recognition of my literary achievements, while Admiral Irving had received a replica of the mounted statue of Peter the Great which stands in the centre of St. Petersburg; on this latter occasion, at a dinner in my honour, I too became a recipient of Peter the Great.

A fine new hydrographic office had been built since last I was in Leningrad and here I was received by Captains Faleev and Burkho, old friends from many a conference. Commander Mark Maliavko, who had been our interpreter onboard *Bellinghausen*, and was now in charge of the Notices to Mariners division, was my guide; together with the chief hydrographic interpreter, a woman of great charm, we went to the Hermitage, Mark pointing out that it was not only an enormous haven of culture, but a warm refuge from Leningrad's November weather.

On my last night I was taken to the Kirov Theatre, not this time for a classical ballet but for the Kirov school end-of-term exposition. After seeing first and second year students perform, we watched a series of six pas-de-deux danced by graduates who were being closely assessed by an audience of note-taking directors from ballet companies throughout the U.S.S.R.; contracts could be offered to these young dancers as soon as the performance was over. Despite obvious nervousness on the part of some of the couples the half dozen dances by these talented youngsters thrilled me.

The next morning I set off by air for Nice, anxious that, despite two changes of aircraft *en route*, I should arrive back in Monaco in time to attend the reception at the Palace on the evening prior to National Day. All went smoothly and with some pleasure I was able to describe to Princess Grace, who directed her own ballet school in Monaco, what I had been witnessing at the Kirov but twenty-four hours earlier.

On Tuesday 20th April 1979, the fiftieth anniversary of the laying of the foundation stone of the Bureau by Prince Louis II, Prince Rainier III, his grandson, unveiled a bronze plaque that we had erected on the pillar above the original stone. In welcoming Prince Rainier I thanked him on behalf of the fifty Member States for the generous hospitality which had always been extended by the Princely Government to the Bureau. Prince Rainier had been present as a small boy at the earlier ceremony, which added to the intimacy of this anniversary.

The plaque is not only commemorative but also serves a modern purpose. It marks with great accuracy the position based on 'World Geodetic System 1972' to which satellite ship location was related; surveying vessels which were, in 1979, increasingly using satellite observations, could then check, when in the Port of Monaco, the precision of their satellite receivers against the known position of the plaque.

After the brief ceremony Prince Rainier made an inspection of current work in the Bureau and Tony Cooper showed him some interesting plots which had already been made by visiting ships to test the agreement between their own satellite positions and that of the plaque; most positions differed by only a hundred or so metres in various directions.

This happy day continued when the three Directors and their wives were entertained by Prince Rainier and Princess Grace at a convivial lunch at the Palace.

Though never proficient at ball games, while I was in Monaco I came to delight in the cut and thrust of pétanque, the game played with steel balls on the hard-baked ground beneath the plane trees in every French village. The satisfying clink as your boule displaces your opponent's in the vicinity of the cochonnet (jack), the ribaldry and mock fury of the players, and the lengthy post mortems over glasses of pastis are all components of this intriguing game.

The staff of the Bureau revived the Monegasque love of an annual summer picnic, but we had to travel further than formerly to find the grassy slopes on which to open our food baskets, or 'cavagnetu', as they were once called. We would deliberate for weeks beforehand as to which beauty spot we should head for, but as soon as we were out of the coach at our selected destination the search was on for a clear bare piece of ground where pétanque could be played; and there, except for the long break for lunch, most of us would spend the day, only a few exploring the beauties of nature. As the sun began to set and the coach driver became restless to be on his way, the boulistes played on, led by

Antoine Ferrero-Regis, a professional assistant who had served over thirty years in the Bureau; he loved the picnic, pizzas and pétanque.

As the dates for the Twelfth (1982) Conference drew nearer, it began to be overshadowed by the growing crisis in the Falklands. By the time the delegates were assembling in Monaco the British forces were well on their way to the South Atlantic. Once assembled, with the Argentine delegation seated a few feet behind the United Kingdom, Rear Admiral Haslam, the U.K. Hydrographer, who had been elected as President of the Conference by the Heads of Delegation, addressed the assembly. He said we were living in difficult times but reminded the delegates that we were not politicians and that should political questions be raised he would have to veto them. The Conference continued in complete harmony and ended without the slightest rancour only a day or so before the British forces landed in the Falklands. It was a triumph for the International Hydrographic Organisation and its total disregard of political issues.

This 1982 Conference was held in the new Conference Centre Auditorium, where the President, the Directing Committee and speakers occupied a spacious stage. As the Conference closed delegates surged onto the stage to congratulate David Haslam on his conduct of the ten-day meeting, and many shook my hand in thanking me for my ten years' work as President. I felt overwhelmed, like an actor on the last night of a long-running successful show – a fitting end to my forty-six years of hydrographic endeavour.

Three months later, on the first day of September 1982, having turned over to my successor, I went to the Palace to say goodbye to His Serene Highness; he regretted that Princess Grace was absent in Paris. The Prince gave me a pair of beautiful gold plated pens inscribed 'G.S.R. – Monaco – I.H.B. 1972-1982' around the princely crown. With these pens I have written this book.

Index

Index of personal and ships' names. Entries are in word-by-word alphabetical order.

A

Abel (stoker, *Challenger*) 99–100
Acheron 133
Adamant 187
Adams, Rear Admiral John 206
Akoglu, Admiral 173
Albert, Prince of Monaco 223, 224, 225, 230
Alexander, Commander 39, 46
Allan, Dr. Tom 154
Allot, Lieutenant 34, 35
Amethyst 233
Anderson, Barbara 212
Anderson, Captain Neil 211, 212
Andrew, Prince, son of Q. Elizabeth II 167
Angelo, Sargeant 185
Anita Dan 206
Anne, Princess, daughter of Q. Elizabeth II 209, 210
Arden-Clark, Sir Charles 76
Argenlieu, Vice Admiral Thierry d' 59
Argonaut 213
Asbeck, Rear Admiral Baron van 81
Asch, Van 137